Fundamental Mathematical Structures

ELEMENTARY FUNCTIONS

Charles J. A. Halberg, Jr.

John F. Devlin

Response book

Scott, Foresman and Company

This response book contains answers for all
exercises in *FMS: Elementary Functions*.
Responses are keyed to the student's book by
page numeral and exercise numeral. The page
reference at the bottom of each even-numbered
page of this book refers to the first response
that appears on the page. The page reference
at the bottom of each odd-numbered page refers
to the last response on that page.

Chapter 1
Introduction

Pages 14-16

1 a Not a function. Both (31, January) and (31, March), for example, are determined by this correspondence.

   b Not a function. Because every state has two senators, every state will occur as the first component of two different ordered pairs.

   c A function

   d A function

   e A function

   f Not a function. Both (Chicago, White Sox) and (Chicago, Cubs), for example, are determined by this correspondence.

2 a (a, b), (e, f), (i, j), (o, p), (u, v), and (y, z)

   b (Sunday, 24), (Monday, 24), (Tuesday, 24), . . . , (Saturday, 24)

3 a $(0, -3)$, $(\frac{1}{2}, -2\frac{1}{2})$, $(16, 13)$, $(-\pi, -\pi - 3)$, and $(6\frac{2}{3}, 3\frac{2}{3})$ are some of the ordered pairs in this set. The set is a function.

   b $(-1, -1)$, $(2, 8)$, $(\frac{1}{3}, \frac{1}{27})$, $(\sqrt{2}, 2\sqrt{2})$ and $(\sqrt[3]{5}, 5)$ are some of the ordered airs contained in this set. The set is a function.

   c $(0, 32)$, $(100, 212)$, $(-40, -40)$, $(5, 41)$, and $(-10, 14)$ are some of the pairs contained in this set. The set is a function.

   d $(1, -2)$, $(1, -4)$, $(\frac{1}{4}, -2\frac{1}{2})$, and $(\frac{1}{4}, -3\frac{1}{2})$ are some of the pairs contained in this set. The set is not a function because at least two distinct elements of the set have the same first component.

4 a $(-2, 3)$, $(-1, 4)$, $(1, 6)$ and $(2, 7)$. The correspondence is a function.

   b $(-2, -\frac{2}{25})$, $(-1, -\frac{1}{25})$, $(1, \frac{1}{25})$, and $(2, \frac{2}{25})$. The correspondence is a function.

   c $(-2, -2)$, $(-2, 2)$, $(-1, -1)$, $(-1, 1)$, $(1, -1)$, $(1, 1)$, $(2, -2)$, and $(2, 2)$. The correspondence is not a function because at least two distinct pairs determined by the correspondence have the same first component.

   d $(-2, 6)$, $(-1, 9)$, $(1, 9)$, and $(2, 6)$. The correspondence is a function.

5 a A: {(Mr. J., A), (Mrs. W., B), (Mr. W., C), (Mrs. J., D), (Mr. T., E), (Mrs. T., F)};

      B: {(Mr. J., A), (Mrs. T., B), (Mr. T., C), (Mrs. J., D), (Mr. W., E), (Mrs. W., F)};

      C: {(Mr. J., A), (Mrs. W., B), (Mr. T., C), (Mrs. J., D), (Mr. W., E), (Mrs. T., F)};

      D: {(Mr. J., A), (Mrs. T., B), (Mr. W., C), (Mrs. J., D), (Mr. T., E), (Mrs. W., F)}.

   b Functions C and D

6 a The second component of each pair is the additive inverse of the first. The missing components are 2.5, 0, −0.7, and 2.2.

   b The second component is greater by 2 than the first component. The missing components are -4.5, $\frac{1}{3}$, 1.1, and $-5\frac{1}{3}$.

   c The second component is the product of 2 and the first component. The missing components are $3\frac{2}{3}$, $-27\frac{1}{3}$, $-\frac{2}{3}$, and 0.0032.

   d The second component is the product of $\frac{1}{3}$ and the first component. The missing components are $-\frac{3}{7}$, 1.95, -0.27, and $34\frac{7}{8}$.

e The second component is the reciprocal of the first. The missing components are $\frac{3}{7}$, 5, −1, and −0.8.

f The second component is the square of the first. The missing components are 0, 16, 2.25, and 0.0009.

g The second component is the absolute value of the first. The missing components are 0, 4, 1.5, and 0.03.

h The second component is 1 greater than the product of 2 and the first component. The missing components are 21, 13, −5, and −1.

Chapter 2
The real and complex number fields

Pages 22-23

1 a Ambiguous. The word "outstanding" will be interpreted differently by different people.

  b Not ambiguous. { } or ϕ

  c Not ambiguous. $\{0, \frac{1}{2}\}$

  d Ambiguous. Because the set of permissible replacements for z is not specified, the elements of the set cannot be tabulated. If z is an integer, then the set is $\{0\}$; if z is a rational or a real number, then the set is $\{0, \frac{1}{2}\}$.

2 a True   b True   c False   d False

3 a $\{-4, -3, -2, -1, 0, 1, 2, 3, 4\}$

  b $\{-2, -1, 0\}$

  c $\{5\}$

  d $\{1, 2, 3, 4, 5\}$

4 a $\{1, 2, 3, \ldots, 11\}$

  b $\{-1, -2\}$

  c $\{-1, -2\}$

  d $\{-1, -2, -3\}$

5 a True   b True   c False   d True   e False   f True

6 [1] − [b]   [5] − [h]

  [2] − [e]   [6] − [c]

  [3] − [g]   [7] − [i]

  [4] − [i]   [8] − [h]

7 a $\{x \mid x \,\epsilon\, \Re \text{ and } x > 7\}$

  b $\{x \mid x \,\epsilon\, \mathcal{I} \text{ and } x \leqq 7\}$

  c $\{x \mid x \,\epsilon\, \mathcal{I} \text{ and } -6 < x < 4\}$

  d $\{x \mid x \,\epsilon\, \Re \text{ and } 23 \leqq x \leqq 35\}$

Pages 24-25

1 a $x = 2; y = -3.$ d $x = \frac{1}{3}; y = \frac{1}{2}.$

  b $x = -1; y = 1.$ e $x = -\frac{1}{5}; y = -\frac{1}{2}.$

  c No solution   f $x = \frac{c}{b + a}; y = \frac{c}{b + a}.$

2 a $5! = 120.$　　　**b** $5 \cdot 4 \cdot 3 = 60.$

3 a 450　　　**b** 90　　　**c** 90　　　**d** 180

4 a 32　　　**b** 2^n subsets. This includes the null set as a subset.

5 a 720　　**b** 120　　**c** 24　　**d** 4　　**e** 30　　**f** 4

6 a $\dfrac{n!}{(n-1)!} = \dfrac{n \cdot (n-1) \cdot (n-2) \cdot \ldots \cdot 3 \cdot 2 \cdot 1}{(n-1) \cdot (n-2) \cdot \ldots \cdot 3 \cdot 2 \cdot 1} = n.$

b $\dfrac{n!}{(n-2)!} = \dfrac{n \cdot (n-1) \cdot (n-2) \cdot (n-3) \cdot \ldots \cdot 3 \cdot 2 \cdot 1}{(n-2) \cdot (n-3) \cdot \ldots \cdot 3 \cdot 2 \cdot 1}$

$= n(n-1) = n^2 - n.$

c $\dfrac{n!}{(n-3)!} = \dfrac{n \cdot (n-1) \cdot (n-2) \cdot (n-3) \cdot (n-4) \cdot \ldots \cdot 3 \cdot 2 \cdot 1}{(n-3) \cdot (n-4) \cdot \ldots \cdot 3 \cdot 2 \cdot 1}$

$= n(n-1)(n-2) = n(n^2 - 3n + 2) = n^3 - 3n^2 + 2n.$

d $\dfrac{n!}{(n-4)!} = \dfrac{n \cdot (n-1) \cdot (n-2) \cdot (n-3) \cdot (n-4) \cdot (n-5) \cdot \ldots \cdot 3 \cdot 2 \cdot 1}{(n-4) \cdot (n-5) \cdot \ldots \cdot 3 \cdot 2 \cdot 1}$

$= n(n-1)(n-2)(n-3) = (n^3 - 3n^2 + 2n)(n-3)$

$= n^4 - 6n^3 + 11n^2 - 6n.$

7 a Since $\dfrac{n!}{(n-1)!} = n$, we have $\dfrac{2!}{(2-1)!} = 2$ when $n = 2.$

Thus, $(2-1)! = 1!$ must equal 1.

b Yes. Yes. Yes

8 a $0!$ must equal 1 since $\dfrac{1!}{0!} = 1$ if and only if $0! = 1.$

b Yes. Yes. Yes

Pages 27-29

1 a True

b False. *Multiplication*

c False. *Nonzero*

d False. *Addition*

e False. *Multiplication*

2 Suppose that the measure of $\angle A$ is $90°$. Then $\angle A$ and its supplement have the same measure, since $180 - 90 = 90.$

3 Suppose that points A, B, and C are collinear. Then there are infinitely many planes containing points A, B, and C.

4 2 is a prime integer, but 2 is an even integer.

5 -6 is an integer, but it is not the case that -6 is greater than $-(-6) = 6.$

6 Suppose that $a = -3$ and $b = 2.$ Then $a < b$, but it is not the case that $a^2 = 9$ is less than $b^2 = 4.$

7 Suppose that $a = -5$ and $b = 5.$ Then $a^2 = b^2$, but $a \neq b.$

8 Suppose that $x = 0.$ Then $\dfrac{x^2 + x}{x}$ is undefined.

9 Suppose that $x = 1.$ Then $x + 2 = 3$ is not an even integer.

10 9 is an odd integer, but 9 is not prime since 3 is a divisor of 9.

11 Suppose that $a = 3$ and $b = 5$. Then $a + b = 8$ is even, but neither a nor b is an even integer.

12 a 1) $a = b$.   Given
       2) $b = a$.   Symmetric property of equality
       3) $c = c$.   Reflexive property of equality
       4) $b + c = a + c$.   Addition is uniquely defined.
       5) $a + c = d$.   Given
       6) $b + c = d$.   Transitive property of equality
    b 1) $a = b$.   Given
       2) $b = a$.   Symmetric property of equality
       3) $c = c$.   Reflexive property of equality
       4) $bc = ac$.   Multiplication is uniquely defined.
       5) $ac = d$.   Given
       6) $bc = d$.   Transitive property of equality

13 a 1) $a = b$.   Given
       2) $c = c$.   Reflexive property of equality
       3) $a + c = b + c$.   Addition is uniquely defined.
    b 1) $a = b$.   Given
       2) $c = c$.   Reflexive property of equality
       3) $ac = bc$.   Multiplication is uniquely defined.

14 a 1) $a = b$.   Given
       2) $c = b$.   Given
       3) $b = c$.   Symmetric property of equality
       4) $a = c$.   Transitive property of equality
    b 1) $a = b$.   Given
       2) $b = d$.   Given
       3) $a = d$.   Transitive property of equality
       4) $a = c$.   Given
       5) $c = a$.   Symmetric property of equality
       6) $a = d$.   Step 3
       7) $c = d$.   Transitive property of equality

Pages 31-32

1 a Closed under both addition and multiplication
   b Closed under both addition and multiplication
   c Closed under addition but not under multiplication. For example, $-3 \cdot (-3) = 9$, and $9 \notin \mathcal{I}^-$.
   d Closed under both addition and multiplication.
   e Closed under multiplication but not under addition. For example, $-5 + 5 = 0$, and $0 \notin \mathcal{I}^+ \cup \mathcal{I}^-$.
   f Closed under both addition and multiplication
   g Closed under multiplication but not under addition. For example, $5 + 5 = 10$, and 10 is not an odd integer.
   h Closed under both addition and multiplication

2 a Closed under both addition and multiplication

b Closed under both addition and multiplication

c Closed under both addition and multiplication

d Closed under addition but not under multiplication. For example, $-3 \cdot (-\frac{1}{4}) = \frac{3}{4}$, and $\frac{3}{4}$ is not a negative rational number.

e Closed under multiplication but not under addition. For example, $-\frac{5}{2} + \frac{5}{2} = 0$, and 0 is not a nonzero rational number.

f Closed under multiplication but not under addition. For example, $\frac{1}{4} + \frac{1}{2} = \frac{3}{4}$ and $\frac{3}{4}$ is not an element of the given set.

3 a Closed under both addition and multiplication.

b Closed under both addition and multiplication.

c Closed under addition but not under multiplication. For example, $-\sqrt{5} \cdot (-\sqrt{5}) = 5$, and 5 is not a negative real number.

d Closed under addition but not under multiplication. For example, $(3\sqrt{2})(\frac{1}{3}\sqrt{2}) = 2$, and 2 is not an element of this set.

e Closed under both addition and multiplication.

f Not closed under addition and multiplication. For example, $(2 + 3\sqrt{5}) + (3 + 2\sqrt{3}) = 5 + 3\sqrt{5} + 2\sqrt{3}$, which is not in the given set. Also, $(2\sqrt{3})(3 + 5\sqrt{2}) = 6\sqrt{3} + 10\sqrt{6}$, which is not an element of this set.

4 a False. $6 - 3 \neq 3 - 6$.   **b** True

c False. $(-8 - 5) - \frac{1}{2} \neq 8 - (5 - \frac{1}{2})$.   **d** True

e False. $6 + (2 \cdot 3) \neq (6 + 2) \cdot (6 + 3)$.   **f** False. $3 \cdot (8 \div 2) \neq (3 \cdot 8) \div (3 \cdot 2)$.

5 a $2xy + 5 + x + 10y = 2y(x + 5) + 1(x + 5) = (2y + 1)(x + 5)$.

b $x^2 - xy - x + y = x(x - y) - 1(x - y) = (x - 1)(x - y)$.

c $x^2 + xy + 2x + 2y = x(x + y) + 2(x + y) = (x + 2)(x + y)$.

d $3z^3 - 2z^2 + 3z - 2 = z^2(3z - 2) + 1(3z - 2) = (z^2 + 1)(3z - 2)$.

e $3xy - 20wz - 15xw + 4yz = 3x(y - 5w) + 4z(y - 5w) = (3x + 4z)(y - 5w)$.

f $3x^2 - 2xy - 3x + 2y = x(3x - 2y) - 1(3x - 2y) = (x - 1)(3x - 2y)$.

g $x^3 + y^3 = (x^3 - x^2y + xy^2) + (x^2y - xy^2 + y^3) = x(x^2 - xy + y^2) + y(x^2 - xy + y^2)$
$= (x + y)(x^2 - xy + y^2)$.

h $x^3 - y^3 = x^3 + (x^2y + xy^2) - (x^2y + xy^2) - y^3 = (x^3 + x^2y + xy^2) - (x^2y + xy^2 + y^3)$
$= x(x^2 + xy + y^2) - y(x^2 + xy + y^2) = (x - y)(x^2 + xy + y^2)$.

6 a Yes. Since $b \in \mathfrak{R}$, $a \circ b = b$ must be in $\mathfrak{R}$.

b No. Suppose that $a = 3$ and $b = -1$. Then $a \circ b = -1$ and $b \circ a = 3$.

c Yes. $(a \circ b) \circ c = b \circ c = c$, and $a \circ (b \circ c) = a \circ c = c$.

7 a (a) Yes. $a^2 + b^2 \in \mathfrak{R}$ if a, $b \in \mathfrak{R}$.

    (b) Yes. $a \circ b = a^2 + b^2 = b^2 + a^2 = b \circ a$.

    (c) No. $(a \circ b) \circ c = (a^2 + b^2) \circ c = (a^4 + 2a^2b^2 + b^4) + c^2$.
But $a \circ (b \circ c) = a^2 + (b^4 + 2b^2c^2 + c^4)$. It is not the case that
$(a^4 + 2a^2b^2 + b^4) + c^2 = a^2 + (b^4 + 2b^2c^2 + c^4)$ for all a, b, $c \in \mathfrak{R}$.

b (a) Yes. If a, $b \in \mathfrak{R}$, then $2(a + b) \in \mathfrak{R}$.

    (b) Yes. $a \circ b = 2(a + b) = 2(b + a) = b \circ a$.

    (c) No. $(a \circ b) \circ c = 2(a + b) \circ c = 2(2(a + b) + c)$, and
$a \circ (b \circ c) = a \circ (2(b + c)) = 2(a + 2(b + c))$. It is not the case that
$2(2(a + b) + c) = 2(a + 2(b + c))$ for all a, b, $c \in \mathfrak{R}$.

c (a) Yes. If a, b, $\epsilon \,\Re$, then $-a - b \,\epsilon\, \Re$.

   (b) Yes. $a \circ b = -a - b = -(a + b) = -(b + a) = -b - a = b \circ a$.

   (c) No. $(a \circ b) \circ c = (-a - b) \circ c = a + b - c$.
   $a \circ (b \circ c) = a \circ (-b - c) = -a + b + c$. It is not the case that
   $a + b - c = -a + b + c$ for all a, b, c, $\epsilon\, \Re$.

d (a) Yes. If a, $b\,\epsilon\, \Re$, then $a + 2b\, \epsilon\, \Re$.

   (b) No. $a \circ b = a + 2b$ and $b \circ a = b + 2a$. $a + 2b \neq b + 2a$ for all a, b, $\epsilon\, \Re$.

   (c) No. $(a \circ b) \circ c = (a + 2b) \circ c = a + 2b + 2c$, and
   $a \circ (b \circ c) = a \circ (b + 2c) = a + 2(b + 2c)$. $a + 2b + 2c \neq a + 2(b + 2c)$ for all
   a, b, $c\, \epsilon\, \Re$.

8 a Yes. $a + c\,\epsilon\, \mathcal{I}$ and $b + d\,\epsilon\, \mathcal{I}$, so $(a + c, b + d)\,\epsilon\,$ S.

  b Yes. $(a, b) \circ (c, d) = (a + c, b + d) = (c + a, d + b) = (c, d) \circ (a, b)$.

  c Yes. $\big((a, b) \circ (c, d)\big) \circ (e, f) = (a + c, b + d) \circ (e, f)$
$$= \big((a + c) + e, (b + d) + f\big)$$
$$= \big(a + (c + e), b + (d + f)\big)$$
$$= (a, b) \circ (c + e, d + f)$$
$$= (a, b) \circ \big((c, d) \circ (e, f)\big).$$

9 a Yes. ac, bd, ad, and $bc\,\epsilon\, \mathcal{I}$ because $\mathcal{I}$ is closed under multiplication. $ac - bd\,\epsilon\, \mathcal{I}$
   because $\mathcal{I}$ is closed under subtraction, and $ad + bc\,\epsilon\, \mathcal{I}$ because $\mathcal{I}$ is closed under
   addition. Hence, $(a, b) \,\square\, (c, d) = (ac - bd, ad + bc)\, \epsilon\,$ S.

  b Yes. $(a, b) \,\square\, (c, d) = (ac - bd, ad + bc)$
$$= (ca - db, da + cb)$$
$$[\times \text{ is commutative on } \mathcal{I}]$$
$$= (ca - db, cb + da)$$
$$[+ \text{ is commutative on } \mathcal{I}]$$
$$= (c, d) \,\square\, (a, b).$$

  c $\big((a, b) \,\square\, (c, d)\big) \,\square\, (e, f) = (ac - bd, ad + bc) \,\square\, (e, f)$
$$= \big((ac - bd)e - (ad + bc)f, (ac - bd)f + (ad + bc)e\big)$$
$$= (ace - bde - adf - bcf, acf - bdf + ade + bce)$$
$$= (ace - adf - bcf - bde, acf + ade + bce - bdf)$$
$$= \big(a(ce - df) - b(cf + de), a(cf + de) + b(ce - df)\big)$$
$$= (a, b) \,\square\, (ce - df, cf + de)$$
$$= (a, b) \,\square\, \big((c, d) \,\square\, (e, f)\big).$$

Steps 1 and 2 and 6 and 7 follow from the definition of operation $\square$. The other
steps follow from the distributive, associative and commutative properties of
addition and multiplication of integers.

Pages 35-37

1 a No. $-0.001 + 1.001 = 1$, but 0, not 1, is the additive identity.

  b Yes. $0 + 0 = 0$.

  c Yes. $\frac{1}{500} = 0.002$ and $0.002 + (-0.002) = 0$.

  d No. $|5| = 5$ and $|-5| = 5$; $5 + 5 \neq 0$.

  e No. $10^{-4} = \frac{1}{10^4} = 0.0001$ and $10^4 = 10,000$. $10,000 + 0.0001 \neq 0$.

  f No. $\left(-\frac{1}{2}\right)^3 = -\frac{1}{8}$ and $-\left(\frac{1}{2}\right)^3 = -\frac{1}{8}$. $-\frac{1}{8} + \left(-\frac{1}{8}\right) \neq 0$.

g No. $(3 + \sqrt{2}) + (3 - \sqrt{2}) \neq 0.$

h No. $-\sqrt{\frac{1}{2}} = -\frac{\sqrt{2}}{2}$ and $\sqrt{2} + \left(-\frac{\sqrt{2}}{2}\right) \neq 0.$

i Yes. $\sqrt{\frac{1}{3}} = \frac{\sqrt{3}}{3}$ and $-\frac{1}{\sqrt{3}} = -\frac{\sqrt{3}}{3}.$ $\frac{\sqrt{3}}{3} + \left(-\frac{\sqrt{3}}{3}\right) = 0.$

j Yes. $\frac{1}{1 - \frac{1}{2}} = 2$ and $\frac{1}{\frac{1}{2} - 1} = -2.$ $2 + (-2) = 0.$

2 a No. $-5 \cdot (-0.02) = 0.1$: the multiplicative identity is 1.

b No. $\frac{2}{3} \cdot \left(-\frac{3}{2}\right) \neq 1.$

c Yes. $1.6 \cdot 0.625 = 1.$

d Yes. $-\sqrt{3} \cdot \left(-\frac{\sqrt{3}}{3}\right) = \frac{3}{3} = 1.$

e Yes. $(3 + 2\sqrt{2}) \cdot (3 - 2\sqrt{2}) = 9 - 8 = 1.$

f Yes. $-1 \cdot (-1) = 1.$

g Yes. $\frac{1}{2^4} = \frac{1}{16}$ and $\frac{1}{16} \cdot 16 = 1.$

h Yes. $3\frac{4}{7} = \frac{25}{7}$ and $\frac{25}{7} \cdot \frac{7}{25} = 1.$

i Yes. $(-2)^3 = -8,$ $-\left(\frac{1}{2}\right)^3 = -\frac{1}{8}$ and $-8 \cdot -\frac{1}{8} = 1.$

j Yes. $\frac{1}{1 - \frac{1}{2}} = 2$ and $2 \cdot \frac{1}{2} = 1.$

3 a b and h

b c and g

4 a a and f

b d and e

5 a, d, f and g

6 b, c, e, and h

7 e, f, and g

8 a, b, c, and d

9 a 2 Additive-inverse axiom

4 Associative axiom for addition

5 Additive-inverse axiom

6 Additive-identity axiom

b The commutative axiom for addition

10 1 Additive-identity axiom

2 Multiplication is uniquely defined.

3 Distributive axiom

4 Additive-identity axiom

5 Corollary to theorem in exercise 9

11 a 1 Hypothesis

2 Multiplicative-inverse axiom

3 Multiplication is uniquely defined.

4 Associative axiom for multiplication

5 Theorem from exercise 10

6 Multiplicative-inverse axiom

7 Multiplicative-identity axiom

b $ab = 0;\ b \neq 0.$ Hypothesis
   $ba = 0.$ Commutative property of multiplication

   $a = 0.$ Theorem from exercise 11a.

12 $\{0,\ 7\}$ 17 $\{-3,\ 0\}$
13 $\{-\frac{1}{3},\ 5\}$ 18 $\{-1,\ 2\}$
14 $\{\sqrt{2},\ -\sqrt{2}\}$ 19 $\{-7,\ 7\}$
15 $\{3 - \sqrt{3},\ 3 + \sqrt{3}\}$ 20 $\{-\frac{1}{2},\ 2\}$
16 $\{-\frac{1}{2},\ \frac{1}{3}\}$ 21 $\{\frac{2}{3},\ \frac{3}{2}\}$

Pages 39-40

1 a The multiplicative-inverse property is not satisfied, since 1 and −1 are the only integers that have multiplicative inverses.

   b The additive-inverse property is not satisfied, since 0 is the only element of the set that has an additive inverse.

   c The closure property of addition is not satisfied.

   d The closure property of multiplication is not satisfied.

2 a $-10 + 15\sqrt{2}$ e $16 + 2\sqrt{2}$
   b $-4 - 8\sqrt{2}$ f $2 - \sqrt{2}$
   c $73 - 12\sqrt{2}$ g $(a + c) + (b + d)\sqrt{2}$
   d $7 + 5\sqrt{2}$ h $(ac + 2bd) + (ad + bc)\sqrt{2}$

3 a $0 + 0\sqrt{2}$
   b $1 + 0\sqrt{2}$
   c $-a - b\sqrt{2}$

4 a $-1 - \sqrt{2}$ d $2 + \frac{3}{2}\sqrt{2}$
   b $-1 + \sqrt{2}$ e $-1 + \frac{1}{2}\sqrt{2}$
   c $3 - 2\sqrt{2}$ f $-2 - 2\sqrt{2}$

5 $(a + b\sqrt{2}) + (a - b\sqrt{2}) = 2a + 0\sqrt{2} = 2a.$

   Since the rational numbers are closed under multiplication, $2a$ is rational.

$$(a + b\sqrt{2})(a - b\sqrt{2}) = a^2 - 2b^2 + (ab - ab)\sqrt{2}$$
$$= a^2 - 2b^2 + 0\sqrt{2}$$
$$= a^2 - 2b^2.$$

   Since the rational numbers are closed under both multiplication and addition (of inverses), $a^2 - 2b^2$ is a rational number.

6 a $1 + \frac{1}{2}\sqrt{2}$ c $-2 - \frac{3}{2}\sqrt{2}$ e $\frac{6}{7} - \frac{2}{7}\sqrt{2}$
   b $3 + 2\sqrt{2}$ d $1 + \sqrt{2}$ f $\frac{2}{17} + \frac{6}{17}\sqrt{2}$

Pages 42-44

1 a $5i,\ -6$ d $-1 - 4i,\ 21 + 7i$
   b $-7i,\ -12$ e $1 + i,\ -66 + 43i$
   c $2 + 11i,\ -24 + 16i$ f $14 - 12i,\ 13 - 82i$

g $2 - 2i,\ 27 + 34i$

h $2,\ 2$

i $5 - 5i,\ -13i$

j $6,\ 13$

k $10 + 10i,\ 50i$

l $-\frac{1}{5} + \frac{7}{5}i,\ -\frac{24}{25} - \frac{7}{25}i$

m $-\frac{4}{3} + \frac{11}{18}i,\ -\frac{11}{18} - \frac{43}{54}i$

n $-9.9 + 99.4i,\ 59 + 16i$

o $3\sqrt{2} + 4i,\ 1 + 7\sqrt{2}i$

p $0,\ -i$

2 a $0 + 0i = 0.$

  b $1 + 0i = 1.$

  c $-a - bi$

3 a $-1 - 4i$ **d** $-2 - 5i$

  b $-1 - 8i$ **e** $6 + 4i$

  c $5 + 6i$ **f** $-7 - 4i$

4 a If $a \in \Re$, then $a^{1} = a$. If $a \in \Re$ and $k \in \mathcal{I}^{+}$, then $a^{k+1} = a^{k} \cdot a$.
If $a + bi \in \mathcal{C}$, then $(a + bi)^{1} = a + bi$. If $a + bi \in \mathcal{C}$ and $k \in \mathcal{I}^{+}$, then
$(a + bi)^{k+1} = (a + bi)^{k} \cdot (a + bi)$.

  b $1 \cdot i = i.$ $i^{8} \cdot i = 1 \cdot i = i.$

    $i^{5} \cdot i = i \cdot i = -1.$ $i^{9} \cdot i = i \cdot i = -1.$

    $i^{6} \cdot i = (-1)i = -i.$ $i^{10} \cdot i = (-1)i = -i.$

    $i^{7} \cdot i = (-i)i = -i^{2} = 1.$ $i^{11} \cdot i = (-i)i = -i^{2} = 1.$

5 a i **c** $-i$ **e** -1 **g** 1 **i** -1

  b -1 **d** 1 **f** i **h** i **j** $-i$

6 a $-i$ **c** $-2 - 5i$ **e** $-\frac{1}{10} + \frac{1}{5}i$ **g** $2 - i$ **i** $-\frac{8}{5} + \frac{1}{5}i$

  b $-5i$ **d** $1 - 4i$ **f** $\frac{3}{2} + \frac{3}{2}i$ **h** $-\frac{4}{5} + \frac{2}{5}i$ **j** $-\frac{17}{10} - \frac{9}{10}i$

7 $(ai)^{2} = a^{2}i^{2} = a^{2} \cdot (-1) = -a^{2}.\ \ (-ai)^{2} = (-a)^{2}i^{2} = a^{2} \cdot (-1) = -a^{2}.$

8 a $\{-2i,\ 2i\}$ **e** $\{-25i,\ 25i\}$ **i** $\{-6\sqrt{2}i,\ 6\sqrt{2}i\}$

  b $\{-3i,\ 3i\}$ **f** $\{-2\sqrt{5}i,\ 2\sqrt{5}i\}$ **j** $\{-2\sqrt{2}i,\ 2\sqrt{2}i\}$

  c $\{-5i,\ 5i\}$ **g** $\{-6\sqrt{2}i,\ 6\sqrt{2}i\}$

  d $\{-6i,\ 6i\}$ **h** $\{-8i,\ 8i\}$

Pages 46-47

1 a $(9, 8);\ (0, 72)$ **h** $(10, 0);\ (34, 0)$

  b $(6, 3);\ (0, 0)$ **i** $(6, -4);\ (5, -12)$

  c $(6, 3\frac{1}{2});\ (2, 24)$ **j** $(11, 1);\ (36, 3)$

  d $(0, 5\sqrt{2});\ (-8, 0)$ **k** $(1.2, -2.6);\ (1.4, -0.2)$

  e $(0, 10);\ (-25, 0)$ **l** $(0, 0);\ (0, \frac{1}{2})$

  f $(4, -2);\ (11, -10)$ **m** $(2\sqrt{3}, 2\sqrt{2});\ (1, 2\sqrt{6})$

  g $(5, 3);\ (16, 11)$ **n** $(0, \sqrt{3});\ (-1, 0)$

2 a Let $(a, b) \in \mathcal{C}$. $(0, 0) \in \mathcal{C}$ since $0 \in \Re$. Then, by the definition of addition in
$(\mathcal{C}, +, \cdot)$, $(a, b) + (0, 0) = (a + 0, b + 0) = (a, b)$. Also $(0, 0) + (a, b) =$
$(0 + a, 0 + b) = (a, b)$.

  b $(1, 0) \in \mathcal{C}$ since $1 \in \Re$ and $0 \in \Re$. Let $(a, b) \in \mathcal{C}$. Then, by the definition of
multiplication in $(\mathcal{C}, +, \cdot)$, $(a, b) \cdot (1, 0) = (a \cdot 1 - b \cdot 0, a \cdot 0 + b \cdot 1) = (a, b)$.
Also, $(1, 0) \cdot (a, b) = (1 \cdot a - 0 \cdot b, 1 \cdot b + 0 \cdot a) = (a, b)$.

3 a $(-\frac{2}{29}, -\frac{5}{29})$ **c** $(0, -\frac{1}{5})$

  b $(-\frac{1}{4}, 0)$ **d** $\frac{4}{25} + \frac{3}{25}i$

e $-\frac{1}{5} - \frac{2}{5}i$

h $\frac{1}{3}i$

f $\frac{1}{4} + \frac{\sqrt{3}}{4}i$

i $\frac{\sqrt{2}}{2} - \frac{\sqrt{2}}{2}i$

g $-i$

j $\left(\dfrac{a}{a^2 + b^2}, \dfrac{-b}{a^2 + b^2} \right)$

4 a Let $(a, b), (c, d) \in \mathcal{C}$. Then $(a, b) + (c, d) = (a + c, b + d)$ by definition of addition in $(\mathcal{C}, +, \cdot)$. $a + c \in \mathfrak{R}$ and $b + d \in \mathfrak{R}$ since $\mathfrak{R}$ is closed under addition. Hence, $(a + c, b + d) \in \mathcal{C}$. Similarly, $(c, d) + (a, b) \in \mathcal{C}$.

b Let $(a, b), (c, d) \in \mathcal{C}$. Then $(a, b) \cdot (c, d) = (ac - bd, ad + bc)$ by definition of multiplication in $(\mathcal{C}, +, \cdot)$. $ac, bd, ad, bc \in \mathfrak{R}$ because $\mathfrak{R}$ is closed under multiplication. $ac - bd \in \mathfrak{R}$ because $\mathfrak{R}$ is closed under subtraction, and $ad + bc \in \mathfrak{R}$ because $\mathfrak{R}$ is closed under addition. Hence, $(ac - bd, ad + bc) \in \mathcal{C}$. Similarly, $(c, d) \cdot (a, b) \in \mathcal{C}$.

c Let $(a, b), (c, d) \in \mathcal{C}$. Then, by the definition of addition in $(\mathcal{C}, +, \cdot)$, $(a, b) + (c, d) = (a + c, b + d)$. But addition is commutative on $\mathfrak{R}$ so that $a + c = c + a$ and $b + d = d + b$. Hence, $(a + c, b + d) = (c + a, d + b)$. Since $(c + a, d + b) = (c, d) + (a, b)$, we have $(a, b) + (c, d) = (c, d) + (a, b)$.

d Let $(a, b), (c, d) \in \mathcal{C}$. Then by the definition of multiplication in $(\mathcal{C}, +, \cdot)$, $(a, b) \cdot (c, d) = (ac - bd, ad + bc)$. Because multiplication is commutative on $\mathfrak{R}$, $ac = ca, bd = db, ad = da$, and $bc = cb$. Also, because addition is commutative on $\mathfrak{R}$, $da + cb = cb + da$. Hence, $(ac - bd, ad + bc) = (ca - bd, cb + da)$. Since $(ca - db, cb + da) = (c, d) \cdot (a, b)$, we have $(a, b) \cdot (c, d) = (c, d) \cdot (a, b)$.

e Let $(a, b), (c, d), (e, f) \in \mathcal{C}$. Then, by the definition of addition in $(\mathcal{C}, +, \cdot)$ and the associative property of addition in $(\mathfrak{R}, +, \cdot)$, we can justify the following steps.

$$\big((a, b) + (c, d)\big) + (e, f) = (a + c, b + d) + (e, f)$$
$$= \big((a + c) + e, (b + d) + f\big)$$
$$= \big(a + (c + e), b + (d + f)\big)$$
$$= (a, b) + (c + e, d + f)$$
$$= (a, b) + \big((c, d) + (e, f)\big).$$

f Let $(a, b), (c, d), (e, f) \in \mathcal{C}$. Then, by the definition of addition in $(\mathcal{C}, +, \cdot)$ and the associative, commutative and distributive properties of addition and multiplication in $\mathfrak{R}$, we have

$$\big((a, b) \cdot (c, d)\big) \cdot (e, f) = (ac - bd, ad + bc) \cdot (e, f)$$
$$= \big((ac - bd)e - (ad + bc)f, (ac - bd)f + (ad + bc)e\big)$$
$$= (ace - bde - adf - bcf, acf - bdf + ade + bce)$$
$$= \big(a(ce - df) - b(cf + de), a(cf + de) + b(ce - df)\big)$$
$$= (a, b) \cdot (ce - df, cf + de)$$
$$= (a, b) \cdot \big((c, d) \cdot (e, f)\big).$$

g If every element (a, b) of $\mathcal{C}$ has an additive inverse in $\mathcal{C}$, then, for each (a, b), there exists an element (x, y) such that $(a, b) + (x, y) = (0, 0) = (x, y) + (a, b)$. By the definition of addition in $\mathcal{C}$, we have $(a, b) + (x, y) = (a + x, b + y)$. Since we want $(a + x, b + y) = (0, 0)$, we have $a + x = 0$, and $b + y = 0$. Hence, $x = -a$ and $y = -b$. Similarly, $(x, y) + (a, b) = (0, 0)$ implies that $x = -a$ and $y = -b$. $(-a, -b) \in \mathcal{C}$ because, by the additive-inverse property of $\mathfrak{R}$, $-a \in \mathfrak{R}$ and $-b \in \mathfrak{R}$. Hence, every element (a, b) of $\mathcal{C}$ has an additive inverse in $\mathcal{C}$

that is of the form $(-a, -b)$. The following computation verifies that $(-a, -b)$ is the inverse of (a, b). $(a, b) + (-a, -b) = \big(a + (-a), b + (-b)\big) = (0, 0) = (-a, -b) + (a, b)$.

h If every nonzero element (a, b) of $\mathcal{C}$ has a multiplicative inverse in $\mathcal{C}$, then for each such element (a, b), there exists an element (x, y) such that $(a, b) \cdot (x, y) = (1, 0) = (x, y) \cdot (a, b)$. By the definition of multiplication in $\mathcal{C}$, we have $(a, b) \cdot (x, y) = (ax - by, ay + bx)$. Since we want $(ax - by, ay + bx) = (1, 0)$, we have $ax - by = 1$ and $ay + bx = 0$. From these equations, we get $x = \dfrac{a}{a^2 + b^2}$ and $y = \dfrac{-b}{a^2 + b^2}$. Since either a or b is nonzero, $\dfrac{a}{a^2 + b^2} \in \mathfrak{R}$ and $\dfrac{-b}{a^2 + b^2} \in \mathfrak{R}$. Hence, $\left(\dfrac{a}{a^2 + b^2}, \dfrac{-b}{a^2 + b^2}\right) \in \mathcal{C}$, and every nonzero element (a, b) of $\mathcal{C}$ has a multiplicative inverse in $\mathcal{C}$ of the form $\left(\dfrac{a}{a^2 + b^2}, \dfrac{-b}{a^2 + b^2}\right)$.

i $(a, b) \cdot \big((c, d) + (e, f)\big) = (a, b) \cdot (c + e, d + f)$
$= \big(a(c + e) - b(d + f), a(d + f) + b(c + e)\big)$
$= (ac + ae - bd - bf, ad + af + bc + be)$
$= (ac - bd + ae - bf, ad + bc + af + be)$
$= (ac - bd, ad + bc) + (ae - bf, af + be)$
$= (a, b) \cdot (c, d) + (a, b) \cdot (e, f)$.

Similarly, $\big((a, b) + (c, d)\big) \cdot (e, f) = (a, b) \cdot (e, f) + (c, d) \cdot (e, f)$.

5 a $(a, b) + (a, -b) = \big(a + a, b + (-b)\big) = (2a, 0)$. $(2a, 0)$ corresponds to the number $2a + 0i$, which is a real number.

b $(a, b) \cdot (a, -b) = (a^2 + b^2, -ab + ab) = (a^2 + b^2, 0)$. $(a^2 + b^2, 0)$ corresponds to the real number $(a^2 + b^2) + 0i$.

6 a $\frac{1}{15} + \frac{2}{15}i$ c $4 + 2i$ e $0 - i$ g $-\frac{13}{5} + \frac{4}{5}i$
  b $\frac{6}{13} + \frac{9}{13}i$ d $\frac{39}{5} - \frac{13}{5}i$ f $3 - 2i$ h $\frac{5}{2} - \frac{1}{2}i$

7 Let $(a, b), (c, d) \in \mathcal{C}$. Then $(a, b) + (c, d) = (a + c, b + d)$. Now the conjugate of $(a + c, b + d)$ is $\big(a + c, -(b + d)\big) = (a + c, -b - d)$. The conjugate of (a, b) is $(a, -b)$, the conjugate of (c, d) is $(c, -d)$, and $(a, -b) + (c, -d) = (a + c, -b -d)$. Hence, the conjugate of the sum of (a, b) and (c, d) is the sum of the conjugates of (a, b) and (c, d).

8 Let $(a, b), (c, d) \in \mathcal{C}$. Then $(a, b) \cdot (c, d) = (ac - bd, ad + bc)$. The conjugate of this product is $(ac - bd, -ad - bc)$. The product of the conjugates of (a, b) and (c, d) is $(a, -b) \cdot (c, -d) = (ac - bd, -ad - bc)$.

Pages 53-54

1 a $\{x \mid x > 20\}$ g $\{x \mid x > 0\}$
  b $\{x \mid x \geq 3\}$ h $\{x \mid x \geq -12\frac{4}{5}\}$
  c $\{x \mid x \leq -5\}$ i $\{x \mid x > -13\}$
  d $\{x \mid x > -7\frac{11}{15}\}$ j $\{x \mid x < 1\frac{2}{3}\}$
  e $\{x \mid x > -2\}$ k $\{x \mid x > -\frac{b}{a}\}$
  f $\{x \mid x > 5\}$ l $\{x \mid x < -\frac{b}{a}\}$

2 a $(a + c) - (b + c) = a + c - b - c = a - b + c - c = a - b$. Therefore, if $a - b$ is positive, then $(a + c) - (b + c)$ is positive.

b If $a > b$, then $a - b > 0$ by definition. By the theorem in part a, it follows that $(a + c) - (b + c) > 0$. But $(a + c) - (b + c) > 0$ implies that $a + c > b + c$. Hence, if $a > b$, then $a + c > b + c$.

c

$a < 0$.	Hypothesis
$0 > a$.	Definition of $>$
$0 + (-a) > a + (-a)$.	Theorem of part b
$-a > 0$.	Additive-identity and additive-inverse properties.

3 a If $a - b$ is positive, then $(a - b)c$ is positive because the product of two positive numbers is positive. By the distributive property of multiplication over addition, $(a - b)c = ac - bc$. Hence, $ac - bc$, which is equal to a positive number, is positive.

b If $a > b$, then $a - b > 0$ by definition. But $a - b > 0$ and $c > 0$, together with the results from part a imply that $ac - bc > 0$. From this, it follows that $ac > bc$.

4 If $c < 0$, then $-c > 0$ by exercise 1c. Also, if $a > b$, then $a - b > 0$. Hence, by exercise 3a, $(a - b)(-c) = bc - ac$ is greater than 0. $bc - ac > 0$ implies that $bc > ac$, which means that $ac < bc$.

5 a By Theorem 3/2, if $a > b$ and c is a real number, then $a + c > b + c$. Again by Theorem 3/2, $c > d$ and $b \, \epsilon \, \Re$ imply that $c + b > d + b$. But, since $c + b = b + c$ and $d + b = b + d$, this means that $b + c > b + d$. By Theorem 2/2, $a + c > b + c$ and $b + c > b + d$ imply that $a + c > b + d$.

b By Theorem 4/2, $a > b$ and $c > 0$ imply that $ac > bc$. Also by Theorem 4/2, $c > d$ and $b > 0$ imply that $cb > db$. $cb > db$ and the commutative property of multiplication imply that $bc > bd$. Hence, by Theorem 2/2, it follows that, since $ac > bc$ and $bc > bd$, $ac > bd$.

6 a True

b False. If $a = 2$ and $b = -2$, then $2 > -2$, but it is not true that $\frac{1}{2} > -\frac{1}{2}$.

c True   **d** True   **e** True   **f** True

7 a If $a > b$, then, by definition of "greater than," $a - b > 0$. Since $a - b = -b - (-a)$, we have $-b - (-a) > 0$. Again, by the definition of "greater than," $-b - (-a) > 0$ implies that $-b > -a$. But $-b > -a$ means that $-a < -b$.

b $-1 < 0$. Hence, by the theorem from exercise 4, $a > b$ and $-1 < 0$ imply that $a(-1) < b(-1)$. Since $a(-1) = -a$ and $b(-1) = -b$, we have $-a < -b$.

8 Suppose that $a > 0$ and that $\frac{1}{a} < 0$. By Theorem 5/2, these assumptions imply that $a(\frac{1}{a}) < 0(\frac{1}{a})$, or $1 < 0$. Since $1 < 0$ is false, we conclude that if $a > 0$, then it is not true that $\frac{1}{a} < 0$. Now suppose that $a > 0$ and $\frac{1}{a} = 0$. If $\frac{1}{a} = 0$, then, because multiplication is uniquely defined, we have $a \cdot \frac{1}{a} = a \cdot 0$, or $1 = 0$. Since $1 = 0$ is false, we conclude that if $a > 0$, then it is not the case that $\frac{1}{a} = 0$. Hence if $a > 0$, then $\frac{1}{a} \not< 0$ and $\frac{1}{a} \neq 0$; so we conclude that if $a > 0$, then $\frac{1}{a} > 0$.

9 a Assume that, if a and b are positive and $a > b$, then $\frac{1}{a} > \frac{1}{b}$. Since $a > 0$ and $b > 0$, $ab > 0$, so, by Theorem 4/2, $\frac{1}{a} > \frac{1}{b}$ and $ab > 0$ imply that $\frac{1}{a} \cdot ab > \frac{1}{b} \cdot ab$.

Since $\frac{1}{a} \cdot ab = b$ and $\frac{1}{b} \cdot ab = a$, we have $b > a$. Since $b > a$ contradicts the assumption that $a > b$, we conclude that if $a > b$, it is not the case that $\frac{1}{a} > \frac{1}{b}$. Now assume that $a > b > 0$ implies that $\frac{1}{a} = \frac{1}{b}$. If $\frac{1}{a} = \frac{1}{b}$, the fact that multiplication is uniquely defined implies that $\frac{1}{a} \cdot ab = \frac{1}{b} \cdot ab$. This implies that $b = a$, which contradicts the assumption that $a > b$. Hence we conclude that if $a > b > 0$, then $\frac{1}{a} < \frac{1}{b}$.

b Positive. Yes. If $0 > a > b$, then $\frac{1}{a} < \frac{1}{b}$.

10 a If $a \geq b$ and c is a real number, then $a + c \geq b + c$.
b If $a \leq 0$, then $-a \geq 0$.
c If $a \geq b$ and $c \geq 0$, then $ac \geq bc$.
d If $a \geq b$ and $c \leq 0$, then $ac \leq bc$.
e If $a, b, c, d \in \mathfrak{R}$, $a \geq b$, and $c \geq d$, then $a + c \geq b + d$.
f If $a, b, c,$ and d are positive, $a \geq b$, and $c \geq d$, then $ac \geq bd$.
g If $a \geq b$, then $-a \leq -b$.

Pages 59-60

1 Left half-line, closed on the right

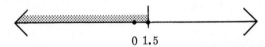

2 Half-open interval, open on the left, with endpoints $-3\frac{1}{4}$(left) and $5\frac{2}{3}$(right)

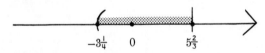

3 Right half-line, open on the left.

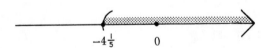

4 Closed interval with left endpoint 0 and right endpoint 6.1.

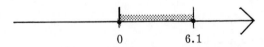

5 Open interval with left endpoint $-4\frac{1}{3}$ and right endpoint $1\frac{2}{3}$.

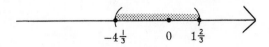

6 Right half-line, closed on the left.

0   3.3

7 Half-open interval, open on the right, with left endpoint 2.1 and right endpoint 7.9.

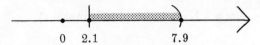

0   2.1   7.9

8 Left half-line, open on the right.

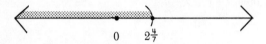

0    $2\frac{4}{7}$

9 $A \cap B = \emptyset$. $A \cup B = \{x \mid x \leqq 5\frac{1}{2}\}$.

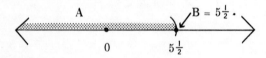

A $B = 5\frac{1}{2}$.

0              $5\frac{1}{2}$

10 $A \cap B = \{x \mid -1.4 \leqq x \leqq 3.6\}$. $A \cup B = \{x \mid x \in \Re\}$.

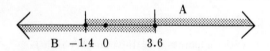

A

B   −1.4 0   3.6

11 $A \cap B = \{x \mid -5 < x \leqq 1\}$. $A \cup B = \{x \mid x \in \Re\}$.

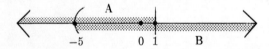

A

−5   0 1   B

12 $A \cap B = \{x \mid x \geqq 12\}$. $A \cup B = \{x \mid x \geqq -3\}$.

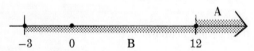

A

−3   0   B   12

13 $A \cap B = \{x \mid x < -1\}$. $A \cup B = \{x \mid x \leqq 1\frac{1}{3}\}$.

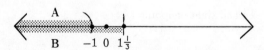

A

B   −1 0 $1\frac{1}{3}$

14 $A \cap B = \{x \mid -1 < x < 3\}$. $A \cup B = \{x \mid x \in \Re\}$.

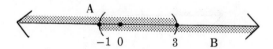

15 $A \cap B = \{x \mid 0 \leqq x < 6\}$. $A \cup B = \{x \mid -4 < x \leqq 6\}$.

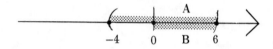

16 $A \cap B = \{x \mid -1 < x < 3\frac{1}{2}\}$. $A \cup B = \{x \mid -6 \leqq x \leqq 7\}$.

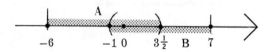

17 $A \cap B = \{x \mid -4 < x \leqq 0\}$. $A \cup B = \{x \mid -5 \leqq x < 4\frac{1}{3}\}$.

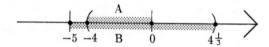

18 $A \cap B = \{x \mid \frac{1}{5} < x < 3\}$. $A \cup B = \{x \mid -7.5 < x < 33.9\}$.

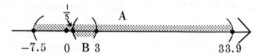

19 a

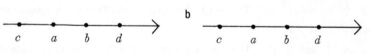

b

c

d

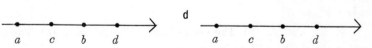

e

f

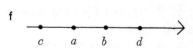

1 a
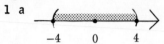
$-4 \quad 0 \quad 4$

b
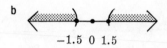
$-1.5\ 0\ 1.5$

c
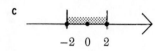
$-2\ 0\ 2$

d
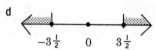
$-3\frac{1}{2} \quad 0 \quad 3\frac{1}{2}$

e
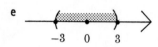
$-3 \quad 0 \quad 3$

f ∅

g
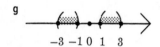
$-3\ -1\ 0\ 1\ \ 3$

h

$-5 \quad -2\ 0\ 2 \quad 5$

2 a $\{x \mid |x| < 3.5\}$ **e** $\{x \mid 2 \leq |x| \leq 4\}$

  b $\{x \mid |x| > 3\}$ **f** $\{x \mid 1 < |x| < 5\}$

  c $\{x \mid |x| \geq 1.1\}$ **g** $\{x \mid 1.5 \leq |x| < 2.5\}$

  d $\{x \mid |x| \leq 2\frac{1}{4}\}$ **h** $\{x \mid 3 < |x| \leq 8\}$

3 (a) 2, 4, 6, 8, and 10. (b) The set is bounded below only. (c) The set is contained in the right half-line $\{x \mid x \geq 2\}$.

4 (a) 2, 4, 8, 16, and 32. (b) The set is bounded below only. (c) The set is contained in the right half-line $\{x \mid x \geq 2\}$.

5 (a) $\frac{1}{2}$, $\frac{1}{4}$, $\frac{1}{8}$, $\frac{1}{16}$, and $\frac{1}{32}$. (b) The set is bounded. (c) The set is contained in the interval $\{x \mid 0 < x \leq \frac{1}{2}\}$.

6 (a) 1, 3, 5, 7 and 9. (b) The set is bounded below only. (c) The set is contained in the right half-line $\{x \mid x \geq 1\}$.

7 (a) 1, $\frac{1}{2}$, $\frac{1}{3}$, $\frac{1}{4}$, and $\frac{1}{5}$. (b) The set is bounded. (c) The set is contained in the interval $\{x \mid 0 < x \leq 1\}$.

8 (a) $\frac{1}{2}$, $\frac{2}{3}$, $\frac{3}{4}$, $\frac{4}{5}$, and $\frac{5}{6}$. (b) The set is bounded. (c) The set is contained in the interval $\{x \mid \frac{1}{2} \leq x < 1\}$.

9 (a) 0, $\frac{3}{2}$, $\frac{8}{3}$, $\frac{15}{4}$, and $\frac{24}{5}$. (b) The set is bounded below only. (c) The set is contained in the right half-line $\{x \mid x \geq 0\}$.

10 (a) $\frac{2}{3}$, $\frac{8}{9}$, $\frac{26}{27}$, $\frac{80}{81}$, and $\frac{242}{243}$. (b) The set is bounded. (c) The set is contained in the interval $\{x \mid \frac{2}{3} \leq x < 1\}$.

11 (a) 1, $\frac{1}{4}$, $\frac{1}{27}$, $\frac{1}{256}$, and $\frac{1}{3125}$. (b) The set is bounded. (c) The set is contained in the interval $\{x \mid 0 < x \leq 1\}$.

12 (a) 1, $\frac{1}{4}$, $-\frac{1}{27}$, $\frac{1}{256}$, and $-\frac{1}{3125}$. (b) The set is bounded. (c) The set is contained in the interval $\{x \mid -1 \leq x \leq \frac{1}{4}\}$.

13 a 1 **b** $\frac{1}{2}$ **c** $\frac{2}{3}$ **d** -1

14 a $\frac{1}{2}$ **b** 1 **c** 1 **d** $\frac{1}{4}$

15 a $3, 2$ **b** $-4, -5$ **c** $-1, -2$ **d** $-4, -5$

16 a 6 **f** 0
   b -5 **g** 6
   c 0 **h** 5
   d 2 **i** 5.6
   e -8 **j** 5.5

17 a

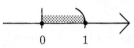

   b The set is bounded.
   c The least member of the set is 0. The set has no greatest member.

Pages 69-70

1   Greatest lower bound   Least upper bound
   a -3 3
   b -3 3
   c Does not exist   Does not exist
   d $-\sqrt{2}$ $\sqrt{2}$
   e 1 Does not exist
   f Does not exist   1
   g 0 1
   h Does not exist   Does not exist

2 a True
   b True
   c False. Suppose that $S = \{x \mid x \geq 1\}$, then S has 1 as its least member.
      $S^- = \{x \mid x \leq -1\}$ which has no least member.
   d False. Suppose that $S^- = \{x \mid x \leq \sqrt{2}\}$, then S^- has $\sqrt{2}$ as its greatest number.
      $S = \{x \mid x \geq -\sqrt{2}\}$ has no greatest member.
   e True

3 a True
   b True
   c False. Let $A = \{x \mid x \leq 3\}$ and let $B = \{x \mid x \geq 0\}$. Then $A \cup B = \{x \mid x \, \epsilon \, \Re\}$, which is not bounded.
   d True, if we specify that the empty set $\emptyset$ is defined to be a bounded set.

4 a $\{n \mid n > 10\}$ **c** $\{n \mid n > 2000\}$
   b $\{n \mid n > 100\}$ **d** $\{n \mid n > \frac{1}{h}\}$

5 a $\{n \mid n > 2\}$ **c** $\{n \mid n > 10\}$
   b $\{n \mid n > 5\}$ **d** $\{n \mid n > \frac{1}{\sqrt{h}}\}$

6 a $\{n \mid n > 1\}$ **c** $\{n \mid n > 2\}$
   b $\{n \mid n > 2\}$ **d** $\{n \mid n > 3\}$

7 a $\{n \mid n > 1\}$ **c** $\{n \mid n > 6\}$
   b $\{n \mid n > 2\}$ **d** $\{n \mid n > 7\}$

8 $n^2 - 1 < n^2$. $\dfrac{1}{n + 1} > 0$ since $n > 0$. Hence $(n^2 - 1)\dfrac{1}{n + 1} < n^2\left(\dfrac{1}{n + 1}\right)$, or

$n - 1 < \dfrac{n^2}{n + 1}$. Since $n > 0$, $\dfrac{1}{n} > 0$. Hence $(n - 1)\dfrac{1}{n} < \left(\dfrac{n^2}{n + 1}\right)\dfrac{1}{n}$, which is equivalent

to $\dfrac{n - 1}{n} < \dfrac{n}{n + 1}$.

9 a $\{n \mid n > 11\}$ c $\{n \mid n > 0\}$

   b $\{n \mid n > 11\}$ d $\{n \mid n > 10\}$

10 By definition of $[\frac{b}{a}]$, $\frac{b}{a} - [\frac{b}{a}] \geq 0$ and $\frac{b}{a} - [\frac{b}{a}] < 1$. Hence $\frac{b}{a} < [\frac{b}{a}] + 1$. Since

$a > 0$, $a \cdot \frac{b}{a} < a([\frac{b}{a}] + 1)$. But $a \cdot \frac{b}{a} = b$; therefore, $b < a([\frac{b}{a}] + 1)$, or $a([\frac{b}{a}] + 1) > b$.

Because $a \cdot \frac{b}{a} = b$ and $[\frac{b}{a}] \leq \frac{b}{a}$, we know that $a \cdot [\frac{b}{a}] \leq b$. But $[\frac{b}{a}] + 1$ is the

smallest integer that is greater than $[\frac{b}{a}]$, hence, it follows that $[\frac{b}{a}] + 1$ is the least

positive integer by which a can be multiplied so that the product is greater than b.

Pages 76-77

1 a Repetend: 0; period: 1

   b Repetend: 5; period: 1

   c Repetend: 0; period: 1

   d Repetend: 3; period: 1

2 a Terminating; $\frac{7}{16} = .4375$.

   b Repeating; a maximum of 10 digits; $-\frac{3}{11} = -.\overline{27}$.

   c Repeating; a maximum of 12 digits; $-\frac{5}{13} = -.\overline{384615}$.

   d Repeating; a maximum of 23 digits; $-\frac{5}{24} = -.208\overline{3}$.

   e Terminating; $\frac{86}{125} = .688$.

3 a $.58 > .5086 > .508 > .5068$.

   b $.1\overline{7} > .177 > .1\overline{7} > .17$.

   c $.30\overline{3} > .\overline{303} > .30\overline{3} > .303$.

   d $.21\overline{54} > .215\overline{4} > .\overline{2154} > .21\overline{54}$.

4 a Rational, because it is a repeating decimal

   b Not rational, because it is a nonterminating, nonrepeating decimal

   c Rational, because it is a terminating decimal

   d Rational, because it is a repeating decimal

   e Rational, because it is a terminating decimal

   f Not rational, because it is a nonterminating, nonrepeating decimal

5 a $\frac{5}{9}$ b $\frac{5}{33}$ c $\frac{8}{9}$ d $\frac{88}{111}$ e $\frac{124}{165}$ f $\frac{899}{1100}$

6 a 8, 8.6, 8.66, and 8.660

   b 4, 4.3, 4.35, and 4.358

   c 12, 12.2, 12.24, and 12.247

   d 14, 14.1, 14.14, and 14.142

7 a If k is an even integer, then $k = 2n$, where n is an integer. Thus,

     $k^2 = (2n)^2 = 4n^2 = 2(2n^2) = 2m$, where $m = 2n^2$. Since $m = 2n^2$ is an integer,

     $k^2 = 2m$ is an even integer.

   b If k is an odd integer, then $k = 2n + 1$, where n is an integer. Thus,

$k^2 = (2n + 1)^2 = 4n^2 + 4n + 1 = 2(2n^2 + 2n) + 1 = 2m + 1$, where $m = 2n^2 + 2n$. Since $m = 2n^2 + 2n$ is an integer, $k^2 = 2m + 1$ is an odd integer.

8 Suppose that k is an odd integer. Then, by exercise 7b, k^2 is an odd integer. But this contradicts the stated hypothesis that k^2 is an even integer. Hence, it is not the case that k is an odd integer, which means that k must be an even integer.

9 Assume that k is an even integer. Then, by exercise 7a, k^2 is an even integer. But this contradicts the stated hypothesis that k^2 is an odd integer. Hence, it is not the case that k is an even integer, which means that k must be an odd integer.

10 Assume that k is not divisible by 3. Then either $k = 3n + 1$ or $k = 3n + 2$, where n is an integer. If $k = 3n + 1$, then $k^2 = (3n + 1)^2 = 9n^2 + 6n + 1 = 3(3n^2 + 2n) + 1$, which is not divisible by 3. Since this contradicts the hypothesis that k^2 is divisible by 3, it follows that $k \neq 3n + 1$. Similarly, if $k = 3n + 2$, then $k^2 = (3n + 2)^2 = 9n^2 + 12n + 4 = 3(3n^2 + 4n + 1) + 1$, which is not divisible by 3. Hence, $k \neq 3n + 2$. Since the only possibility left is $k = 3n$, it must be the case that k is divisible by 3.

11 Assume that $\sqrt{3}$ is rational. Then $\sqrt{3} = \frac{a}{b}$, where a and b are integers with no common factors other than 1. Therefore, $3 = \frac{a^2}{b^2}$, or $3b^2 = a^2$. Since $3b^2$ is divisible by 3, it must be the case that a^2 is divisible by 3. By the theorem from exercise 10, if a^2 is divisible by 3, then a is divisible by 3. Thus, $a = 3c$, where c is an integer. Substituting in $3b^2 = a^2$, we have $3b^2 = (3c)^2 = 9c^2$. Hence, $b^2 = 3c^2$. But, because $3c^2$ is divisible by 3, it must be the case that b^2 is divisible by 3, which in turn implies that b is divisible by 3. But a divisible by 3 and b divisible by 3 contradicts the assumption that a and b have no common factors except 1. This contradiction shows that the initial hypothesis that $\sqrt{3} = \frac{a}{b}$ must be false. Hence, it must be the case that $\sqrt{3}$ is irrational.

12 By analogy with exercise 10, it can be shown that if k is an integer and if k^2 is divisible by 5, then k is also divisible by 5. Every integer can be written in one of the following forms: $5n$, $5n + 1$, $5n + 2$, $5n + 3$, or $5n + 4$. If $k = 5n + 1$, then $k^2 = 25n^2 + 10n + 1$, which is not divisible by 5. If $k = 5n + 2$, then $k^2 = 25n^2 + 20n + 4$, which is not divisible by 5. If $k = 5n + 3$, then $k^2 = 25n^2 + 30n + 9$, which is not divisible by 5. If $k = 5n + 4$, then $k^2 = 25n^2 + 40n + 16$, which is not divisible by 5. Hence, if k^2 is divisible by 5, then $k = 5n$, which means that k is divisible by 5.

The theorem just proved can now be used to prove that $\sqrt{5}$ is irrational. If $\sqrt{5}$ were rational, then $\sqrt{5}$ would equal $\frac{p}{q}$, where p and q are integers with no common factors other than 1. From this, we would have: $5 = \frac{p^2}{q^2}$; $5q^2 = p^2$; $p = 5r$ (by the theorem just proved); $5q^2 = 25r^2$; $q^2 = 5r^2$; and $q = 5s$ (by the theorem just proved). Hence, p and q would have 5 as a common factor, which contradicts the assumption that $\frac{p}{q}$ is in lowest terms. Therefore, $\sqrt{5}$ cannot be expressed as the quotient of two integers and, hence, must be irrational.

Chapter review
Pages 77-79

1	c	5	c	9	c	13	d	17	b	21	a
2	c	6	b	10	c	14	d	18	b	22	d
3	a	7	c	11	c	15	b	19	a	23	c, d
4	b	8	d	12	c	16	a	20	b	24	b

Chapter 3
The Cartesian plane

Pages 82–83

1 a {(−2, 1), (−2, 3), (−2, 5), (−4, 1), (−4, 3), (−4, 5), (0, 1), (0, 3), (0, 5), (2, 1),
(2, 3), (2, 5), (4, 1), (4, 3), (4, 5)}

b {(−2, −2), (−2, −1), (−4, −2), (−4, −1), (0, −2), (0, −1), (2, −2), (2, −1),
(4, −2), (4, −1)}

c {(1, −2), (1, −1), (3, −2), (3, −1), (5, −2), (5, −1)}

d {(1, 1), (1, 3), (1, 5), (3, 1), (3, 3), (3, 5), (5, 1), (5, 3), (5, 5)}

e {(−2, −2), (−2, −1), (−1, −2), (−1, −1)}

f {(−2, 1), (−2, 3), (−2, 5), (−1, 1), (−1, 3), (−1, 5)}

2 a

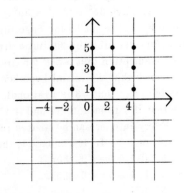

b

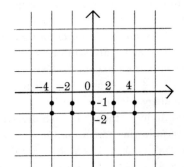

c

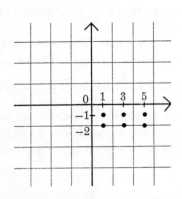

d

e

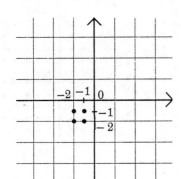

f

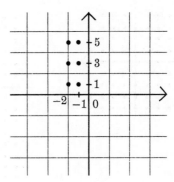

3 G = {0, 2}; H = {2, 4, 6, 8}.

4 a A subset   c A subset   e A subset
   b Not a subset   d Not a subset   f A subset

5 (1, 5), (1, 4), (3, 2), (3, 4), (5, 2) and (5, 5)

6 {3, 2} is the set with the two elements 3 and 2.

   (3, 2) is an ordered pair whose first component is 3 and whose second component
is 2.

   {(3, 2)} is the set containing the ordered pair (3, 2) as its only elements.

7

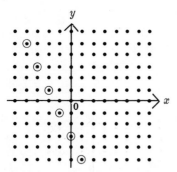

8

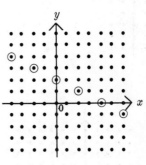

9

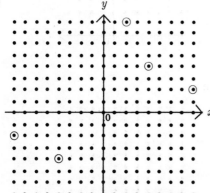

10

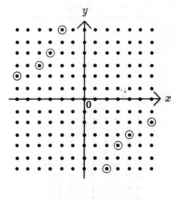

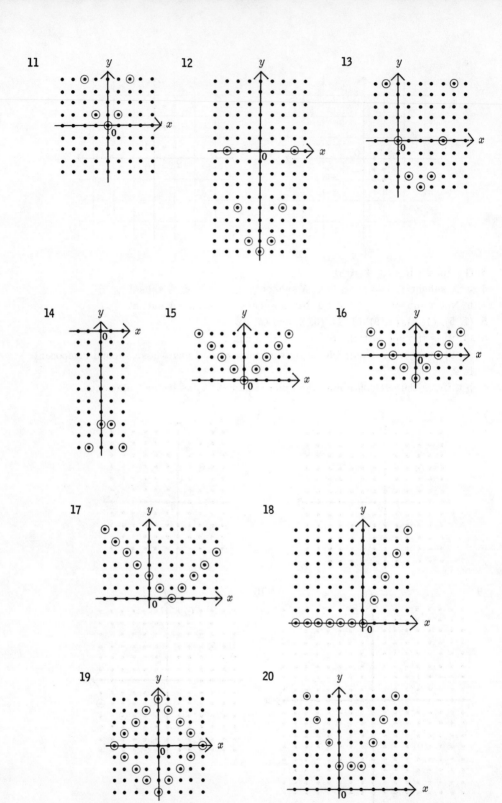

Pages 86-87

1 a Area: 20 sq. units

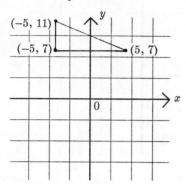

b Area: 60.5 sq. units

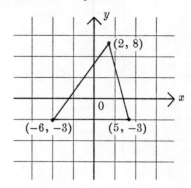

c Area: 25 sq. units

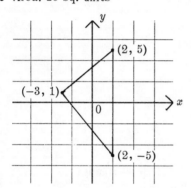

d Area: 20 sq. units

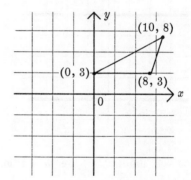

2 $2\sqrt{29}$

3 $(0, 0)$, $(a, 0)$, (a, a) and $(0, a)$

4 a $(b, \sqrt{3}b)$ **b** $(b, -\sqrt{3}b)$

5 a

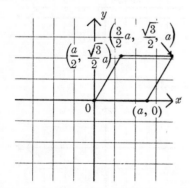

b

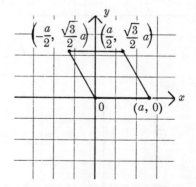

6 a $(-2, 0)$ **b** $(0, -3)$

7 a 3 units

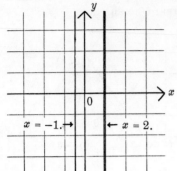

b 3 units

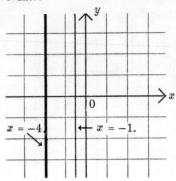

c 8 units

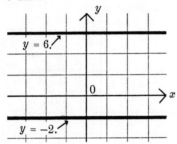

d $|4 - d|$ units　　**e** $|a - b|$ units　　**f** $|c - d|$ units

8 a 4 units

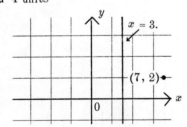

b 3 units

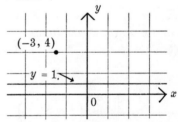

c 4 units

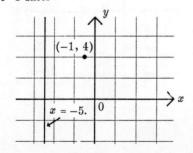

d 5 units

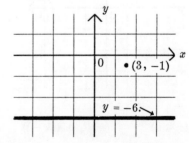

e $|a - c|$ units   **f** $|b - d|$ units

Pages 89-92

1 a

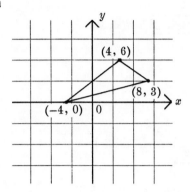

Scalene

b

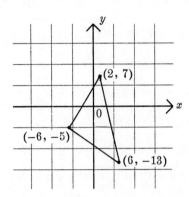

Isosceles

c

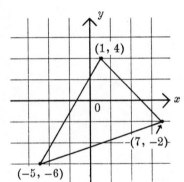

Scalene

d

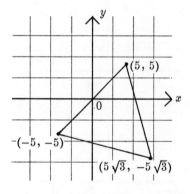

Equilateral

2 a $d(P, M) = \sqrt{(a - \frac{a + c}{2})^2 + (b - \frac{b + d}{2})^2}$

$\qquad = \sqrt{(\frac{a - c}{2})^2 + (\frac{b - d}{2})^2}$

$\qquad = \frac{\sqrt{a^2 - 2ac + c^2 + b^2 - 2bd + d^2}}{2}.$

$\quad d(M, R) = \sqrt{(\frac{a + c}{2} - c)^2 + (\frac{b + d}{2} - d)^2}$

$\qquad = \sqrt{(\frac{a - c}{2})^2 + (\frac{b - d}{2})^2}$

$$= \frac{\sqrt{a^2 - 2ac + c^2 + b^2 - 2bd + d^2}}{2}.$$

$$d(P, R) = \sqrt{(a - c)^2 + (b - d)^2} = \sqrt{a^2 - 2ac + c^2 + b^2 - 2bd + d^2}.$$

Hence, $d(P, M) + d(M, R) = d(P, R)$.

b Yes. $d(P, M) = \dfrac{\sqrt{a^2 - 2ac + c^2 + b^2 - 2bd + d^2}}{2} = d(M, R)$.

c $x = \dfrac{a + c}{2}; \ y = \dfrac{b + d}{2}.$

3 a $(0, 3)$, $(6, 4\frac{1}{2})$, and $(2, 1\frac{1}{2})$

b $(-2, 1)$, $(4, -3)$, and $(0, -9)$

c $(4, 1)$, $(1, -4)$, and $(-2, -1)$

d $(0, 0)$, $\left(\dfrac{-5 + 5\sqrt{3}}{2}, \dfrac{-5 - 5\sqrt{3}}{2} \right)$, and $\left(\dfrac{5 + 5\sqrt{3}}{2}, \dfrac{5 - 5\sqrt{3}}{2} \right)$

4 a $\sqrt{(x - 4)^2 + (y - 7)^2} = \sqrt{(x - 10)^2 + (y - 3)^2}.$

$x^2 - 8x + 16 + y^2 - 14y + 49 = x^2 - 20x + 100 = y^2 - 6y + 9.$

$12x - 8y = 44$, or $3x - 2y = 11.$

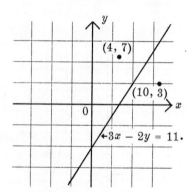

b $\sqrt{(x + 4)^2 + (y - 2)^2} = \sqrt{(x - 8)^2 + (y + 4)^2}.$

$x^2 + 8x + 16 + y^2 - 4y + 4 = x^2 - 16x + 64 + y^2 + 8y + 16.$

$24x - 12y = 60$, or $2x - y = 5.$

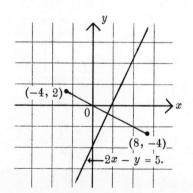

c $\sqrt{(x-0)^2 + (y-0)^2} = 10.$

$\qquad x^2 + y^2 = 100.$

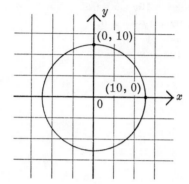

d $\sqrt{(x-0)^2 + (y+5)^2} = 3$ or $x^2 + (y+5)^2 = 9.$

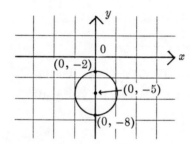

e $\sqrt{(x+6)^2 + (y-2)^2} = 4$ or $(x+6)^2 + (y-2)^2 = 16.$

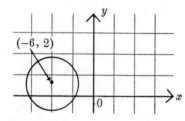

f $\sqrt{(-6-5)^2 + (2-1)^2} = \sqrt{122}.$

Hence, $r^2 = 122.$

$(x+6)^2 + (y-2)^2 = 122.$

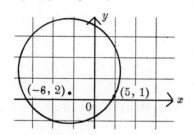

5 a $(x - h)^2 + (y - k)^2 = r^2.$

  b $x^2 + y^2 = r^2.$

6 a $(x - 4)^2 + (y - 5)^2 = 36.$ $x^2 + y^2 - 8x - 10y + 5 = 0.$

  b $(x - 0)^2 + (y + 2)^2 = 9.$ $x^2 + y^2 + 0x + 4y - 5 = 0.$

  c $(x - 3)^2 + (y + 4)^2 = 100.$ $x^2 + y^2 - 6x + 8y - 75 = 0.$

  d $(x - 5)^2 + (y - 0)^2 = 25.$ $x^2 + y^2 - 10x + 0y + 0 = 0.$

7 a

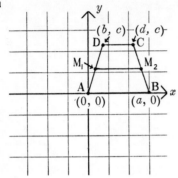

M_1 has coordinates $(\frac{b}{2}, \frac{c}{2})$; M_2 has coordinates $(\frac{a + d}{2}, \frac{c}{2})$.

Thus, $d(M_1, M_2) = \frac{a + d - b}{2}$. $d(A, B) = a$ and $d(D, C) = d - b$. Hence, $\frac{1}{2}\big(d(A, B) + d(D, C)\big) = \frac{1}{2}(a + d - b)$. Therefore, $d(M_1, M_2) = \frac{1}{2}\big(d(A, B) + d(D, C)\big) = \frac{a + d - b}{2}$.

b

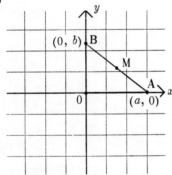

The coordinates of M, the midpoint of $\overline{AB}$, are $(\frac{a}{2}, \frac{b}{2})$.

$$d(A, M) = \sqrt{\left(a - \frac{a}{2}\right)^2 + \left(0 - \frac{b}{2}\right)^2} = \frac{\sqrt{a^2 + b^2}}{2}.$$

$$d(M, B) = \sqrt{\left(\frac{a}{2} - 0\right)^2 + \left(\frac{b}{2} - b\right)^2} = \frac{\sqrt{a^2 + b^2}}{2}.$$

$$d(M, O) = \sqrt{\left(\frac{a}{2} - 0\right)^2 + \left(\frac{b}{2} - 0\right)^2} = \frac{\sqrt{a^2 + b^2}}{2}.$$

Hence, $d(A, M) = d(M, B) = d(M, O)$, which means that M is equidistant from points A, B, and O.

c

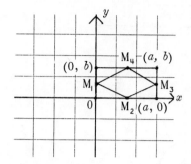

The coordinates of M_1 are $(0, \frac{b}{2})$; the coordinates of M_2 are $(\frac{a}{2}, 0)$; the coordinates of M_3 are $(a, \frac{b}{2})$; and the coordinates of M_4 are $(\frac{a}{2}, b)$.

$$d(M_1, M_2) = \sqrt{\left(0 - \frac{a}{2}\right)^2 + \left(\frac{b}{2} - 0\right)^2} = \frac{\sqrt{a^2 + b^2}}{2}.$$

$$d(M_2, M_3) = \sqrt{\left(\frac{a}{2} - a\right)^2 + \left(0 - \frac{b}{2}\right)^2} = \frac{\sqrt{a^2 + b^2}}{2}.$$

$$d(M_3, M_4) = \sqrt{\left(a - \frac{a}{2}\right)^2 + \left(b - \frac{b}{2}\right)^2} = \frac{\sqrt{a^2 + b^2}}{2}.$$

$$d(M_4, M_1) = \sqrt{\left(\frac{a}{2} - 0\right)^2 + \left(b - \frac{b}{2}\right)^2} = \frac{\sqrt{a^2 + b^2}}{2}.$$

Hence, $M_1 M_2 M_3 M_4$ is a rhombus.

d

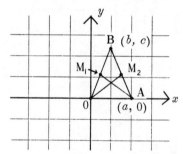

M_1 is the midpoint of $\overline{OB}$, with coordinates $(\frac{b}{2}, \frac{c}{2})$; and M_2 is the midpoint of $\overline{AB}$, with coordinates $(\frac{a + b}{2}, \frac{c}{2})$. If $\overline{AM_1} \cong \overline{OM_2}$, then $d(A, M_1) = d(O, M_2)$.

Hence, $\sqrt{\left(a - \frac{b}{2}\right)^2 + \left(0 - \frac{c}{2}\right)^2} = \sqrt{\left(0 - \frac{a + b}{2}\right)^2 + \left(0 - \frac{c}{2}\right)^2}$, or

$\sqrt{\left(\frac{2a - b}{2}\right)^2 + \left(\frac{c}{2}\right)^2} = \sqrt{\left(\frac{a + b}{2}\right)^2 + \left(\frac{c}{2}\right)^2}$. This is possible if and only if

$(2a - b)^2 = (a + b)^2$, or $4a^2 - 4ab + b^2 = a^2 + 2ab + b^2$. Thus, if the medians are congruent, then $3a^2 - 6ab = 0$, or $3a(a - 2b) = 0$. Since $a \neq 0$, this means that $a = 2b$.

$d(O, B) = \sqrt{(0 - b)^2 + (0 - c)^2} = \sqrt{b^2 + c^2}.$

$d(A, B) = \sqrt{(a - b)^2 + (0 - c)^2} = \sqrt{(a - b)^2 + c^2}.$

Since $a = 2b$, we have $d(A, B) = \sqrt{(2b - b)^2 + c^2} = \sqrt{b^2 + c^2}.$

Hence $d(O, B) = d(A, B)$, and $\triangle OAB$ is isosceles.

Pages 96-97

1

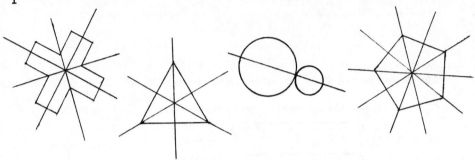

2 a

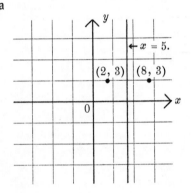

b

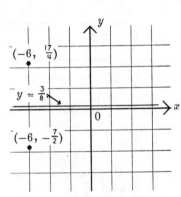

c

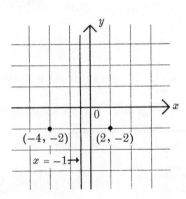

d

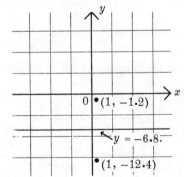

e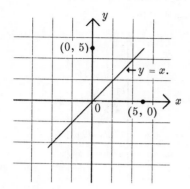

f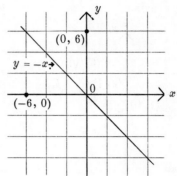

3 a $(5, -5)$ and $(-5, 5)$

b $(-2, -3)$ and $(2, 3)$

c $(-4, 1)$ and $(4, -1)$

d $(8, 6)$ and $(-8, -6)$

e $(0, -2 -\sqrt{3})$ and $(0, 2 + \sqrt{3})$

f $(2 - \sqrt{3}, 0)$ and $(-2 + \sqrt{3}, 0)$

4 a Not symmetric with respect to either axis

b Symmetric with respect to the y–axis

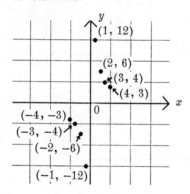

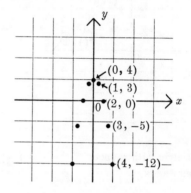

c Symmetric with respect to both axes

d Not symmetric with respect to either axis

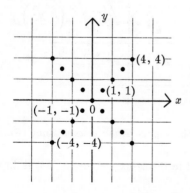

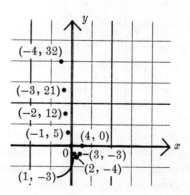

e Symmetric with respect to the x-axis

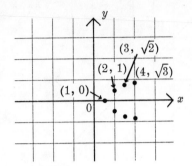

f Not symmetric with respect to either axis

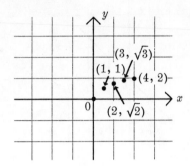

g Symmetric with respect to both axes

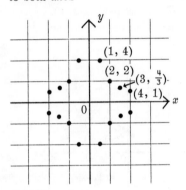

h Symmetric with respect to the y-axis.

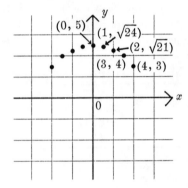

i Symmetric with respect to both axes

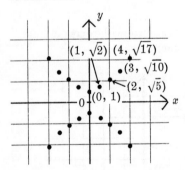

j Symmetric with respect to both axes

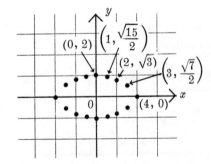

5 a The graph of such a set is symmetric with respect to the y-axis since $(-a, b)$ is in the set whenever (a, b) is in the set.

b The graph of S is symmetric with respect to the x-axis since $(a, -b)$ is in the set whenever (a, b) is in the set.

c The graph of S is symmetric with respect to both axes since $(-a, b)$ and $(a, -b)$ are in the set whenever (a, b) is in the set.

Page 100

1 a $(-\frac{1}{2}, -5)$ c $(1, 2)$ e $(2, 2)$
   b $(7, -.5)$ d $(-1, -5.6)$ f $(-\frac{5}{2}, \frac{5}{2})$

2 a $(-5, -5)$ c $(4, 1)$ e $(0, -2 -\sqrt{3})$
   b $(2, -3)$ d $(-8, 5)$ f $(-2 + \sqrt{3}, 0)$

3 a Symmetric with respect   b Symmetric with respect to
      to the origin   the y–axis

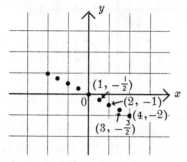

   c Symmetric with respect   d Symmetric with respect
      to the x-axis   to the origin

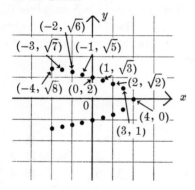

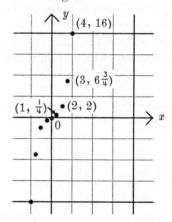

   e Symmetric with respect   f Symmetric with respect
      to the x–axis   to the y–axis

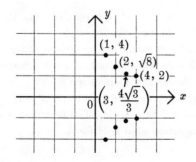

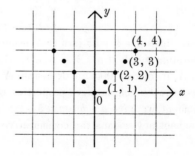

g Symmetric with respect to both axes and the origin

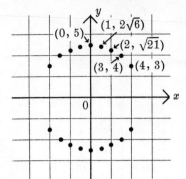

h Symmetric with respect to both axes and the origin

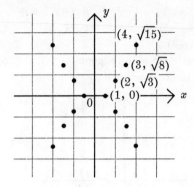

4 a The graph is symmetric with respect to the y–axis only.

  b The graph is symmetric with respect to the x–axis only.

5 Symmetry with respect to the origin implies that $(-a, -b)$ is in $\mathcal{S}$ whenever (a, b) is in $\mathcal{S}$. Symmetry with respect to the x–axis implies that $(-a, b)$ is in $\mathcal{S}$ whenever $(-a, -b)$ is in $\mathcal{S}$. Hence, $(-a, b)$ is in $\mathcal{S}$ whenever (a, b) is in $\mathcal{S}$, which implies that $\mathcal{S}$ is symmetric with respect to the y–axis.

6 Symmetry with respect to the origin implies that $(-a, -b)$ is in $\mathcal{S}$ whenever (a, b) is in $\mathcal{S}$. Symmetry with respect to the y–axis implies that $(a, -b)$ is in $\mathcal{S}$ whenever $(-a, -b)$ is in $\mathcal{S}$. Hence, $(a, -b)$ is in $\mathcal{S}$ whenever (a, b) is in $\mathcal{S}$, which implies that $\mathcal{S}$ is symmetric with respect to the x–axis.

Chapter review
Pages 100-102

1 d	4 c	7 a	10 b	13 c	16 a
2 c	5 b	8 c	11 b	14 d	17 d
3 b	6 d	9 c	12 a	15 b	18 d

Cumulative review
Pages 102- 104

1 a $\{-3, -2, -1, 1, 2, 3\}$

  b $\{1, 2\}$

  c ϕ

  d $\{-2, -1, 1, 2, 3\}$

  e $\{(1, -3), (1, -2), (1, -1), (2, -3), (2, -2), (2, -1)\}$

  f $\{(1, -2), (1, -1), (2, -2), (2, -1)\}$

2 a Yes. Since $a + b - ab$ is a real number, the set would *not* be closed under operation $\circ$ only if $a + b - ab = 1$. But this is possible only if $a = 1$. Since $a \in A$, it follows that $a = 1$; hence, A is closed under operation $\circ$.

  b Yes. By the commutative properties of addition and multiplication of real numbers, we have $a \circ b = a + b - ab = b + a - ba = b \circ a$. The fact that A is a subset of $\mathfrak{R}$ means the commutative properties also hold for A.

c Yes. Using the commutative, associative and distributive properties of real numbers, which also hold for set A, we have

$$(a \circ b) \circ c = (a + b - ab) \circ c$$
$$= (a + b - ab) + c - (a + b - ab)c$$
$$= a + b - ab + c - ac - bc + abc$$
$$= a + b + c - bc - ab - ac + abc$$
$$= a + (b + c - bc) - a(b + c - bc)$$
$$= a \circ (b + c - bc)$$
$$= a \circ (b \circ c).$$

d The identity is 0 since $0 \circ a = 0 + a - 0 \cdot a = a$ for all a in A.

e Since 0 is the identity element under operation $\circ$, the inverse of a, if it exists, is the element x such that $a \circ x = 0$. Since $a \circ x = a + x - ax$, we want to find the value for x such that $a + x - ax = 0$. Solving for x, we get

$$x = \frac{-a}{1 - a} = \frac{a}{a - 1}. \quad \text{That } \frac{a}{a - 1} \text{ is the inverse of } a \text{ is verified as follows.}$$

$$a \circ \frac{a}{a - 1} = a + \frac{a}{a - 1} - a \cdot \frac{a}{a - 1} = \frac{a^2 - a + a}{a - 1} - \frac{a^2}{a - 1} = 0.$$

3 a $-\frac{5}{17}$ **b** $\frac{11}{1}$ **c** $3 + 2\sqrt{2}$ **d** $-1i$ **e** $\frac{3}{25} - \frac{4}{25}i$

4 a The set is not closed under multiplication. For example, $3i \cdot 3i = -9$, and -9 is not in the set.

   b The set is not closed under addition. For example, $1 + 1 = 2$, and 2 is not in the set.

   c Not every nonzero element of the set has a multiplicative inverse in the set. For example, $3 + 2i$ does not have a multiplicative inverse in the set.

   d The set is not closed under addition. For example, $(1 + i) + (-1 - i) = 0$ is not in the set.

5 a True

   b False. $\{x \mid x \in \Re$ and $x > -4\}$ does not have a least member, but -4 is the greatest lower bound of this set.

   c False. $\{x \mid x \in \Re$ and $x < \sqrt{5}\}$ has $\sqrt{5}$ as its least upper bound, but this set not have a greatest member.

   d True

6 a $-\frac{1}{10}$ is the greatest lower bound. $\frac{1}{100}$ is the least upper bound.

   b $\frac{1}{3}$ is the greatest lower bound. 1 is the least upper bound.

   c -4 is the greatest lower bound, and 4 is the least upper bound.

   d -1 is the greatest lower bound, and 1 is the least upper bound.

7 a $(7, -20)$ **b** $10 - 12i$ **c** $(1, 0)$ **d** $\frac{34}{5} + \frac{2}{5}i$

8 a Assume that $a > 0$ and $\frac{1}{a} < 0$. Then $a \cdot \frac{1}{a} < 0 \cdot 0$, or $1 < 0$. Since 1 is not less than 0, the assumption that $\frac{1}{a} < 0$ must be incorrect. Now assume that $a > 0$ and $\frac{1}{a} = 0$. Then $a \cdot \frac{1}{a} = a \cdot 0$, or $1 = 0$, which is false. Therefore, it cannot be that $\frac{1}{a} = 0$. Hence, it must be the case that $\frac{1}{a} > 0$.

   b If $ab > 0$, then, by part a $\frac{1}{ab} > 0$. Since $a > b$, $\frac{1}{ab} \cdot a > \frac{1}{ab} \cdot b$, or $\frac{1}{b} > \frac{1}{a}$. Hence, $\frac{1}{a} < \frac{1}{b}$.

9 a $A \cup B = \{x \mid x > 5\}$. $A \cap B = \{x \mid x > 9\}$.

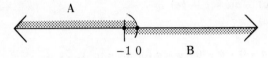

b $A \cup B = \{x \mid x \in \Re\}$. $A \cap B = \{x \mid -1 \leq x < 0\}$.

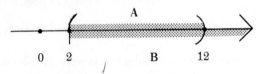

c $A \cup B = \{x \mid -3 \leq x < 5\}$. $A \cap B = \{x \mid -1 \leq x \leq 1\}$.

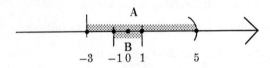

d $A \cup B = \{x \mid x \geq 2\}$. $A \cap B = \{x \mid 2 < x < 12\}$.

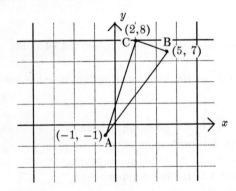

10 $(2b, 2c)$ and $(2b - a, 2c)$

11

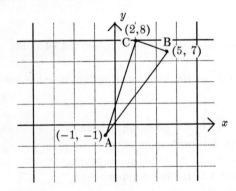

a $d(A, B) = \sqrt{(5 - (-1))^2 + (7 - (-1))^2} = \sqrt{36 + 64} = \sqrt{100}$.

$d(A, C) = \sqrt{(2 - (-1))^2 + (8 - (-1))^2} = \sqrt{9 + 81} = \sqrt{90}$,

$d(B, C) = \sqrt{(2 - 5)^2 + (8 - 7)^2} = \sqrt{9 + 1} = \sqrt{10}$.

Hence, $[d(A, B)]^2 = 100 = 90 + 10 = [d(A, C)]^2 + [d(B, C)]^2$. Therefore, $\triangle ABC$ is a right triangle.

b $\left(\dfrac{5-1}{2}, \dfrac{7-1}{2}\right) = (2, 3)$.

c $(x - 2)^2 + (y - 3)^2 = 25$.

12 a Symmetric with respect to the y-axis

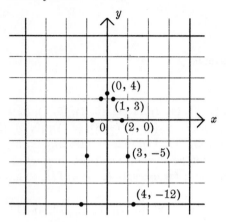

b Symmetric with respect to the x-axis

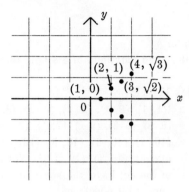

c Symmetric with respect to both axes and the origin

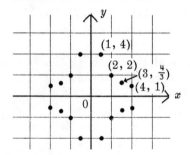

d Symmetric with respect to the origin

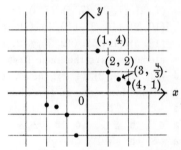

13

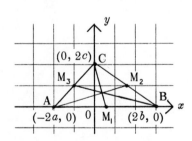

The coordinates of M_1, the midpoint of $\overline{AB}$, are $(b - a, 0)$; the coordinates of M_2, the midpoint of $\overline{BC}$, are (b, c), and the coordinates of M_3, the midpoint of $\overline{AC}$, are $(-a, c)$. $[d(A, M_2)]^2 = (b + 2a)^2 + c^2$. $[d(M_1, C)]^2 = (b - a)^2 + (2c)^2$. $[d(B, M_3)]^2 = (2b + a)^2 + c^2$. Hence, the sum of the squares of the lengths of the medians of $\triangle ABC$ is

$(b + 2a)^2 + c^2 + (b - a)^2 + (2c)^2 + (2b + a)^2 + c^2 = 6b^2 + 6a^2 + 6c^2 + 6ab.$

$[d(A, B)]^2 = (2b + 2a)^2.$ $[d(B, C)]^2 = (2b)^2 + (2c)^2.$ $[d(A, C)]^2 = (2a)^2 + (2c)^2.$
Hence, three fourths of the sum of the squares of the lengths of the three sides
of $\triangle ABC$ is $\frac{3}{4}[(2b + 2a)^2 + (2b)^2 + (2c)^2 + (2a)^2 + (2c)^2] = 6a^2 + 6b^2 + 6c^2 + 6ab.$

Chapter 4
Real-valued functions of a single real variable

Pages 112-113

1 a {(1, 1), (2, 1), (2, 2), (3, 1), (3, 3), (4, 1), (4, 2), (4, 4), (5, 1), (5, 5), (6, 1),
(6, 2), (6, 3), (6, 6), (7, 1), (7, 7), (8, 1), (8, 2), (8, 4), (8, 8), (9, 1), (9, 3), (9, 9),
(10, 1), (10, 2), (10, 5), (10, 10), (11, 1), (11, 11), (12, 1), (12, 2), (12, 3),
(12, 4), (12, 6), (12, 12)}. Not a function because at least two distinct elements
of the set have the same first component; for example (2, 1) and (2, 2) have the
same first component.

b {(1, 1), (2, 2), (3, 2), (4, 3), (5, 2), (6, 4), (7, 2), (8, 4), (9, 3), (10, 4), (11, 2),
(12, 6)}. A function because no two elements have the same first component.

c {(2, 2), (3, 2), (3, 3), (4, 2), (4, 3), (5, 2), (5, 3), (5, 5), (6, 2), (6, 3), (6, 5),
(7, 2), (7, 3), (7, 5), (7, 7), (8, 2), (8, 3), (8, 5), (8, 7), (9, 2), (9, 3), (9, 5), (9, 7),
(10, 2), (10, 3), (10, 5), (10, 7), (11, 2), (11, 3), (11, 5), (11, 7), (11, 11), (12, 2),
(12, 3), (12, 5), (12, 7), (12, 11)}. Not a function because at least two distinct
elements have the same first component.

d {(2, 1), (3, 2), (4, 2), (5, 3), (6, 3), (7, 4), (8, 4), (9, 4), (10, 4), (11, 5), (12, 5)}.
A function since no two elements have the same first component.

2 a -3 b -3 c 4 d $6 - 4a^2$ e $5 - 9a^2 + 6a$

3 a 6 b $\frac{3}{4}$ c $10 + 2\sqrt{3}$ d $3a^2 - 8a + 6$ e $12a^2 + 8a + 2$

4 a -8 b $\frac{8}{27}$ c $-\frac{1}{27}$ d a^6 e $1 - 3a + 3a^2 - a^3$

5 a 5.3 b $-\frac{1}{4}$ c $8\frac{1}{2}$ d $\frac{7}{2} + \frac{3}{2}a$ e $-\frac{7}{4} + \frac{9}{4}a.$

6 a Domain: $\{x \mid x \in \mathfrak{R}\}$
  Range: $\{y \mid y \in \mathfrak{R}\}$

b Domain: $\{x \mid x \in \mathfrak{R}\}$
  Range: $\{y \mid y \in \mathfrak{R}\}$

c Domain: $\{x \mid x \in \mathfrak{R}$ and $x \neq 0\}$
  Range: $\{y \mid y \in \mathfrak{R}$ and $y \neq 0\}$

d Domain: $\{x \mid x \in \mathfrak{R}$ and $x > 0\}$
  Range: $\{g(x) \mid g(x) \in \mathfrak{R}$ and $g(x) > 0\}$

e Domain: $\{x \mid x \in \mathfrak{R}$ and $x \geq 0\}$
  Range: $\{y \mid y \in \mathfrak{R}$ and $y \geq 0\}$

f Domain: $\{x \mid x \in \mathfrak{R}$ and $-5 \leq x \leq 5\}$
  Range: $\{h(x) \mid h(x) \in \mathfrak{R}$ and $0 \leq h(x) \leq 5\}$

g Domain: $\{x \mid x \in \mathfrak{R}$ and $\mid x \mid \geq 3\}$
  Range: $\{y \mid y \in \mathfrak{R}$ and $y \geq 0\}$

h Domain: $\{x \mid x \in \Re \text{ and } x \neq 0\}$

Range: $\{G(x) \mid G(x) \in \Re \text{ and } G(x) \neq 1\}$

7 a 0; 3; −3

b −6; 6; 27

c 15; −30; 3000

d No. Only integers of the form $3n$ are in the range of the function. Integers of the form $3n + 1$ and $3n + 2$ are not images of domain elements in this mapping.

e Yes. If x is in $\Re$, then x is the image of $\frac{x}{3}$ in $\Re$, so that every element of $\Re$ is is the image of a domain element in this mapping.

8 a

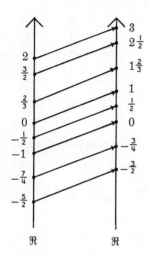

b

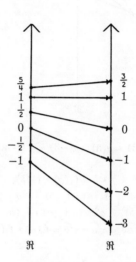

c

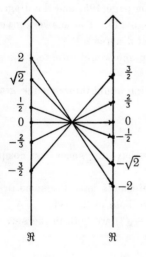

d

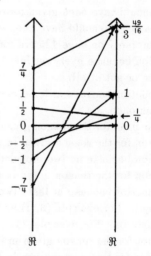

e 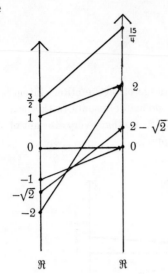 f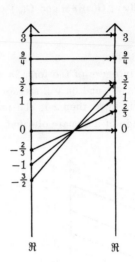

9 $g(0) = g(0 + 3) = g(3)$. $g(-3) = g\big((-3) + 3\big)^. = g(0)$. Hence, because $g(0) = g(3)$,
   $g(-3) = g(3)$.

10 a $f_1(ab) = ab = a \cdot b = f_1(a) \cdot f_1(b)$.
    b $f_2(ab) = -ab$. $f_2(a) \cdot f_2(b) = -a \cdot (-b) = ab$. Hence, $f_2(ab) \neq f_2(a) \cdot f_2(b)$.
    c $f_3(ab) = (ab)^3 = a^3 b^3 = f_3(a) \cdot f_3(b)$.
    d $f_4(ab) = \sqrt{ab} = \sqrt{a} \cdot \sqrt{b} = f_4(a) \cdot f_4(b)$.

Pages 119-121

1 [Note: In the first edition of the text, the diagrams given for exercise 1 on
   page 119 should have been given for exercise 7 on page 125, and the diagrams
   given on page 125 should have been given on page 119. The answers given here
   and for exercise 7 on page 125 are for the correct diagrams.]
   a A function because every vertical line in the plane would intersect the graph
      only once or not at all.
   b Not a function because at least one vertical line would intersect the graph
      more than once.
   c Not a function for the reason given in part b.
   d A function for the reason given in part a.
2 a A function because no two elements of the set have the same first component.
   b A function for the reason given in part a.
   c Not a function because at least two distinct elements have the same first
      component. For example $(3, 1)$ and $(3, -1)$ are both in the set.
   d Not a function. For example, $(1, \sqrt{3})$ and $(1, -\sqrt{3})$ are both in the set.
   e A function for the reason given in part a.
   f A function for the reason given in part a.

3 One possible graph is shown below.

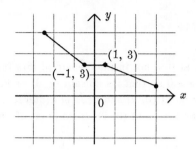

4 a False. In this case, the function would not be decreasing since $-5 < -1$ would not imply that $g(-5) \geq g(-1)$.

 b False. If this were the case then $g(0)$ would be less than $g(1)$, which would mean that g is not a decreasing function. Since $g(-1) = g(1) = 3$ and g is a decreasing function, it must also be true that $g(1) = 3$.

 c True. Since $g(0) = 3$ and g is a decreasing function, $0 \leq x_1$ implies that $3 \geq g(x_1)$, or $g(x_1) \leq 3$.

 d True. Since $g(0) = 3$ and g is a decreasing function, $x_1 \leq 0$ implies that $g(x_1) \geq 0$.

 e False. Suppose that $k = 3$. Then $-5 < -1 < 5$ and $-5 < 1 < 5$. But we know that $g(-1) = g(1) = 3$.

5 One possible graph is shown below.

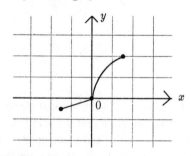

6 a True. The least element of the domain is -3 and the least element of the range is -1. Since f is a strictly increasing function, $x_1 < x_2$ implies that $f(x_1) < f(x_2)$. Hence, $-3 < x_2$ implies that $-1 < f(x_2)$.

 b True. Since 4 is the greatest element of the range and 3 is the greatest element element of the domain and f is an increasing function, it must be the case that $f(3) = 4$. But because f is *strictly* increasing, $x_1 < 3$ implies that $f(x_1) < 4$.

 c True. Since $f(0) = 0$, $x_1 < 0$ implies that $f(x_1) < 0$.

 d True. Since $f(0) = 0$, $0 < x_2$ implies that $0 < f(x_2)$, or $f(x_2) > 0$.

 e True. Let $-3 < c_1 < 3$ and $-3 < c_2 < 3$. If $c_1 < c_2$, then $f(c_1) < f(c_2)$. Hence, $f(c_1) = f(c_2)$ if and only if $c_1 = c_2$. This property follows from the fact that f is a strictly increasing function.

7 **a** $y = x.$

d $y = \dfrac{2x + 1}{3x - 1}.$

b $y = x - 1.$

e $y = 6 + x.$

c $y = \dfrac{x - 3}{x + 3}.$

f $y = \dfrac{-1}{4 + 2x}.$

8 **a** Function f is not defined for $x = 0$, so that 0 is not in the domain of this function. The function g: $y = x + 2$ is defined for $x = 0$ so that its domain is all of $\Re$.

b The graph of f has a "break" in it at the point (0, 2) and does not intersect the y−axis. The graph of function g contains the point (0, 2) as its point of intersection with the y−axis.

Pages 124-125

1 Increasing: $-3 \leqq x \leqq 0$. Decreasing: $-6 \leqq x \leqq -3$.

2 Increasing: $-5 \leqq x \leqq -1$. Decreasing: $-1 \leqq x \leqq 3$.

3 Increasing: $3 \leqq x \leqq 6$. Decreasing: $0 \leqq x \leqq 3$.

4 Increasing: $-2 \leqq x \leqq 2$. Decreasing: $-3 \leqq x \leqq -2$ and $2 \leqq x \leqq 3$.

5 One possible graph is shown below.

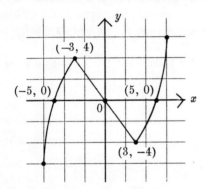

6 **a** True. Since f is strictly increasing in the interval $-5 \leqq x \leqq -3$ and since f(5) = 0 and f(−3) = 4, if $5 < x \leqq -3$, it must be the case that $0 < f(x) \leqq 4$. Also, since f is strictly decreasing in the interval $-3 \leqq x \leqq 0$ and since f(−3) = 4 and f(0) = 0, if $-3 < x < 0$, it must be the case that $4 > f(x) > 0$. Hence, for the interval $-5 < x < 0$, f(x) > 0.

b True. Since f is strictly decreasing over the interval $0 \leqq x \leqq 3$ and since f(0) = 0 and f(3) = −4, if $0 < x \leqq 3$, it must be the case that $0 > f(x) \leqq -4$. Also, since f is strictly increasing over the interval $3 \leqq x \leqq 5$ and since f(3) = −4 and f(5) = 0, if $3 < x < 5$, then it must be the case that $-4 < f(x) < 0$. Hence, for the interval $0 < x < 5$, f(x) < 0.

c True. The condition $|h| < 1$ means that h is in the open interval from −1 to 1. If h is in the interval $-1 < h \leqq 0$, then x is in the interval $-4 < x \leqq -3$. Since f is a strictly increasing function for this interval, it follows that f(x) $\leqq$ f(−3) for $-4 < x \leqq -3$. If h is in the interval $0 \leqq h < 1$, then x is in the interval $-3 \leqq x < -2$. Since f is a strictly decreasing function for this interval, it follows that f(x) $\leqq$ f(−3) for all h such that $|h| < 1$.

d True. Since f is a strictly decreasing function for the interval $-3 \leq x \leq 3$, it follows that $f(x) \geq f(3)$ for $2 < x \leq 3$. Also, since f is strictly increasing for the interval $3 \leq x \leq 6$, it follows that $f(x) \geq f(3)$ for $3 \leq x < 4$. Hence, $f(3) \leq f(3 + h)$ for all h such that $|h| < 1$.

7 a (See note for exercise 1, page 119).
Increasing: $\{x \mid -3 \leq x \leq -1\}$; decreasing: $\{x \mid -1 \leq x \leq 1\}$
b Increasing: $\{x \mid 3 \leq x \leq 3\frac{1}{2}\}$; decreasing: $\{x \mid -3 \leq x \leq 3\}$
c Increasing: $\{x \mid -5 \leq x \leq -2\}$; decreasing: $\{x \mid -2 \leq x \leq 2\}$
d Increasing: $\{x \mid -1 \leq x \leq 1\}$; decreasing: $\{x \mid -3 \leq x \leq -1\}$ or $\{x \mid 1 \leq x \leq 3\}$

8 a Assume that $x_2 > x_1$. Now $f(x_2) - f(x_1) = (2x_2 - 3) - (2x_1 - 3) = 2(x_2 - x_1)$. Since $x_2 > x_1$, it follows that $(x_2 - x_1) > 0$ and, hence, that $2(x_2 - x_1) > 0$. Thus, since $f(x_2) - f(x_1) = 2(x_2 - x_1)$, we have $f(x_2) - f(x_1) > 0$, or $f(x_2) > f(x_1)$. Therefore, f is a strictly increasing function.
b Assume that $x_2 > x_1$. Now $f(x_2) - f(x_1) = (mx_2 + b) - (mx_1 + b) = m(x_2 - x_1)$. Since $x_2 > x_1$, we have $(x_2 - x_1) > 0$; therefore, since $m > 0$, $m(x_2 - x_1) > 0$. Because $f(x_2) - f(x_1) = m(x_2 - x_1)$, it follows that $f(x_2) - f(x_1) > 0$, or $f(x_2) > f(x_1)$. Hence, f is a strictly increasing function.

9 Assume that $x_2 > x_1$. Now $g(x_2) - g(x_1) = (x_2)^3 - (x_1)^3 = (x_2 - x_1)((x_2)^2 + x_2 x_1 + (x_1)^2)$. Since $x_2 > x_1$, we have $(x_2 - x_1) > 0$, and $x_2^2 + x_1^2 > x_2 x_1$. Thus $\left((x_2)^2 + x_2 x_1 + (x_1)^2\right) > 0$. Therefore, the product $(x_2 - x_1)\left((x_2^2) + x_2 x_1 + (x_1)^2\right) > 0$. Hence, $g(x_2) - g(x_1) > 0$, or $g(x_2) > g(x_1)$. Thus, g is a strictly increasing function.

Pages 127-129

1 One-to-one
2 Not one-to-one; a possible restriction on the domain of g: $\{x \mid x \geq 0\}$.
3 Not one-to-one; a possible restriction on the domain of h: $\{x \mid x \leq 0\}$
4 One-to-one
5 Not one-to-one; a possible restriction on the domain of G: $\{x \mid x \geq 0\}$
6 Not one-to-one; a possible restriction on the domain of H: $\{x \mid -12 \leq x \leq 0\}$
7 Not one-to-one; a possible restriction on the domain of k: $\{x \mid x \geq 4\}$
8 Not one-to-one; a possible restriction on the domain of K: $\{x \mid x \leq -4\}$
9 a 2 seconds. $\{t \mid 0 \leq t \leq 2\}$. $\{s \mid 0 \leq s \leq 32\}$
   b 8 feet. 24 feet. No; the velocity increases as the time increases since the ball travels only 8 feet in the first second and 24 feet in the second second.
   c 8 feet per second. 14 feet per second
10 a Strictly decreasing. As x increases, $g(x)$ decreases.
   b The decrease is 7.5 foot-candles. The decrease is .225 foot-candles. No, the amount of decrease decreases as the distance increases.
   c −480 foot-candles per foot. −.3 foot-candles per foot.
   d The results are negative because the function is a decreasing one so that $g(x)$ decreases as x increases. Hence, the average rate of change represents a rate of decrease.

11 a −7 units per unit increase in x.

   b f is decreasing over this interval so the average rate of change represents a rate of decrease.

12 a 12   **b** 36   **c** $-\frac{29}{36}$ **d** $11 + 6h + h^2$

13 a −25   **b** 9   **c** −11   **d** $35 + 2h$

Pages 133-135

1 a $f(a) = -5$; $f(-a) = -5$; and $-f(-a) = 5$. The function is even.

  b $f(a) = -10a^2$; $f(-a) = -10(-a)^2 = -10a^2$; and $-f(-a) = 10a^2$. The function is even.

  c $f(a) = -\frac{1}{a^3}$; $f(-a) = -\frac{1}{(-a)^3} = \frac{1}{a^3}$; and $-f(-a) = -\frac{1}{a^3}$. The function is odd.

  d $f(a) = a^2 - 6a$; $f(-a) = a^2 + 6a$; and $-f(-a) = -a^2 - 6a$. The function is neither even nor odd.

  e $f(a) = a^2 - 9$; $f(-a) = a^2 - 9$; and $-f(-a) = 9 - a^2$. The function is even.

  f $f(a) = -a^2 + 4a - 5$; $f(-a) = -a^2 - 4a - 5$; $-f(-a) = a^2 + 4a - 5$. The function is neither even nor odd.

  g $f(a) = a^2 - \frac{1}{a}$; $f(-a) = a^2 + \frac{1}{a}$; and $-f(-a) = -a^2 - \frac{1}{a}$. The function is neither even nor odd.

  h $f(a) = a^2 - 4a + 4$; $f(-a) = a^2 + 4a + 4$; and $-f(-a) = -a^2 - 4a - 4$. The function is neither even nor odd.

2 a

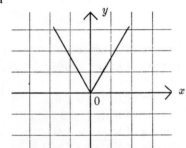

b

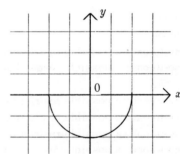

c

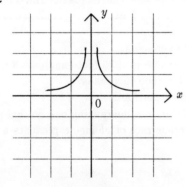

d

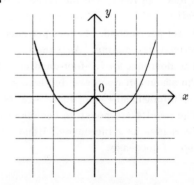

e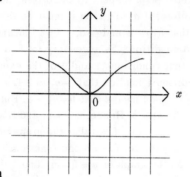

f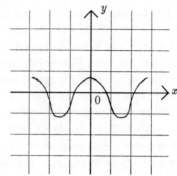

3 a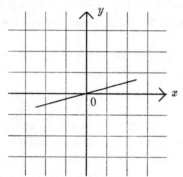

b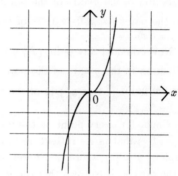

c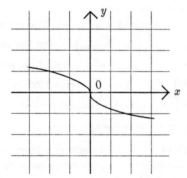

d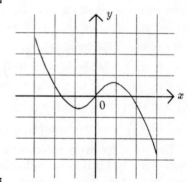

e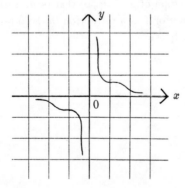

f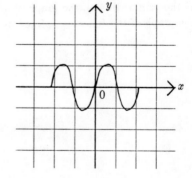

4 If f is an odd function and, hence, symmetric with respect to the origin, then $(a, b) \in f$ implies that $(-a, -b) \in f$. Therefore, if $a \in D$, then it must be the case that $-a \in D$. Now $(a, b) \in f$ means that $f(a) = b$ and $(-a, -b) \in f$ means that $f(-a) = -b$. Hence $f(a) = -f(-a)$, and condition 2 is necessary for f to be an odd function. Conversely, assume that conditions 1 and 2 of the exercise are satisfied. If $(a, b) \in f$, then condition 1 implies that $(-a, c) \in f$. Now $(a, b) \in f$ means that $f(a) = b$ and $(-a, c) \in f$ means that $f(-a) = c$. But condition 2 of the exercise implies that $-f(-a) = b$. Hence, $c = -b$, and $(-a, -b) \in f$. Thus, $(a, b) \in f$ implies that $(-a, -b) \in f$, so that the graph of f is symmetric with respect to the origin. Therefore, f is an odd function.

5 Consider any point $(x_0, y_0) = \left(x_0,\ f(-x_0)\right)$ on the graph of $y = f(-x)$. The reflection in the y-axis of the point (x_0, y_0) is the point $(-x_0, y_0) = \left(-x_0,\ f(-x_0)\right)$. But the point $\left(-x_0,\ f(-x_0)\right)$ is of the form $\left(x,\ f(x)\right)$ and, hence, lies on the graph of $y = f(x)$.

Now consider any point $(x_1, y_1) = \left(x_1,\ f(x_1)\right)$ on the graph of $y = f(x)$. The reflection in the y-axis of the point (x_1, y_1) is the point $(-x_1, y_1) = \left(-x_1,\ f(x_1)\right)$. But the point $\left(-x_1,\ f(x_1)\right)$ is of the form $\left(x,\ f(-x)\right)$ and, hence, lies on the graph of $y = f(-x)$.

Since, for every point on the graph of $y = f(-x)$, there is a point on the graph of $y = f(x)$ that is its reflection in the y-axis and since, for every point on the graph of $y = f(x)$, there is a point on the graph of $y = f(-x)$ that is its reflection in the y-axis; it follows that the graph of any function f is a reflection in the y-axis of the graph of the function defined by $y = f(-x)$.

6 Let $(x_0, y_0) = \left(x_0,\ -f(-x_0)\right)$ be a point on the graph of $y = -f(-x)$. The reflection in the origin of the point (x_0, y_0) is $(-x_0, -y_0) = \left(-x_0,\ f(-x_0)\right)$. Since the point $\left(-x_0,\ f(-x_0)\right)$ is of the form $\left(x,\ f(x)\right)$, it is on the graph of $y = f(x)$. Now let $(x_1, y_1) = \left(x_1,\ f(x_1)\right)$ be a point on the graph of $y = f(x)$. The reflection in the origin of the point (x_1, y_1) is $(-x_1, -y_1) = \left(-x_1,\ -f(x_1)\right)$. Since the point $\left(-x_1,\ -f(x_1)\right)$ is of the form $\left(x_1,\ -f(-x_1)\right)$, it is on the graph of $y = -f(-x)$.

Therefore, for every point on the graph of $y = -f(-x)$ there is a point on the graph of $y = f(x)$ that is its reflection in the origin; and, for every point on the graph of $y = f(x)$, there is a point on the graph of $y = -f(-x)$ that is its reflection in the origin. Hence, the graph of any function f is a reflection in the origin of the graph of the function defined by $y = -f(-x)$.

1 a

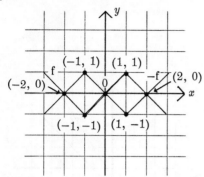

b

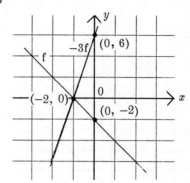

c

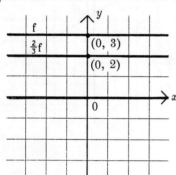

d

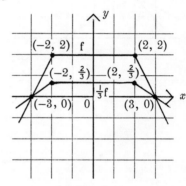

2 Condition a

3 Condition c

4 Condition a

5 Condition c

6 Condition b

7 Condition d

8 Suppose that the graphs of f and af intersect at a point on the y-axis. Any point on the y-axis that is on the graph of f is of the form $\left(0,\ f(0)\right)$, and any point on the y-axis that is on the graph of af is of the form $\left(0,\ af(0)\right)$. For any point of intersection of the two graphs on the y-axis, it must be the case that $\left(0,\ f(0)\right) = \left(0,\ af(0)\right)$. Hence, $f(0) = af(0)$. But if $a \neq 1$, then $f(0) = af(0)$ if and only if $f(0) = 0$.

9 Any point on the graph of f is of the form $\left(x,\ f(x)\right)$ and any point on the graph of af is of the form $\left(x,\ af(x)\right)$. If a given point is a point of intersection of the two graphs, then it must be the case that $\left(x,\ f(x)\right) = \left(x,\ af(x)\right)$. Hence, for a point of intersection, we have $f(x) = af(x)$. Since $a \neq 1$, $f(x) = af(x)$ if and only if $f(x) = 0$. Thus, every point of intersection is of the form $(x,\ 0)$ and must lie on the x-axis.

10 The average rate of change of a function f over the interval $x_1 \leq x \leq x_2$ is $\dfrac{f(x_2) - f(x_1)}{x_2 - x_1}$. The average rate of change of function af over this interval is

$$\frac{a\mathrm{f}(x_2) - a\mathrm{f}(x_1)}{x_2 - x_1} = \frac{a\left(\mathrm{f}(x_2) - \mathrm{f}(x_1)\right)}{x_2 - x_1} = a \cdot \frac{\left(\mathrm{f}(x_2) - \mathrm{f}(x_1)\right)}{x_2 - x_1}.$$

Pages 147-150

1 a

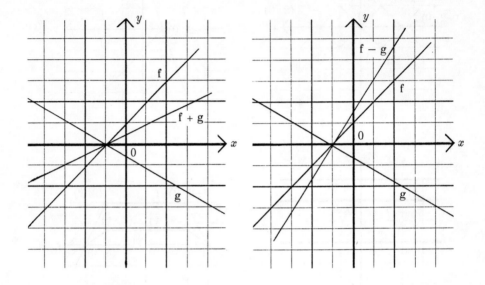

b

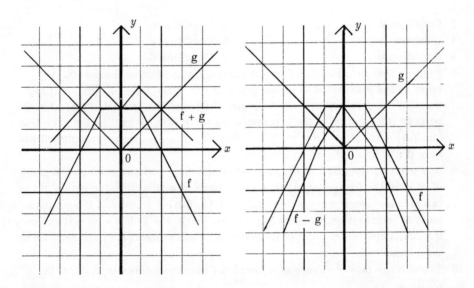

c

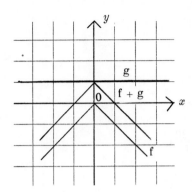

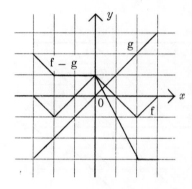

d

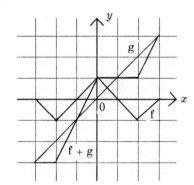

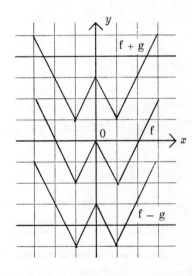

2 a   b

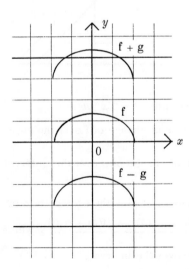

3 Each point in the graph of f + g is *a* units above the point with the same abscissa
   in the graph of f. Each point in the graph of f + g is |*a*| units below the point with
   the same abscissa in the graph of f.

4 a $(f + g)(x) = \dfrac{4x - 2}{x^2}$. $\quad (f - g)(x) = \dfrac{2x - 8}{2x^2}$.

b $(f + g)(x) = \dfrac{x^2 + 6}{x + 1}$. $\quad (f - g)(x) = \dfrac{x^2 - 8}{1 + x}$.

c $(f + g)(x) = \dfrac{41}{14x}$. $\quad (f - g)(x) = \dfrac{-29}{14x}$.

d $(f + g)(x) = \dfrac{-x + 12}{x - 2}$. $\quad (f - g)(x) = \dfrac{3x + 6}{x - 2}$.

e $(f + g)(x) = \dfrac{-2x + 20}{15x^2}$. $\quad (f - g)(x) = \dfrac{8x - 20}{15x^2}$.

f $(f + g)(x) = \dfrac{3x - 4}{2x(x - 1)}$. $\quad (f - g)(x) = \dfrac{3x + 4}{2x(x - 1)}$.

5

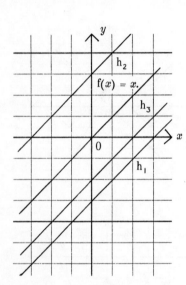

6

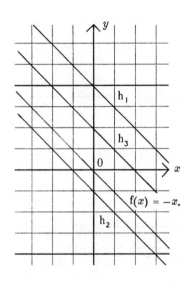

7 The average rate of change of f + g over the interval $a \leqq x \leqq b$ is

$\dfrac{\big(f(b) + g(b)\big) - \big(f(a) + g(a)\big)}{b - a}$. The average rate of change of f over the same

interval is $\dfrac{f(b) - f(a)}{b - a}$, and the average rate of change of g over this interval is

$\dfrac{g(b) - g(a)}{b - a}$. Hence, the average rate of change of f plus the average rate of

change of g is $\dfrac{f(b) - f(a)}{b - a} + \dfrac{g(b) - g(a)}{b - a} = \dfrac{\big(f(b) + g(b)\big) - \big(f(a) + g(a)\big)}{b - a}$, which is

equal to the average rate of change of f + g over the interval.

8 The average rate of change of f − g over the interval $a \leqq x \leqq b$ is

$\dfrac{\big(f(b) - g(b)\big) - \big(f(a) - g(a)\big)}{b - a} = \dfrac{\big(f(b) - f(a)\big) - \big(g(b) - g(a)\big)}{b - a}$. The difference of the average rates of change of f and g over this same interval is

$$\frac{f(b) - f(a)}{b - a} - \frac{g(b) - g(a)}{b - a} = \frac{\left(f(b) - f(a)\right) - \left(g(b) - g(a)\right)}{b - a}.$$

9 Since f is an increasing function, $x_1 < x_2$ implies that $f(x_1) \leq f(x_2)$. Since g is an increasing function $x_1 < x_2$ implies that $g(x_1) \leq g(x_2)$. Therefore, $x_1 < x_2$ implies that $f(x_1) + g(x_1) \leq f(x_2) + g(x_2)$. But $f(x_1) + g(x_1) = (f + g)(x_1)$ and $f(x_2) + g(x_2) = (f + g)(x_2)$. Thus, $x_1 < x_2$ implies that $(f + g)(x_1) \leq (f + g)(x_2)$, and, hence, $f + g$ is an increasing function.

Pages 151-153

1 a $5f(x) = \dfrac{15x}{(x - 3)^2}$; $5g(x) = \dfrac{5}{x - 3}$; hence, $5f(x) + 5g(x) = \dfrac{20x - 15}{(x - 3)^2}$.

$f(x) + g(x) = \dfrac{4x - 3}{(x - 3)^2}$; hence, $5\left(f(x) + g(x)\right) = \dfrac{20x - 15}{(x - 3)^2}$.

b $2f(x) = \dfrac{28}{x^2 - x}$; $2g(x) = \dfrac{2x}{1 - x}$; hence, $2f(x) + 2g(x) = \dfrac{28 - 2x^2}{x^2 - x}$.

$f(x) + g(x) = \dfrac{14 - x^2}{x^2 - x}$; hence, $2\left(f(x) + g(x)\right) = \dfrac{28 - 2x^2}{x^2 - x}$.

c $3f(x) = \dfrac{3x}{x + 6}$; $3g(x) = \dfrac{3x}{x^2 + 4x - 12}$; hence, $3f(x) + 3g(x) = \dfrac{3x^2 - 3x}{x^2 + 4x - 12}$.

$f(x) + g(x) = \dfrac{x^2 - x}{x^2 + 4x - 12}$; hence, $3\left(f(x) + g(x)\right) = \dfrac{3x^2 - 3x}{x^2 + 4x - 12}$.

d $2f(x) = \dfrac{2}{x^2 - 25}$; $2g(x) = \dfrac{2}{x^2 - 4x - 5}$; hence, $2f(x) + 2g(x) = \dfrac{4x + 12}{(x^2 - 25)(x + 1)}$.

$f(x) + g(x) = \dfrac{2x + 6}{(x^2 - 25)(x + 1)}$; hence, $2\left(f(x) + g(x)\right) = \dfrac{4x + 12}{(x^2 - 25)(x + 1)}$.

2 a

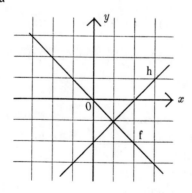

b

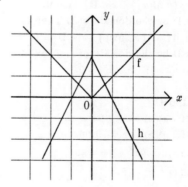

c

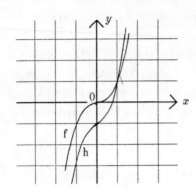

d

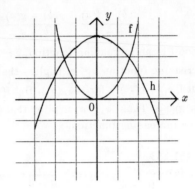

3 $(f + g)(x) = \dfrac{3}{2x}$. $\dfrac{3}{2x} = \dfrac{1}{6}$ if and only if $x = 9$.

4 $(f + g)(x) = \dfrac{16}{3x}$. $\dfrac{16}{3x} = 1$ if and only if $x = \dfrac{16}{3}$.

5 $(f + g)(x) = \dfrac{x^2 + x + 3}{x^2 - 1}$. $\dfrac{x^2 + x + 3}{x^2 - 1} = 1$ if and only if $x = -4$.

6 $(f + g)(x) = \dfrac{9x^2 - 10x}{3x^2 - 11x - 4}$. $\dfrac{9x^2 - 10x}{3x^2 - 11x - 4} = 3$ if and only if $x = -\dfrac{12}{23}$.

7 Let D be the domain of f. Then $(a + b)f = \{(x, (a + b)\, f(x)) \mid x \in D\}$. Also, $af = \{(x, af(x)) \mid x \in D\}$ and $bf = \{(x, bf(x)) \mid x \in D\}$. Hence, $af + bf = \{(x, af(x) + bf(x)) \mid x \in D\}$. Since multiplication is distributive over addition of real numbers, we have $af(x) + bf(x) = (a + b)\, f(x)$, so that $af + bf = \{(x, (a + b)\, f(x)) \mid x \in D\} = (a + b)f$.

8 Let D be the domain of f. Then $(ab)f = \{(x, (ab)f(x)) \mid x \in D\}$. Also, $bf = \{(x, bf(x)) \mid x \in D\}$, so that $a(bf) = \{(x, a[bf(x)]) \mid x \in D\}$. Since multiplication of real numbers is associative, $a[bf(x)] = (ab)f(x)$. Hence, $a(bf) = \{(x, (ab)f(x)) \mid x \in D\} = (ab)f$.

9 Let D be the domain of f. Then $1f = \{(x, 1 \cdot f(x)) \mid x \in D\}$. Since $1 \cdot f(x) = f(x)$, $1f = \{(x, f(x)) \mid x \in D\} = f$.

10 Let D be the domain of f. Then $0f = \{(x, 0 \cdot f(x)) \mid x \in D\}$. Since $0 \cdot f(x) = 0$, $0f = \{(x, 0) \mid x \in D\} = \overline{0}$.

Pages 156-157

1 a $(f \cdot g)(x) = x^2 + 2x - 8$.

 b $(f \cdot g)(x) = x^4 - 0.09$.

2 a $g(x) = -2x^2 + 3x + 8$.

 b $g(x) = x + 12$.

 c $g(x) = 2x + 7$.

 c $(f \cdot g)(x) = x^3 + 1$.

 d $(f \cdot g)(x) = x^3 - 3x^2 + 2x - 6$.

 d $g(x) = 4x^2 + 2x - 1$.

 e $g(x) = x^2 + 2x - 1$.

 f $g(x) = x^2 + x + 1$.

3 $\frac{f}{g}(x) = \frac{3x-1}{5x-4}$. If $\frac{3x-1}{5x-4} = \frac{2}{3}$, then $3(3x-1) = 2(5x-4)$. Hence, $\frac{f}{g}(x) = \frac{2}{3}$ when $x = 5$.

4 $x = 3$.   **5** $x = 3$ or $x = -3$.

6 a Average rate of change of f: $\frac{7-3}{4-2} = 2$. Average rate of change of g:

$\frac{15-3}{2} = 6$. Average rate of change of f · g: $\frac{105-9}{2} = 48$. Average rate of

change of $\frac{f}{g}$: $\frac{\frac{7}{15}-1}{2} = -\frac{4}{15}$.

b No, $2 \cdot 6 \neq 48$. No, $\frac{2}{6} \neq -\frac{4}{15}$.

7 $f \cdot g = \left\{ \left(x, f(x) \cdot g(x) \right) \mid f(x) \cdot g(x) \text{ is defined} \right\}$. Now $f(x) \cdot g(x) = g(x) \cdot f(x)$, by the commutative property of multiplication of real numbers. Hence, $f \cdot g = \left\{ \left(x, g(x) \cdot f(x) \right) \mid g(x) \cdot f(x) \text{ is defined} \right\} = g \cdot f$.

8 $g \cdot h = \left\{ \left(x, g(x) \cdot h(x) \right) \mid g(x) \cdot h(x) \text{ is defined} \right\}$. Hence, $f \cdot (g \cdot h) = \left\{ \left(x, f(x) \cdot [g(x) \cdot h(x)] \right) \mid f(x) \cdot [g(x) \cdot h(x)] \text{ is defined} \right\}$. $f \cdot g = \left\{ \left(x, f(x) \cdot g(x) \right) \mid f(x) \cdot g(x) \text{ is defined} \right\}$. Hence, $(f \cdot g) \cdot h = \left\{ \left(x, [f(x) \cdot g(x)] \cdot h(x) \right) \mid [f(x) \cdot g(x)] \cdot h(x) \text{ is defined} \right\}$. By the associative property of multiplication of real numbers, $f(x) \cdot [g(x) \cdot h(x)] = [f(x) \cdot g(x)] \cdot h(x)$. Therefore, $f \cdot (g \cdot h) = (f \cdot g) \cdot h$.

9 $g + h = \left\{ \left(x, g(x) + h(x) \right) \mid g(x) + h(x) \text{ is defined} \right\}$. Thus, $f \cdot (g + h) = \left\{ \left(x, f(x) \cdot [g(x) + h(x)] \right) \mid f(x) \cdot [g(x) + h(x)] \text{ is defined} \right\}$. Since multiplication is distributive over addition of real numbers, $f(x) \cdot [g(x) + h(x)] = [f(x) \cdot g(x)] + [f(x) \cdot h(x)]$. Hence, $f \cdot (g + h) = \left\{ \left(x, [f(x) \cdot g(x)] + [f(x) \cdot h(x)] \right) \mid [f(x) \cdot g(x)] + [f(x) \cdot h(x)] \text{ is defined} \right\} = (f \cdot g) + (f \cdot h)$.

10 $g + h = \left\{ \left(x, g(x) + h(x) \right) \mid g(x) + h(x) \text{ is defined} \right\}$. Therefore, $\frac{g+h}{f} =$

$\left\{ \left(x, \frac{g(x)+h(x)}{f(x)} \right) \mid \frac{g(x)+h(x)}{f(x)} \text{ is defined} \right\}$. By the distributive property,

$\frac{g(x)+h(x)}{f(x)} = \left(g(x) + h(x) \right) \cdot \frac{1}{f(x)} = g(x) \cdot \frac{1}{f(x)} + h(x) \cdot \frac{1}{f(x)} = \frac{g(x)}{f(x)} + \frac{h(x)}{f(x)}$. Hence,

$\frac{g+h}{f} = \left\{ \left(x, \frac{g(x)}{f(x)} + \frac{h(x)}{f(x)} \right) \mid \frac{g(x)}{f(x)} + \frac{h(x)}{f(x)} \text{ is defined} \right\} = \frac{g}{f} + \frac{h}{f}$.

11 $f \cdot \frac{1}{g} = \left\{ \left(x, f(x) \cdot \frac{1}{g(x)} \right) \mid f(x) \cdot \frac{1}{g(x)} \text{ is defined} \right\}$. By definition of multiplication

of real numbers, $f(x) \cdot \frac{1}{g(x)} = \frac{f(x)}{g(x)}$. Hence, $f \cdot \frac{1}{g} = \left\{ \left(x, \frac{f(x)}{g(x)} \right) \mid \frac{f(x)}{g(x)} \text{ is defined} \right\} = \frac{f}{g}$.

Pages 159-161

1 a $f \circ g = \{(0, 4), (2, 4), (4, 0), (6, 8), (8, 4)\}$.

b **c**

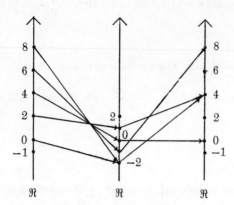 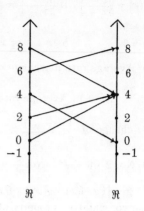

2 a g o f = {(−2, 0), (−1, −2), (0, −2), (1, 0), (2, −1)}.

b **c**

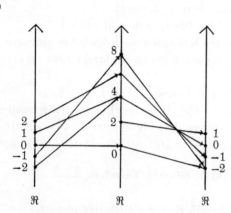 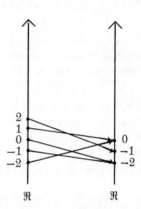

3 a (f o g)(1) = f(3) = 4.   c f$\big($f(1)$\big)$ = f(0) = 1.

  b (g o f)(−2) = g(9) = 19.   d g$\big($g(−3.5)$\big)$ = g(−6) = −11.

4 a (f o g)(x) = f(2x + 1) = (2x + 1 − 1)^2 = 4x^2. Hence, x = ±2.

  b (g o f)(x) = g $(x − 1)^2$ = 2(x − 1)^2 + 1 = 2x^2 − 4x + 3. Hence, x = 2 or x = 0.

  c g$\big($g(x)$\big)$ = g(2x + 1) = 2(2x + 1) + 1 = 4x + 3. Hence, x = −2.

  d f$\big($f(x)$\big)$ = f$\big($(x − 1)$^2\big)$ = $\big($(x − 1)^2 − 1$\big)^2$ = (x^2 − 2x)^2 = x^2(x^2 − 4x + 4). Hence,
    x = 3 or x = −1.

5 a (f o g)(x) = f(x^3) = 5x^3; (g o f)(x) = g(5x) = 125x^3.

  b (f o g)(x) = f(2x^2) = 2x^2 − 3; (g o f)(x) = g(x − 3) = 2(x − 3)^2 = 2x^2 − 12x + 18.

  c (f o g)(x) = f(x + 7) = x; (g o f)(x) = g(x − 7) = x.

  d (f o g)(x) = f$\big($(x − 1)$^2\big)$ = 2(x − 1)^2 − 3 = 2x^2 − 4x − 1; (g o f)(x) = g(2x − 3) =
    (2x − 4)^2 = 4x^2 − 16x + 16.

  e (f o g)(x) = f(3x − 1) = (3x − 1)^2 + 1 = 9x^2 − 6x + 2; (g o f)(x) = g(x^2 + 1) =
    3 (x^2 + 1) −1 = 3x^2 + 2.

f $(f \circ g)(x) = f(5x + 4) = -3; (g \circ f)(x) = g(-3) = -11.$

g $(f \circ g)(x) = f\left(\dfrac{x + 1}{3}\right) = x; (g \circ f)(x) = g(3x - 1) = x.$

h $(f \circ g)(x) = f\left((x + 1)^3\right) = 2(x + 1)^3 = 2x^3 + 6x^2 + 6x + 2; (g \circ f)(x) = g(2x) =$
$(2x + 1)^3 = 8x^3 + 12x^2 + 6x + 1.$

6 $g(x) = x - 2.$

7 a $F(x) = 5x - 3.$

b $G(x) = \dfrac{x + 3}{5}.$

c $(F \circ G)(x) = F\left(\dfrac{x + 3}{5}\right) = x; (G \circ F)(x) = G(5x - 3) = x.$

8 For any function f, $f(x) = f(x)$; hence, $I\left(f(x)\right) = f(x)$. Since $I(x) = x$, $f\left((I)x\right) = f(x).$

9 $(f \circ g)(x) = f(m_2x + b_2) = m_1 m_2 x + (m_1 b_2 + b_1).$ Hence, $\left((f \circ g) \circ h\right)(x) = (f \circ g)(m_3 x + b_3) =$
$m_1 m_2 m_3 x + (m_1 m_2 b_3 + m_1 b_2 + b_1).$ $(g \circ h)(x) = g(m_3 x + b_3) = m_2 m_3 x + (m_2 b_3 + b_2).$
Therefore, $\left(f \circ (g \circ h)\right)(x) = f\left(m_2 m_3 x + (m_2 b_3 + b_2)\right) = m_1 m_2 m_3 x + (m_1 m_2 b_3 + m_1 b_2 + b_1).$
Hence, $(f \circ g) \circ h = f \circ (g \circ h).$

10 a

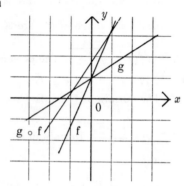

b

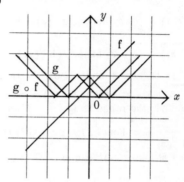

11 a

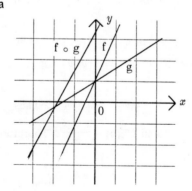

b

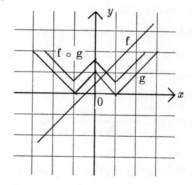

Pages 165-166

1 Function f has no inverse because two of the elements obtained by reversing the
components, $(1, -1)$ and $(1, 1)$, have the same first component.

2 Function g has an inverse. $g^{-1} = \{(5, 0), (4, 1), (3, 2), (2, 3), (1, 4), (0, 5)\} = g$.

3 Function h has an inverse. $h^{-1} = \{(-3, -3), (-1, -2), (0, 0), (2, 1), (3, 3)\}$.

4 Function f has no inverse because all five elements of the set obtained by reversing the components have the same first component.

5 The inverse is the set of all ordered pairs of real numbers in which the second component of each pair is greater by 5 than the first component.

6 The inverse is the set of ordered pairs of real numbers in which the second component of each pair is one half the first component.

7 The function has no inverse because all ordered pairs obtained by reversing the components would have 1 as their first component.

8 The function has no inverse. For example, $(3, 3)$ and $(3, -3)$ are both contained in the set obtained by reversing the components.

9 The function has no inverse. For example, both $(\pi, \sqrt{\pi})$ and $(\pi, -\sqrt{\pi})$ are contained in the set obtained by reversing the components.

10 The inverse function is the set of ordered pairs in which the second component is the square of the first component. The domain is $\{x \mid x \in \Re \text{ and } x \geq 0\}$.

11 $-7(f^{-1}(x)) + 2 = x$; hence, $f^{-1}(x) = \dfrac{x - 2}{-7}$. The domain and range of f^{-1} are $\Re$.

12 $\dfrac{1}{4}(g^{-1}(x)) - \dfrac{5}{4} = x$; hence, $g^{-1}(x) = 4x + 5$. The domain and range of g^{-1} are $\Re$.

13 $\sqrt{(h^{-1}(x))^2 - 3} = x$; hence, $(h^{-1}(x))^2 - 3 = x^2$, or $h^{-1}(x) = \sqrt{x^2 + 3}$. The domain of h^{-1} is $\{x \mid x \in \Re \text{ and } x \geq 0\}$; the range of h^{-1} is $\{y \mid y \in \Re \text{ and } y \geq \sqrt{3}\}$.

14 $\sqrt{F^{-1}(x)} + 5 = x$; hence, $F^{-1}(x) = x^2 - 10x + 25$. The domain of F^{-1} is $\{x \mid x \in \Re \text{ and } x \geq 5\}$; the range is $\{y \mid y \in \Re \text{ and } y \geq 0\}$.

15 $\dfrac{1}{2 + G^{-1}(x)} = x$; hence, $1 = 2x + G^{-1}(x) \cdot x$, or $G^{-1}(x) = \dfrac{1 - 2x}{x}$. Domain of G^{-1}: $\{x \mid x \in \Re \text{ and } x < 0\}$; range of G^{-1}: $\{y \mid y \in \Re \text{ and } y < -2\}$.

16 $4([H^{-1}(x)]^2) + 2 = x$; hence, $H^{-1}(x) = \dfrac{\sqrt{x - 2}}{2}$. Domain of H^{-1}: $\{x \mid x \in \Re \text{ and } x \geq 2\}$; range of H^{-1}: $\{y \mid y \in \Re \text{ and } y \geq 0\}$.

17 Let g be the function $\{(x, y) \mid (x, y) \in g\}$. Then g^{-1} is $\{(y, x) \mid (x, y) \in g\}$ by Definition 29/4. Again by Definition 29/4, $(g^{-1})^{-1}$ is $\{(x, y) \mid (y, x) \in g^{-1}\}$. Hence, $(g^{-1})^{-1} = g$.

18 $(f \circ g)(x) = f(g(x)) = f(m_2 x + b_2) = m_1(m_2 x + b_2) + b_1 = m_1 m_2 x + m_1 b_2 + b_1$. Thus $(f \circ g)^{-1}(x) = \dfrac{x - b_1 - m_1 b_2}{m_1 m_2}$. Now $g^{-1}(x) = \dfrac{x - b_2}{m_2}$ and $f^{-1}(x) = \dfrac{x - b_1}{m_1}$. Therefore,

$$g^{-1} \circ f^{-1} = g^{-1}(f^{-1}(x)) = g^{-1}\left(\dfrac{x - b_1}{m_1}\right) = \dfrac{\dfrac{x - b_1}{m_1} - b_2}{m_2} = \dfrac{x - b_1 - m_1 b_2}{m_1 m_2}.$$ Hence, $(f \circ g)^{-1} = g^{-1} \circ f^{-1}$.

19 $(f \circ g)(x) = f(g(x)) = f(x^3) = mx^3 + b$. Therefore, $(f \circ g)^{-1}(x) = \sqrt[3]{\dfrac{x - b}{m}}$. Now $g^{-1}(x) = \sqrt[3]{x}$ and $f^{-1}(x) = \dfrac{x - b}{m}$. Thus, $g^{-1} \circ f^{-1} = g^{-1}\left(\dfrac{x - b}{m}\right) = \sqrt[3]{\dfrac{x - b}{m}}$.

Hence, $(f \circ g)^{-1} = g^{-1} \circ f^{-1}$.

1

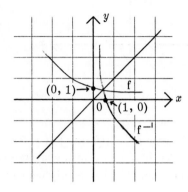

2 The function is its own inverse, so the graphs of f and f^{-1} are identical.

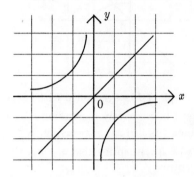

3

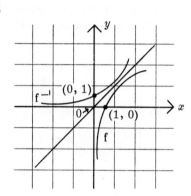

4 The function does not have an inverse. One possible restriction and its inverse are shown below.

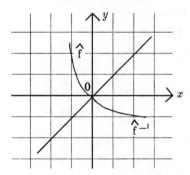

5

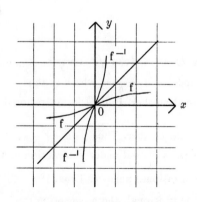

6 The function does not have an inverse. One possible restriction and its inverse are shown below.

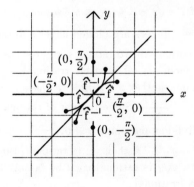

7 The function has no inverse. A restriction and its inverse are shown below.

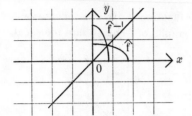

8 The function has no inverse. A restriction and its inverse are shown below.

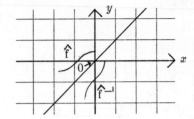

9 The graph of f is symmetric with respect to the line $y = x$.

10 a Let f be a strictly increasing function with inverse $f^{-1} = \{(f(x), x) \mid (x, f(x)) \in f\}$. Since f is strictly increasing, $x_1 > x_2$ implies that $f(x_1) > f(x_2)$ and, conversely, $f(x_1) > f(x_2)$ implies that $x_1 > x_2$. But this means that f^{-1} is a strictly increasing function.

b Let g be a strictly decreasing function with inverse $g^{-1} = \{(g(x), x) \mid (x, g(x)) \in g\}$. Since g is strictly decreasing, $x_1 > x_2$ implies that $g(x_1) < g(x_2)$ and, conversely, $g(x_1) < g(x_2)$ implies that $x_1 > x_2$. Hence, g^{-1} is a strictly decreasing function.

Chapter review
Pages 171-175

1 d	10 c	19 a
2 b	11 b	20 a
3 c	12 b	21 c
4 c	13 c	22 b
5 d	14 b	23 d
6 c	15 a	24 b
7 c	16 c	25 b
8 b	17 c	26 c
9 d	18 b	27 a

Cumulative review
Pages 175-177

1 a If $1 + \sqrt{2} = \frac{a}{b}$ with a, $b \in \mathcal{I}$ and $b \neq 0$, then $\sqrt{2} = \frac{a}{b} - 1$, or $\sqrt{2} = \frac{a - b}{b}$. Since the integers are closed under subtraction and $b \neq 0$, $\frac{a - b}{b}$, which is the quotient of two integers, represents a rational number. But $\sqrt{2}$ is not rational; hence, $1 + \sqrt{2}$ must be irrational.

b Suppose that $x + y\sqrt{2} = r$, where r is a rational number. Then $y\sqrt{2} = r - x$, or $\sqrt{2} = \frac{r - x}{y}$. Since the set of rational numbers is closed under subtraction and division and since $y \neq 0$, $\frac{r - x}{y}$ represents a rational number. Thus, if $x + y\sqrt{2} = r$, then $\sqrt{2}$ is rational. Since $\sqrt{2}$ is irrational, the assumption that $x + y\sqrt{2}$ is rational must be false. Thus, it must be the case that $x + y\sqrt{2}$ is irrational.

2 a Unbounded **c** Bounded below
b Bounded **d** Bounded above
e Bounded, if $\emptyset$ is considered to be a bounded set
f Bounded

3 $(2 - 3i)^2 - 4(2 - 3i) + 13 = -5 - 12i - 8 + 12i + 13 = 0$.

4 a $f(-4) = 8 - \sqrt{25 - 16} = 5$. $f\big(f(3)\big) = f(4) = 5$.
b The greatest lower bound of the domain is -5, and the least upper bound of the domain is 5. The greatest lower bound of the range is 3 and the least upper bound of the range is 8.

5 a The graph of a function g having these properties is shown below.

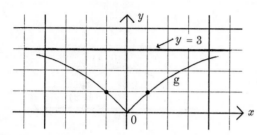

b As $|x|$ increases, the graph of g gets closer and closer to the line $y = 3$.

6 The distance of a point (x, y) from the point $(2, 0)$ is $\sqrt{(x - 2)^2 + y^2}$. The distance of a point (x, y) from the line $x = -2$ is $\sqrt{(x + 2)^2 + (y - y)^2} = \sqrt{(x + 2)^2}$. If these two distances are to be equal, then $\sqrt{(x - 2)^2 + y^2} = \sqrt{(x + 2)^2}$, or $(x - 2)^2 + y^2 = (x + 2)^2$. This equation is equivalent to $x^2 - 4x + 4 + y^2 = x^2 + 4x + 4$, or $y^2 = 8x$.
b No. For example, both $(2, 4)$ and $(2 - 4)$ are contained in the set of ordered pairs determined by this equation.

7 Suppose that $x_1 > x_2$. Then $g(x_1) = (x_1)^2 + 6x_1$ and $g(x_2) = (x_2)^2 + 6x_2$. But since $x_1 > x_2$ and both are greater than or equal to zero, $(x_1)^2 > (x_2)^2$ and $6x_1 > 6x_2$. Hence, $(x_1)^2 + 6x_1 > (x_2)^2 + 6x_2$, which means that $g(x_1) > g(x_2)$.

8 a 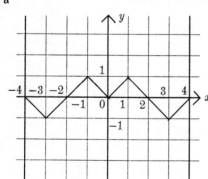   **b**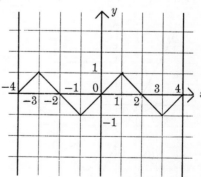

9 a
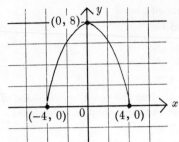

b
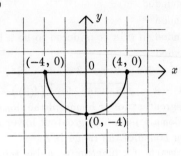

c
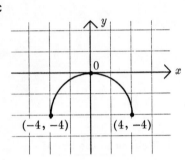

d
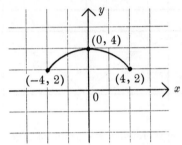

10 a $(f \cdot g)(x) = \dfrac{6x^2}{x^2 - x - 6}$. Hence, $(f \cdot g)(x) = 6$ when $x = -6$.

b $\dfrac{f}{g}(x) = \dfrac{3x^2 - 9x}{2x^2 + 4x}$. Hence, $\dfrac{f}{g}(x) = 2$ when $x = -17$.

c $(f + g)(x) = \dfrac{5x^2 - 5x}{x^2 - x - 6}$. Hence, $(f + g)(x) = 0$ when $x = 0$ and when $x = 1$.

11 $(f \circ g)(x) = f(x - 4) = (x - 4)^2 - (x - 4) + 5 = x^2 - 9x + 25$.

$(g \circ f)(x) = g(x^2 - x + 5) = x^2 - x + 1$. Thus, $(f \circ g)(x) \geq (g \circ f)(x)$ whenever $x^2 - 9x + 25 \geq x^2 - x + 1$; that is, whenever $x \leq 3$.

12 a Yes. Since f is a one-to-one function, it has an inverse.

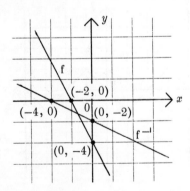

b The graph of f^{-1} is shown on page 62.

c $-2\left(f^{-1}(x)\right) - 4 = x$. Hence, $f^{-1}(x) = \dfrac{x + 4}{-2}$.

13 a Each ordinate of f is doubled and then reflected in the x-axis to obtain each ordinate of g.

b The graph of h is the graph of f shifted upward 3 units.

c The graph of G is the graph of f reflected in the y-axis.

d The graph of f^{-1} is the graph of f reflected in the line $y = x$.

Chapter 5
Constant and linear functions

Pages 183-185

1 a -1 **c** $-\sqrt{3}$ **e** $-\sqrt{3}$

  b 1 **d** $-\dfrac{1}{\sqrt{3}}$ **f** m

2 a Collinear; $\dfrac{-4 - 2}{7 - 3} = \dfrac{8 - (-4)}{-1 - 7}$.

b Not collinear; $\dfrac{3 - (-1)}{0 - (-1)} \neq \dfrac{7 - 3}{3 - 0}$.

c Collinear; $\dfrac{-1 - 6}{1 - 6} = \dfrac{-8 - (-1)}{-4 - 1}$.

d Collinear; $\dfrac{\dfrac{b + d}{2} - b}{\dfrac{a + c}{2} - a} = \dfrac{d - b}{c - a}$.

e Collinear; $\dfrac{\dfrac{2b + d}{3} - b}{\dfrac{2a + c}{3} - a} = \dfrac{d - b}{c - a}$.

f Collinear; $\dfrac{\dfrac{b + 2d}{3} - b}{\dfrac{a + 2c}{3} - a} = \dfrac{2d - 2b}{2c - 2a} = \dfrac{d - b}{c - a}$.

3 a   **b**

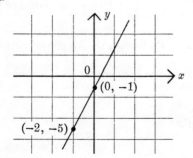

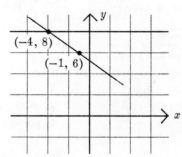

c

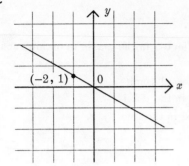

d

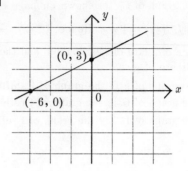

e

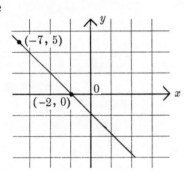

f

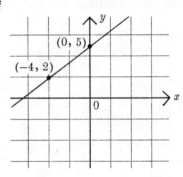

4

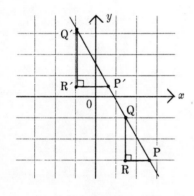

The coordinates of points P, Q, R, P′, Q′, and R′, are as follows: $P(x_1, y_1)$, $Q(x_2, y_2)$, $R(x_2, y_1)$, $P′(x_3, y_3)$, $Q′(x_4, y_4)$, and $R′(x_4, y_3)$.

Since their corresponding angles are congruent, triangles PQR and P′Q′R′ are similar. Hence, $\dfrac{d(R,Q)}{d(R,P)} = \dfrac{d(R′,Q′)}{d(R′,P′)}$. But $\dfrac{d(R,Q)}{d(R,P)} = \dfrac{y_2 - y_1}{x_2 - x_1}$, which is the slope of $\overline{QP}$.

Also, $\dfrac{d(R′,Q′)}{d(R′,P′)} = \dfrac{y_4 - y_3}{x_4 - x_3}$, which is the slope of $\overline{Q′P′}$. Hence, the slopes of these

two segments, which are both contained in the same nonvertical line, are equal.

5 a $0° < \alpha < 90°$.
  b $90° < \alpha < 180°$.
  c $90° < \alpha < 180°$.
  d $0° < \alpha < 90°$.
  e $0° < \alpha < 90°$.
  f $90° < \alpha < 180°$.

6 a

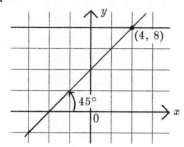

b

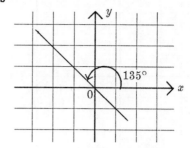

c

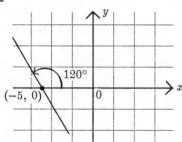

d

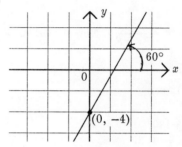

e

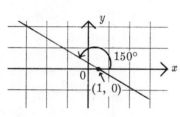

f

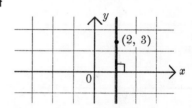

7 a 45°   c 120°   e 72°
  b 135°   d 27°   f 158°

8

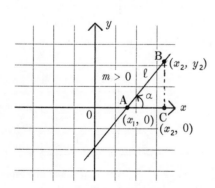

The slope of ℓ is equal to the slope of $\overline{AB}$ in ℓ. Hence, $m = \dfrac{y_2}{x_2 - x_1}$. Also

$\tan \alpha = \dfrac{d(C,B)}{d(A,C)} = \dfrac{y_2}{x_2 - x_1} = m.$

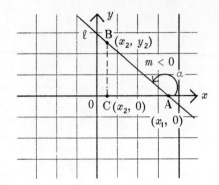

Again, $m = \dfrac{y_2}{x_2 - x_1}$. Now tan $\sphericalangle BAC = \dfrac{y_2}{x_1 - x_2} = \tan(180 - \alpha)$. Hence, $\tan(180 - \alpha) = \dfrac{-y_2}{x_2 - x_1} = -m$.

9 $0°$ or $180°$

Pages 188-190

1 a $y = \frac{2}{3}x - 5$.

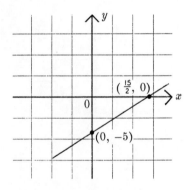

b $y = -2x + 3$.

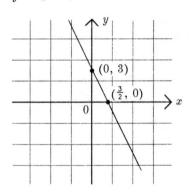

c $y = \frac{3}{4}x + 5$.

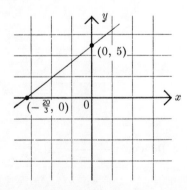

d $y = -\frac{1}{2}x - 8\frac{1}{2}$.

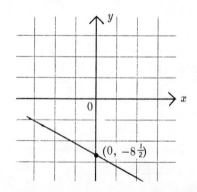

e $y = x + 1.$

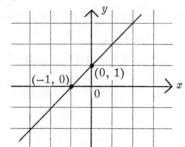

f $y = -\frac{8}{3}x + 12\frac{2}{3}.$

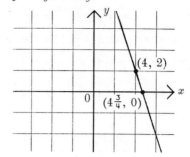

g $y = \frac{2}{3}x - 4.$

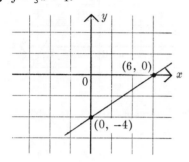

h $y = -\frac{3}{2}x + 3.$

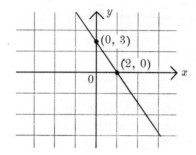

i Since $\tan 45 = 1,\ m = 1.$
$y = x - 2.$

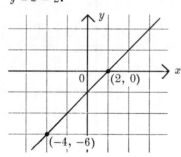

j Since $\tan(180 - 135) = 1,\ m = -1.$
$y = -x + 9.$

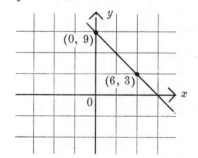

2 The y-intercept of a line that passes through the origin is $(0, 0)$. Hence, b in $y = mx + b$ is zero. Thus, the equation of a line with slope m that contains the origin is $y = mx$.

3 Since the line contains (x_1, y_1) we can substitute these coordinates in $y = mx + b$ to obtain $y_1 = mx_1 + b$. Thus, $b = y_1 - mx_1$. Therefore, the slope-intercept form of the equation becomes $y = mx + y_1 - mx_1$, which is equivalent to $y - y_1 = m(x - x_1)$.

4 Since $(a, 0)$ is contained in the line, we have $0 = ma + b$. Hence, $m = -\frac{b}{a}$, and we have $y = -\frac{b}{a}x + b$. This equation is equivalent to $\frac{b}{a}x + y = b$, or $\frac{x}{a} + \frac{y}{b} = 1$.

5 a Since $AB \neq 0$, both A and B are different from 0. From $Ax + By + C = 0$, we can obtain $By = -Ax - C$, or $y = -\frac{A}{B}x - \frac{C}{B}$, which is the slope-intercept form of the linear equation. From this form of the equation, we know immediately that $m = -\dfrac{A}{B}$ and that $(0, -\dfrac{C}{B})$ is the y-intercept of the graph. Setting y equal to zero, we obtain $(-\dfrac{C}{A}, 0)$ as the x-intercept of the line.

b Yes. $By + C = 0$, or $y = -\dfrac{C}{B}$, is the equation of a line parallel to the x-axis.

c Yes. $Ax + C = 0$, or $x = -\dfrac{C}{A}$, is the equation of a line parallel to the y-axis.

6 $y = -\dfrac{1}{5}x.$

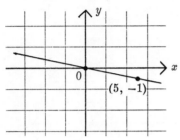

7

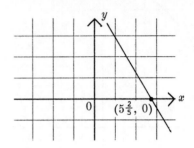

8 The equation is in point-slope form. The slope of the line is -4, and the point $(-1, 2)$ is in the line.

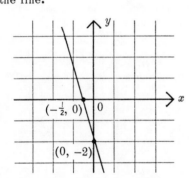

9 The intercepts are $(3, 0)$ and $(0, 5)$.

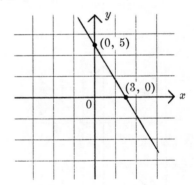

10 $y = -\dfrac{1}{2}x + 4.$

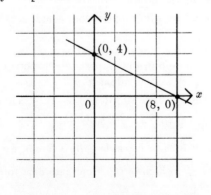

11

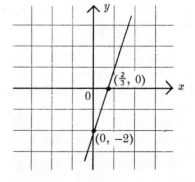

12 The equation is in point-slope form. The slope of the line is $\frac{2}{3}$ and $(2, -3)$ is in the line.

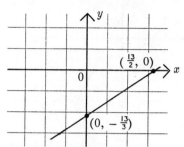

13 The intercepts are $(4, 0)$ and $(0, -7)$.

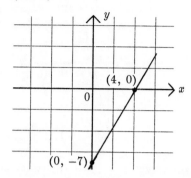

14 The average rate of change of the constant function f, defined by $f(x) = b$, over the interval $x_1 \leqq x \leqq x_2$ is $\dfrac{f(x_2) - f(x_1)}{x_2 - x_1}$. Since $f(x_2) = b = f(x_1)$, we have $\dfrac{b - b}{x_2 - x_1} = 0$.

15 The average rate of change of $f(x) = mx + b$ over the interval $x_1 \leqq x \leqq x_2$ is

$$\frac{f(x_2) - f(x_1)}{x_2 - x_1} = \frac{mx_2 + b - (mx_1 + b)}{x_2 - x_1} = \frac{m(x_2 - x_1)}{x_2 - x_1} = m.$$

Pages 193-194

1 a $y = \frac{1}{2}x + 2\frac{1}{2}$.

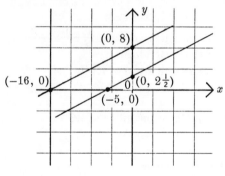

b $-\dfrac{x}{10} - \dfrac{y}{10} = 1$.

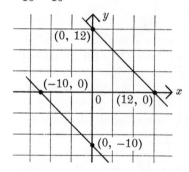

c $y = -\frac{1}{2}x$.

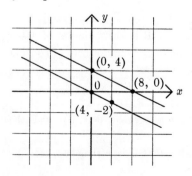

d $y = -\frac{5}{3}x + 1$.

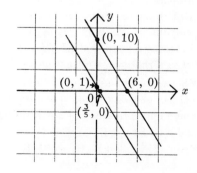

e $y = 4x + 8$.

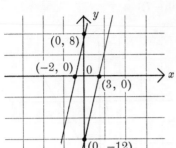

f $y = -2x - 15$.

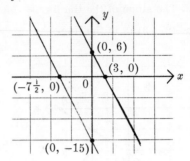

2 a $y = \frac{3}{4}x$ and $y = -\frac{3}{2}x + 18$ are the equations of the lines containing the sides with slopes $\frac{3}{4}$ and $-\frac{3}{2}$. The coordinates of the third vertex are $(8, 6)$.

b $y = \frac{3}{4}x - 9$ and $y = -\frac{3}{2}x$. The coordinates of the third vertex are $(4, -6)$.

3 a $\overline{AD}$ is contained in the line $y = \frac{2}{3}x + 9$. $\overline{CD}$ is contained in the line $y = -\frac{5}{2}x + 37\frac{1}{2}$.

b The coordinates of vertex D are $(9, 15)$.

4 Let EFGH be the quadrilateral formed, where E is the midpoint of $\overline{AB}$, F is the midpoint of $\overline{BC}$, G is the midpoint of $\overline{DC}$, and H is the midpoint of $\overline{AD}$. We must prove that $\overline{EF}$ is parallel to $\overline{HG}$ and $\overline{FG}$ is parallel to $\overline{EH}$.

1) $\overline{FG}$ has endpoints $(b + a, c)$ and $(d + b, e + c)$. Thus, the slope of $\overline{FG}$ is
$$\frac{e + c - c}{d + b - b - a} = \frac{e}{d - a}.$$

2) $\overline{EH}$ has endpoints $(a, 0)$ and (d, e). Thus, the slope of $\overline{EH}$ is $\frac{e - 0}{d - a} = \frac{e}{d - a}$.

3) Therefore, $\overline{FG} \parallel \overline{EH}$, because they have the same slope.

4) $\overline{EF}$ has endpoints $(a, 0)$ and $(b + a, c)$. Thus, the slope of $\overline{EF}$ is
$$\frac{c - 0}{b + a - a} = \frac{c}{b}.$$

5) $\overline{HG}$ has endpoints (d, e) and $(d + b, e + c)$. Thus, the slope of $\overline{HG}$ is
$$\frac{e + c - e}{d + b - d} = \frac{c}{b}.$$

6) Hence, $\overline{EF} \parallel \overline{HG}$, because they have the same slope.

7) Thus, quadrilateral EFGH is a parallelogram, because its opposite sides are parallel.

5 Let EFGH be the quadrilateral formed, where E is the midpoint of $\overline{AB}$, F is the midpoint of $\overline{BC}$, G is the midpoint of $\overline{DC}$, and H is the midpoint of $\overline{AD}$. By exercise 4, we know that EFGH is a parallelogram. Therefore, to prove that EFGH is a rhombus, we must prove that $\overline{EF} \cong \overline{FG} \cong \overline{GH} \cong \overline{HE}$.

1) $\overline{EF}$ has endpoints $(a, 0)$ and $(2a, b)$. Hence, $d(E, F) = \sqrt{a^2 + b^2}$.

2) $\overline{FG}$ has endpoints $(2a, b)$ and $(a, 2b)$. Hence, $d(F, G) = \sqrt{a^2 + b^2}$.

3) Since opposite sides of a parallelogram are congruent, $d(G, H) = d(E, F)$ and $d(H, E) = d(F, G)$.

4) Since $d(E,F) = d(F, G) = d(G, H) = d(H, E)$, EFGH is a rhombus.

6 a The median to the side with endpoints $(0, 0)$ and $(8, 0)$ is contained in the line $y = 4x - 16$; the median to the side with endpoints $(8, 0)$ and $(6, 8)$ is contained in the line $y = \frac{4}{7}x$; and the median to the side with endpoints $(6, 8)$ and $(0, 0)$ is contained in the line $y = -\frac{4}{5}x + 6\frac{2}{5}$.

b The intersection of lines $y = 4x - 16$ and $y = \frac{4}{7}x$ is the point $(4\frac{2}{3}, 2\frac{2}{3})$. Since $2\frac{2}{3} = -\frac{4}{5} \cdot 4\frac{2}{3} + 6\frac{2}{5}$, this point is also contained in the line $y = -\frac{4}{5}x + 6\frac{2}{5}$.

Hence, the medians intersect in a common point.

7 The median to the side with endpoints $(0, 0)$ and $(2a, 0)$ is contained in the line $y = \frac{2c}{2b - a}x - \frac{2ac}{2b - a}$; the median to the side with endpoints $(2a, 0)$ and $(2b, 2c)$ is contained in the line $y = \frac{c}{a + b}x$; and the median to the side with endpoints $(2b, 2c)$ and $(0, 0)$ is contained in the line $y = \frac{c}{b - 2a}x - \frac{2ac}{b - 2a}$. The intersection of lines $y = \frac{2c}{2b - a}x - \frac{2ac}{2b - a}$ and $y = \frac{c}{a + b}x$ is the point $\left(\frac{2}{3}(a + b), \frac{2}{3}c\right)$. Since $\frac{2}{3}c = \frac{c}{b - 2a}\left(\frac{2}{3}(a + b)\right) - \frac{2ac}{b - 2a}$, this point is also contained in the line $y = \frac{c}{b - 2a}x - \frac{2ac}{b - 2a}$. Hence, the medians intersect in the point $\left(\frac{2}{3}(a + b), \frac{2}{3}c\right)$.

8 a Because the product of the slopes of the two lines is -1, the slope of the perpendicular line through $(5, 5)$ is -2. Hence, an equation for the line is $y = -2x + 15$. See the graph at the left below.

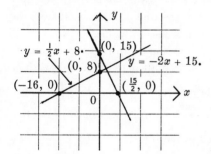
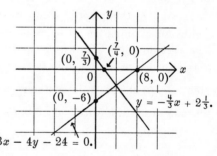

b The slope of the given line is $\frac{3}{4}$; hence, the slope of the perpendicular line is $-\frac{4}{3}$. Therefore, an equation for the perpendicular line is $y = -\frac{4}{3}x + 2\frac{1}{3}$. See the graph at the right above.

c The slope of the perpendicular line is 1; hence, its equation is $y = x + 2$. See the graph at the left below.

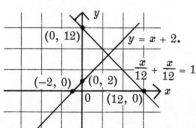
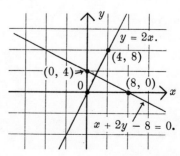

d The slope of the perpendicular line is 2; hence, its equation is $y = 2x$. See the graph on the right at the bottom of page 71.

e The slope of the perpendicular line is $-\frac{1}{4}$; hence, its equation is $y = -\frac{1}{4}x - \frac{1}{2}$. See the graph at the left below.

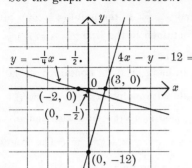

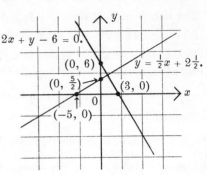

f The slope of the perpendicular line is $\frac{1}{2}$; hence, its equation is $y = \frac{1}{2}x + 2\frac{1}{2}$. See the graph at the right above.

9 a The altitude to the side with endpoints $(-6, 0)$ and $(6, 0)$ is perpendicular to the x-axis; and it is contained in the line $x = 2$. The altitude to the side with endpoints $(6, 0)$ and $(2, 8)$ is contained in the line $y = \frac{1}{2}x + 3$. The altitude to the side with endpoints $(2, 8)$ and $(-6, 0)$ is contained in the line $y = -x + 6$.

b The intersection of the lines $x = 2$ and $y = \frac{1}{2}x + 3$ is the point $(2, 4)$. Since $4 = -2 + 6$, this point is also contained in the line $y = -x + 6$. Hence, the lines containing the altitudes intersect in a common point.

10 The altitude to the side with endpoints $(-a, 0)$ and $(a, 0)$ is perpendicular to the x-axis; and it is contained in the line $x = b$. The altitude to the side with endpoints $(a, 0)$ and (b, c) is contained in the line $y = \dfrac{a - b}{c} x + \dfrac{a(a - b)}{c}$. The altitude to the side with endpoints (b, c) and $(-a, 0)$ is contained in the line $y = \dfrac{-(a + b)}{c} x + \dfrac{a(a + b)}{c}$. The intersection of the lines $x = b$ and $y = \dfrac{a - b}{c}x + \dfrac{a(a - b)}{c}$ is the point $\left(b, \dfrac{a^2 - b^2}{c}\right)$. Since $\dfrac{a^2 - b^2}{c} = \dfrac{-(a + b)}{c} \cdot b + \dfrac{a(a + b)}{c}$, this point is also contained in the line $y = \dfrac{-(a + b)}{c}x + \dfrac{a(a + b)}{c}$. Hence, the altitudes intersect at the point $\left(b, \dfrac{a^2 - b^2}{c}\right)$.

Pages 196-198

1 a $L = 0.1w + 20$.

b $20 \leq L \leq 30$.

c $24.5 = 0.1w + 20;\ 0.1w = 4.5;\ w = 45$. Hence, a 45-pound weight would be required.

2 a $F = g(C) = \frac{9}{5}C + 32$.

c $-17\frac{7}{9}$ degrees centigrade

b $C = g^{-1}(F) = \frac{5}{9}(F - 32)$

d -40 degrees

3 a $f(x) = 2x - 30$.
   b The domain is $0 \leq x \leq 65$. The range is $-30 \leq f(x) \leq 100$.
   c 76
   d 60
4 a $L = 0.0017T + 100$.
   b The slope of the graph is 0.0017. The length increases .0017 cm. for each 1° C.
   c 100.051 cm.; 100.136 cm.
5 a If x represents the number of items answered correctly, then $100 - x$ is the number of items answered incorrectly. The student's score S is then
      $S = x - \frac{1}{4}(100 - x)$, which is equivalent to $S = \frac{5}{4}x - 25$.
   b 60; 80
6 a $s = -11t + 88$.
   b The domain is $0 \leq t \leq 8$. The range is $0 \leq s \leq 88$.
   c 55 feet per second; 22 feet per second
   d The average speed is 44 feet per second and the length of the interval is 8.
      Hence, the distance traveled before the car is brought to a stop is 352 feet.
7 Let t represent the number of seconds the ball rolls down the ramp. Then $18 - t$ represents the number of seconds the ball rolls on level ground. When the ball has rolled for 18 seconds, the speed is 0. Hence, $0 = 12.8t - 1.6(18 - t)$ or $t = 2$. Thus, the ball rolls 2 seconds on the ramp and 16 seconds on the ground.
8 Since it takes 1 second for the sound of the shot to travel 1100 ft., the speed of sound is 1100 ft. per sec. Since it takes the bullet $\frac{1}{2}$ sec. to travel 1100 ft., the speed of the bullet is 2200 ft. per sec.
9 The slope of I^{-1} is the reciprocal of the slope of I. Hence, the slope of I^{-1} is 1. The ordinate of the y-intercept of I^{-1} is the negative of the ordinate of the y-intercept of I divided by the slope of I. That is, the ordinate of the y-intercept of I^{-1} is $\frac{0}{1} = 0$. Hence, an equation for I^{-1} is $I^{-1}(x) = x$. Thus, $I^{-1} = I$.
10 Since f has slope 1 and is different from I, f is defined by an equation of the form $f(x) = x + b$, where $b \neq 0$. Hence, f^{-1} is defined by an equation of the form $f^{-1}(x) = x - b$. Now $x + b = x - b$ if and only if $b = 0$, which is contrary to the hypothesis that $f \neq I$. Hence, it is never the case that $f(x) = f^{-1}(x)$, so that $f \cap f^{-1} = \emptyset$.
11 Let $f(x) = mx + b$, where $m \neq 1$; then $f^{-1}(x) = \frac{1}{m}x + \frac{-b}{m}$. The coordinates of the intersection of f and f^{-1} are:

$$\left(\frac{\frac{-b}{m} - b}{m - \frac{1}{m}}, \frac{m \cdot \frac{-b}{m} - \frac{1}{m} \cdot b}{m - \frac{1}{m}} \right) = \left(\frac{\frac{-b - bm}{m}}{\frac{m^2 - 1}{m}}, \frac{\frac{-b - bm}{m}}{\frac{m^2 - 1}{m}} \right)$$

$$= \left(\frac{-b}{m - 1}, \frac{-b}{m - 1} \right).$$

The coordinates of the intersection of f and I are:

$$\left(\frac{0 - b}{m - 1}, \frac{m \cdot 0 - b}{m - 1}\right) = \left(\frac{-b}{m - 1}, \frac{-b}{m - 1}\right).$$

Therefore, the graphs of f and f^{-1} intersect at the same point where the graph of f intersects the graph of I.

12 a Let f be defined by $f(x) = mx + b$. Then af is defined by $af(x) = amx + ab$. Since the slope of f is m and the slope of af is am, the slope of af is a times the slope of f.

b Let f be defined by $f(x) = m_1 x + b_1$ and let g be defined by $g(x) = m_2 x + b_2$. Then f + g is defined by $f(x) + g(x) = m_1 x + b_1 + m_2 x + b_2 = (m_1 + m_2) x + (b_1 + b_2)$. Hence, the slope of f + g is $m_1 + m_2$, which is the sum of the slope of f and g.

c Let f and g be defined by the equations given in part b. Then $(f \circ g)(x)$ is defined by $f(m_2 x + b_2) = m_1(m_2 x + b_2) + b_1 = m_1 m_2 x + (m_1 b_2 + b_1)$. Hence, the slope of f $\circ$ g is $m_1 m_2$, which is the product of the slopes of f and g.

Pages 200-202

1 a All lines are nonvertical and contain the origin.

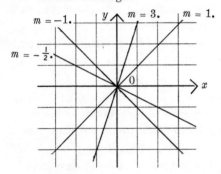

b All lines are horizontal.

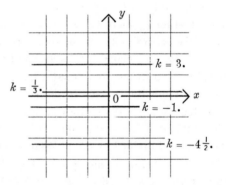

c All lines have slope $\frac{2}{3}$.

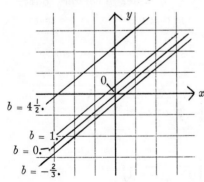

d All lines are nonvertical and contain $(0, -4)$.

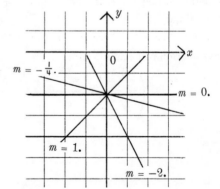

e All lines are nonvertical and contain $(-3, 1)$.

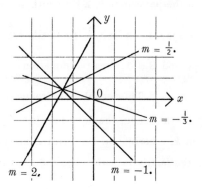

f All lines are nonvertical and contain $(0, 2)$.

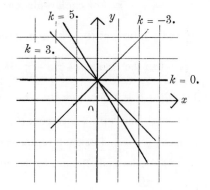

g All lines have slope $-\frac{2}{3}$.

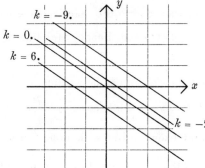

h All lines have slope -1.

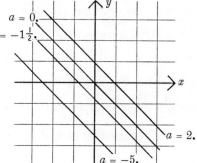

2 a $y = mx - 4$.

 b $y = m(x + 6)$.

 c $y = \frac{1}{2}x + b$.

 d $y - 2 = m(x + 1)$.

 e $\frac{x}{2b} + \frac{y}{b} = 1$ or $y = -\frac{1}{2}x + b$.

3 Approximately 33.8 pounds per square inch.

4 .465 ohms.

5 256 feet per second.

6 a y is doubled.

 b y is divided by 2.

 c y is divided by 3.

 d y is multiplied by 10.

7 a If $A \neq 0$ and $B \neq 0$, the equation $Ax + By + C = 0$ can be written as

 $y = \frac{-A}{B}x - \frac{C}{B}$, which is the linear equation for a line with slope $-\frac{A}{B}$ and

y-intercept $(0, -\frac{C}{B})$. In this case, the equation $Ax + By + k = 0$ can be written

as $y = -\frac{A}{B}x - \frac{k}{B}$. For each replacement of the parameter k, a line with slope

$-\frac{A}{B}$ and y-intercept $(0, -\frac{k}{B})$ is obtained. Hence, each line in the family is

parallel to the line $y = -\frac{A}{B}x - \frac{C}{B}$. If $A = 0$ and $B \neq 0$, then the equation

$Ax + By + C = 0$ becomes $By + C = 0$, or $y = -\frac{C}{B}$. This equation represents a

horizontal line with y-intercept $(0, -\frac{C}{B})$. In this case, the equation $Ax + By + k = 0$

becomes $y = -\frac{k}{B}$. For each replacement of k, a horizontal line with y-intercept

$(0, \frac{-k}{B})$ is obtained. Hence, each line in the family is parallel to the horizontal

line $y = \frac{-C}{B}$.

If $A \neq 0$ and $B = 0$ then the equation $Ax + By + C = 0$ becomes $Ax + C = 0$,

or $x = -\frac{C}{A}$. This equation defines a vertical line with x-intercept $(-\frac{C}{A}, 0)$. In

this case, the equation $Ax + By + k = 0$ becomes $x = \frac{-k}{A}$. For each replacement

of k, a vertical line with x-intercept $(\frac{-k}{A}, 0)$ is obtained. Hence, each line in

the family is parallel to the vertical line $x = \frac{-C}{A}$.

b If $A \neq 0$ and $B \neq 0$, then the equation $Ax + By + C = 0$ can be written as

$y = \frac{-A}{B}x - \frac{C}{B}$. In this case, the equation $Bx - Ay + k = 0$ becomes $y = \frac{B}{A}x + \frac{k}{A}$.

For each replacement of k, this equation represents a line with slope $\frac{B}{A}$ and

y-intercept $(0, \frac{k}{A})$. Since $-\frac{A}{B} \cdot \frac{B}{A} = -1$, each line in this family is perpendicular

to the line $y = -\frac{A}{B}x - \frac{C}{B}$.

If $A = 0$ and $B \neq 0$, the equation $Ax + By + C = 0$, or $y = -\frac{C}{B}$, represents a

horizontal line. In this case, the equation $Bx - Ay + k = 0$ becomes $x = \frac{-k}{B}$.

For each replacement of k, this equation represents a vertical line. Hence,

every line in this family is perpendicular to the line $y = \frac{-C}{B}$.

If $A \neq 0$ and $B = 0$, the equation $Ax + By + C = 0$, or $x = \frac{-C}{A}$ represents a

vertical line. In this case, the equation $Bx - Ay + k = 0$ becomes $y = \frac{k}{A}$. For

each replacement of k, this equation represents a horizontal line. Hence, every

line in this family is perpendicular to the line $x = \frac{-C}{A}$.

8 a $2x - 3y + k = 0$.   c $3x + 2y + k = 0$.
   b $5x - y + k = 0$.   d $-x - 4y + k = 0$.

9 a $k = -1$.   b $k = -22$.   c $k = -21$.   d $k = 17$.

10 a Since (a, b) is contained in ℓ_1 and ℓ_2, it follows that (a, b) satisfies the equations for these lines. Hence, $A_1a + B_1b + C_1 = 0$ and $A_2a + B_2b + C_2 = 0$. Thus, $(A_1a + B_1b + C_1) + k(A_2a + B_2b + C_2) = 0 + k(0) = 0$. The equation $(A_1x + B_1y + C_1) + k(A_2x + B_2y + C_2) = 0$ can be written as $(A_1 + kA_2)x + (B_1 + kB_2)y + (C_1 + kC_2) = 0$. Therefore, this equation does represent a one-parameter family of lines. Hence, for each replacement of k, the line represented by the equation $(A_1x + B_1y + C_1) + k(A_2x + B_2y + C_2) = 0$ contains the point (a, b).

b The line $A_2x + B_2y + C_2 = 0$ is not in the family because there is no replacement of k that results in this equation.

c All the lines in the family are parallel to ℓ_1 and ℓ_2.

11 a $(2x + 3y - 12) + k(x - 2y + 1) = 0$. Since $(4, 5)$ is in this line, $(8 + 15 - 12) + k(4 - 10 + 1) = 0$. Hence, $5k = 11$, or $k = \frac{11}{5}$. Thus, an equation for this line is $3x - y - 7 = 0$.

b $(x + 2y - 5) + k(3x - y + 6) = 0$. Since $(4, -2)$ is in this line, $(4 - 4 - 5) + k(12 + 2 + 6) = 0$. Hence, $20k = 5$, or $k = \frac{1}{4}$. Thus, an equation for the line is $x + y - 2 = 0$.

c $(3x + y - 4) + k(x + 3y + 4) = 0$. Since the slope of the line is 1, the coefficient of x must be 1; that is, $3 + 1k = 1$, or $k = -2$. Thus an equation for the line is $x - 5y - 12 = 0$.

d $(2x + 3y + 21) + k(3x + 2y + 19) = 0$. Since the line is vertical, it must have an equation of the form $x = a$, which means that the coefficient of y in the equation must be 0. Therefore, $3 + 2k = 0$, or $k = -\frac{3}{2}$. Hence, an equation for the line is $-\frac{5}{2}x = 7\frac{1}{2}$, or $x = -3$.

e $(2x + 3y + 21) + k(3x + 2y + 19) = 0$. Since the line is horizontal, its equation must be of the form $y = a$, which means that the coefficient of x in the equation must be 0. Therefore, $2 + 3k = 0$, or $k = -\frac{2}{3}$. Hence, an equation for the line is $\frac{5}{3}y = -8\frac{1}{3}$, or $y = -5$.

12 $10x + 10y = 25(100)$; $6x + 16y = 25(100)$. The coefficient of x is 0 if $6x + 16y = 2500$ is multiplied by $-\frac{5}{3}$ and the two equations are added. $y = 100$; $x = 150$.

13 $x + y = 20$; $.95x + .15y = .45(20)$. Multiplying the first equation by $-.15$ and adding the two equations, we obtain $.8x = 6$, or $x = 7.5$. Hence, $y = 12.5$.

14 Let x represent the reciprocal of one number, and y the reciprocal of the other. $x + y = 1$; $x - y = \frac{2}{3}$. Hence, $y = 6$ and $x = \frac{6}{5}$.

15 Let x denote the tens' digit and let y denote the units' digit. Then $x = 3y + 1$; $10y + x = (10x + y) - 45$. Hence, $x = 7$ and $y = 2$.

16 Let x denote the speed of the boat and let y denote the speed of the current. Then $\frac{1}{3}(x + y) = 6$; $\frac{1}{2}(x - y) = 6$. Hence, $x = 15$ and $y = 3$.

1 a

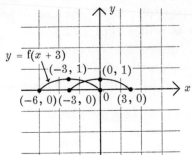

b

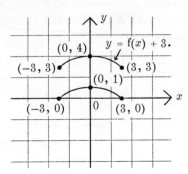

c

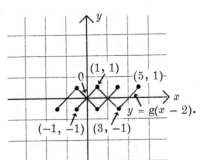

d

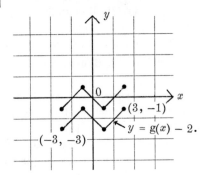

e

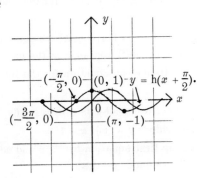

f

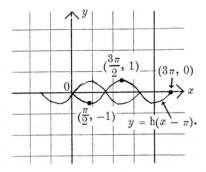

2 $(g \circ f)(x) = 3x.$

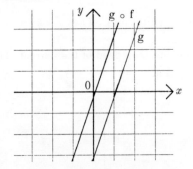

3 $(g \circ f)(x) = 2x + 6.$

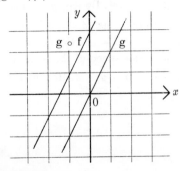

4 $(g \circ f)(x) = 2x.$

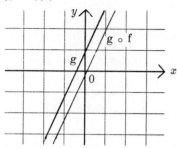

5 $(g \circ f)(x) = x.$

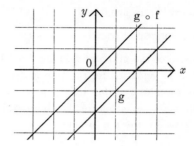

6 $(g \circ f)(x) = 7 - x.$

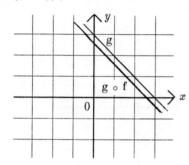

7 $\alpha = -2$. The graph of h is the graph of g translated 2 units to the right.

8 $\alpha = 3\frac{1}{2}$. The graph of h is the graph of g translated $3\frac{1}{2}$ units to the left.

9 $\alpha = -2$. The graph of h is the graph of g translated 2 units to the right.

10 $\alpha = 4$. The graph of h is the graph of g translated 4 units to the left.

11 $\alpha = -1$. The graph of h is the graph of g translated 1 unit to the right.

12 a $\beta = -1$, since $f(x) + \beta = 1 + \sqrt{x + 1} + (-1) = \sqrt{x + 1} = g(x)$.

    b $\alpha = -1$, since $g(x - 1) = \sqrt{(x - 1) + 1} = \sqrt{x} = h(x)$.

    c The graph of $y = g(x)$ is the graph of $h(x)$ translated 1 unit to the left.

    d The graph of $y = f(x)$ is the graph of $y = g(x)$ translated 1 unit upward.

    e The graph of f is the graph of h translated 1 unit to the left and 1 unit upward.

13 a $\alpha = -2$.

    b $\beta = 5$.

    c The graph of $g(x)$ is the graph of $h(x)$ translated 5 units downward.

    d The graph of $f(x)$ is the graph of $g(x)$ translated 2 units to the left.

    e The graph of f is the graph of h translated 5 units downward and 2 units to the left.

14 a $\alpha = -\dfrac{b}{2}$.

    b g is a $\dfrac{b}{2}$ horizontal translate of f, to the left if $b > 0$ and to the right if $b < 0$.

    c $\beta = \dfrac{b^2}{4} - c$.

d The graph of h is a $\frac{b^2}{4} - c$ vertical translate of g, upward if β is positive and downward if β is negative.

e h is a $\frac{b}{2}$ horizontal translate and a $\frac{b^2}{4} - c$ vertical translate of f.

15 a The slope of the graph of $g(x) = mx + b$ is m. In a horizontal translation of α units, the equation for the line is $g(x + \alpha) = m(x + \alpha) + b = mx + (m\alpha + b)$. Hence, the slope of this line is also m.

b No. Since the equation for the line resulting from the translation is $g(x + \alpha) = mx + (m\alpha + b)$, the y-intercept is $(0, m\alpha + b)$.

Pages 210-211

1 a

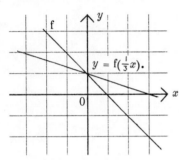

b

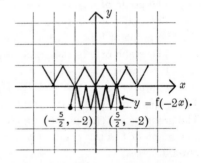

c

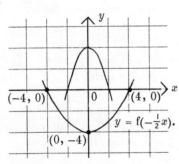

d

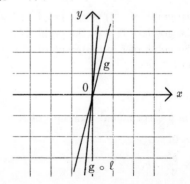

2 The two graphs coincide, since $g \circ \ell(x) = 5 = g(x)$.

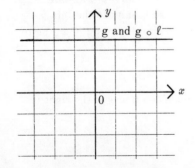

3 $(g \circ \ell)(x) = g(3x) = 4(3x) = 12x$.

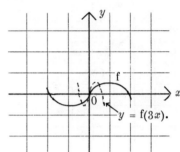

4 $(g \circ \ell)(x) = g(-\frac{1}{2}x) = 5 + 3x.$

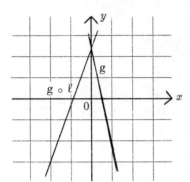

5 $(g \circ \ell)(x) = g(-2x) = 4x^2.$

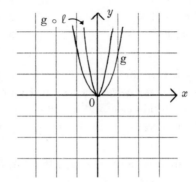

6 $(g \circ \ell)(x) = g(4x) = 16x^2.$

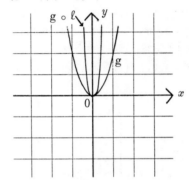

7 $(g \circ \ell)(x) = g(-\frac{1}{2}x) = \frac{1}{4}x^2.$

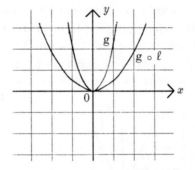

8 $(g \circ \ell)(x) = g(\frac{1}{4}x) = \frac{1}{16}x^2.$

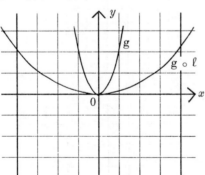

9 $g \circ \ell(x) = g(\frac{3}{2}x) = -\dfrac{\sqrt{400 - 9x^2}}{2}.$

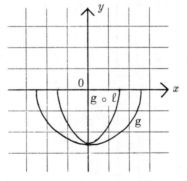

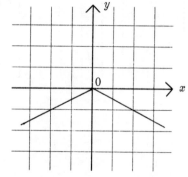

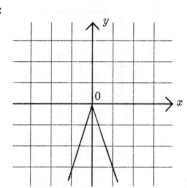

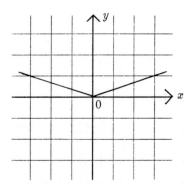

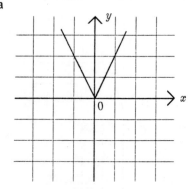

Page 214

1 a $\{x \mid x \geq -5\}$

  b $\{x \mid x \leq -5\}$

  c $\{x \mid x \leq 3\}$

  d $\{x \mid x \geq 3\}$

  e $\{x \mid x \geq \frac{1}{2}\}$

  f $\{x \mid x \geq 2 \text{ or } x \leq -2\}$

  g $\{x \mid x \leq 2\}$

  h $\{x \mid x \geq -3\}$

  i $\{x \mid x = 4\}$

  j $\{x \mid x \leq 1\}$

2 a Suppose that $x > 0$, then $-x < 0$. By Definition 32/5, $|x| = x$ and $|-x| = -(-x) = x$. Hence, in this case, $|x| = |-x|$. Now suppose that $x \leq 0$, then $-x \geq 0$. By Definition 32/5, $|x| = -x$ and $|-x| = -x$. Hence, $|x| = |-x|$. Thus, in all cases, $|x| = |-x|$.

  b If $x \geq 0$, then $|x^2| = x^2 = |x|^2$. If $x < 0$, then $|x^2| = |(-x)^2| = x^2 = |x|^2$. Hence, in all cases, $|x^2| = |x|^2$.

  c If $x \geq 0$, then $|x| = x$ and $-|x| = -x$. Now $-1 \leq 1 \leq 1$, so $-x \leq x \leq x$. Substituting for $-x$ and x, we have $-|x| \leq x \leq |x|$. If $x \leq 0$, then $|x| = -x$. Since $-1 \leq 1 \leq 1$ and $x \leq 0$, $-1(x) \geq x \geq 1(x)$; that is, $x \leq x \leq -x$, or $-(-x) \leq x \leq -x$. Substituting for $-x$, we have $-|x| \leq x \leq |x|$. Thus, in all cases, $-|x| \leq x \leq |x|$.

  d If $x \geq 0$, then $|x| = x$. Since $-1 \leq 1 \leq 1$ and $x \geq 0$, $-1(x) \leq x \leq x$, or $-x \leq x \leq x$. Substituting for x, we have $-x \leq |x| \leq x$.

3 a

b

c

d

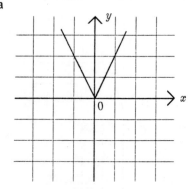

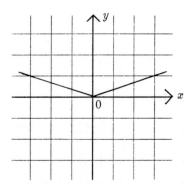

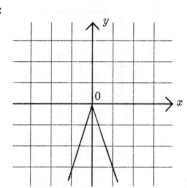

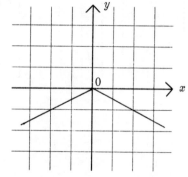

4 a The graphs are the same.

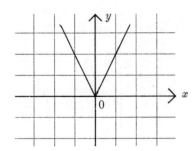

b The graphs are reflections of each other in the x-axis.

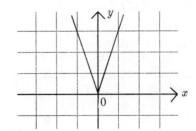

c No. $|ax| = a|x|$ only if $a \geqq 0$. If $a < 0$, $|ax| = -a|x|$.

Pages 218-220

1 $\{x \mid -18 < x < 18\}$

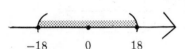

2 $\{x \mid x \geq 89 \text{ or } x \leq -89\}$

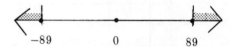

3 $\{x \mid -14\frac{8}{15} \leqq x \leqq 2\frac{2}{15}\}$

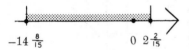

4 $\{x \mid x < -3.97 \text{ or } x > 10.07\}$

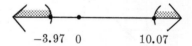

5 $\{x \mid -2 \leqq x \leqq -1\}$

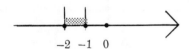

6 $\{x \mid x < -\frac{1}{5} \text{ or } x > 1\}$

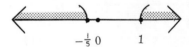

7 a

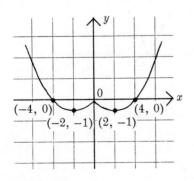

b

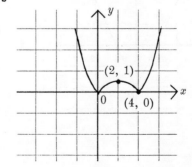

c
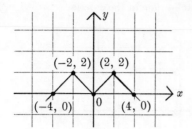

d
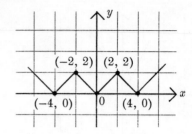

8
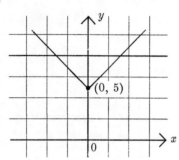

9
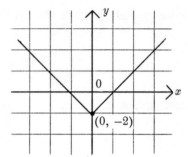

10
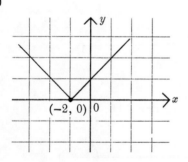

11
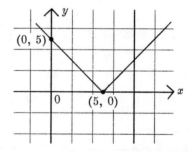

12
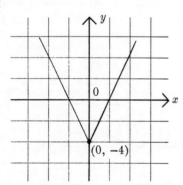

13
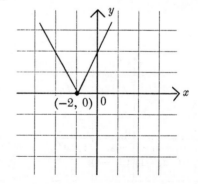

Responses for pages 218--220

14

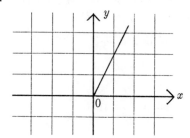

Graph coincides with x-axis to left of origin.

15

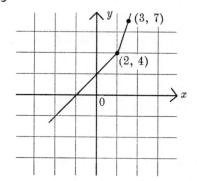

16

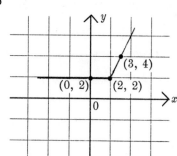

17

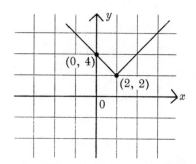

18 a If $ab = 0$, then $a = 0$ or $b = 0$. If $a = b = 0$, then $|ab| = 0 = |0| \cdot |0|$. If $a = 0$ and $b \neq 0$, then $|ab| = 0 = |0| \cdot |b|$. Similarly, if $b = 0$ and $a \neq 0$, then $|ab| = 0 = |a| \cdot |0|$. Hence, in all cases, if $ab = 0$, then $|ab| = |a| \cdot |b|$.

b If $ab > 0$, then $a > 0$ and $b > 0$ or $a < 0$ and $b < 0$. If $a > 0$ and $b > 0$, then $|ab| = ab = |a| \cdot |b|$. If $a < 0$ and $b < 0$, then $|ab| = (-a)(-b) = ab = |a| \cdot |b|$. Hence, in all cases, if $ab > 0$, then $|ab| = |a| \cdot |b|$.

c If $ab < 0$, then $a < 0$ and $b > 0$ or $a > 0$ and $b < 0$. If $a < 0$ and $b > 0$, then $|ab| = -ab = (-a)(b) = |a| \cdot |b|$. If $a > 0$ and $b < 0$, then $|ab| = -ab = (a)(-b) = |a| \cdot |b|$.

19 a If $b > 0$, then $|b| = b$ and $\left|\frac{1}{b}\right| = \frac{1}{b}$. Hence, $\left|\frac{1}{b}\right| = \frac{1}{b} = \frac{1}{|b|}$. If $b < 0$, then $|b| = -b$ and $\left|\frac{1}{b}\right| = -\frac{1}{b} = \frac{1}{-b}$. Hence, $\left|\frac{1}{b}\right| = \frac{1}{-b} = \frac{1}{|b|}$. Hence, in all cases, $\left|\frac{1}{b}\right| = \frac{1}{|b|}$.

b By Theorem 18/5, $\left|\frac{a}{b}\right| = |a| \cdot \left|\frac{1}{b}\right|$. From part a, $\left|\frac{1}{b}\right| = \frac{1}{|b|}$. Thus, $\left|\frac{a}{b}\right| = |a| \cdot \frac{1}{|b|} = \frac{|a|}{|b|}$.

20 $|mx + b| < c$ is equivalent to $|m| \cdot \left|x + \frac{b}{m}\right| < c$, or $\left|x + \frac{b}{m}\right| < \frac{c}{|m|}$. Since $c > 0$,

$$-\frac{c}{|m|} < x + \frac{b}{m} < \frac{c}{|m|}, \text{or} - \frac{c}{|m|} - \frac{b}{m} < x < \frac{c}{|m|} - \frac{b}{m}.$$

21 By Theorem 19/5, $|x| + |y| \geq |x + y|$. Hence, if $x = b$ and $y = a - b$, $|b| + |a - b| \geq |b + (a - b)|$, or $|b| + |a - b| \geq |a|$. Therefore, $|a - b| \geq |a| - |b|$.

22 a $\dfrac{5}{|x|} < 25$, or $5 < 25\,|x|$. Hence, $|x| > \frac{1}{5}$. $\{x \mid x > \frac{1}{5}$ or $x < -\frac{1}{5}\}$

b $\dfrac{3}{|x - 1|} < \frac{1}{3}$, or $9 < |x - 1|$. $\{x \mid x < -8$ or $x > 10\}$

c $\dfrac{10}{|10 - x|} < 0.01$ or $1000 < |10 - x|$. $\{x \mid x < -990$ or $x > 1010\}$

d $2 < |2x + 3|$. $\{x \mid x < -2\frac{1}{2}$ or $x > -\frac{1}{2}\}$.

23 Assume that $|x - 2| < \frac{1}{3}$. Then $3\,|x - 2| < 1$, or $|3x - 6| < 1$. Since $f(x) = -3x$, $f(x) + 6 = -3x + 6 = -(3x - 6)$. Hence, $|f(x) + 6| = |-(3x - 6)| = |3x - 6|$, so that $|f(x) + 6| < 1$. Now assume that $|f(x) + 6| < 1$. Since $f(x) + 6 = -3x + 6$, it follows that $|-3x + 6| < 1$, or $|-3| \cdot |x - 2| < 1$. Hence, $3\,|x - 2| < 1$, or $|x - 2| < \frac{1}{3}$.

24 Assume that $|x - 24| < 2$. Then $\frac{1}{2}|x - 24| < 1$ or $|\frac{1}{2}x - 12| < 1$. Since $f(x) = \frac{1}{2}x$, $|f(x) - 12| = |\frac{1}{2}x - 12|$. Therefore, $|f(x) - 12| < 1$. Now assume that $|f(x) - 12| < 1$. Since $|f(x) - 12| = |\frac{1}{2}x - 12|$, it follows that $|\frac{1}{2}x - 12| < 1$ or $|\frac{1}{2}(x - 24)| < 1$. Hence, $\frac{1}{2} \cdot |x - 24| < 1$ or $|x - 24| < 2$.

25 a By definition, $\max(f, g)(a) = \frac{1}{2}\big(|f(a) - g(a)| + f(a) + g(a)\big)$. Since $g(a) = f(a)$, this becomes $\max(f, g)(a) = \frac{1}{2}\big(|f(a) - f(a)| + f(a) + f(a)\big) = \frac{1}{2}\big(2[f(a)]\big) = f(a)$.

b If $f(a) > g(a)$, then $|f(a) - g(a)| = f(a) - g(a)$. Hence, $\max(f, g)(a) = \frac{1}{2}\big(f(a) - g(a) + f(a) + g(a)\big) = \frac{1}{2}\big(2[f(a)]\big) = f(a)$.

c If $f(a) < g(a)$, then $|f(a) - g(a)| = g(a) - f(a)$. Hence, $\max(f, g)(a) = \frac{1}{2}\big(g(a) - f(a) + f(a) + g(a)\big) = \frac{1}{2}\big(2[g(a)]\big) = g(a)$.

26 a $\min(f, g)(x) = -\frac{1}{2}\big(|f(x) - g(x)| - f(x) - g(x)\big)$.

b If $f(a) = g(a)$, then $\min(f, g)(a) = -\frac{1}{2}\big(|f(a) - f(a)| - f(a) - f(a)\big) = -\frac{1}{2}\big(-2[f(a)]\big) = f(a)$. If $f(a) > g(a)$, then $|f(a) - g(a)| = f(a) - g(a)$. Hence, $\min(f, g)(a) = -\frac{1}{2}\big(f(a) - g(a) - f(a) - g(a)\big) = -\frac{1}{2}\big(-2[g(a)]\big) = g(a)$. If $f(a) < g(a)$, then $|f(a) - g(a)| = g(a) - f(a)$. Hence, $\min(f, g)(a) = -\frac{1}{2}\big(g(a) - f(a) - f(a) - g(a)\big) -\frac{1}{2}\big(-2[f(a)]\big) = f(a)$.

27 a

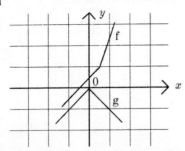

b The graph of f, shown in part a, is the graph of max(f, g).
c The graph of g, shown in part a, is the graph of min(f, g).

28 a

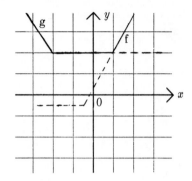

b In the graph for part a, the solid line portions of the graphs of f and g represent the graph of max(f, g).
c In the graph for part a, the dotted-line portions of the graphs of f and g represent the graph of min(f, g).

Pages 226-227

1 Not discontinuous
2 Discontinuous for $x = -1$ since $f(x)$ is not defined for $x = -1$.
3 Discontinuous for $x = 0$ since $f(x)$ is not defined for $x = 0$.
4 Discontinuous for $x = 0$ since $f(x)$ is not defined for $x = 0$.
5 Discontinuous for $x = -2$ since $f(x)$ is not defined for $x = -2$.
6 Discontinuous for $x = 0$ because the values of $f(x)$ for x near 0 are not arbitrarily close to $f(0) = 0$.
7 Not discontinuous
8 Not discontinuous
9 a Maximum width of vertical strip: 0.4 in.

b Maximum width of vertical strip: 0.2 in.

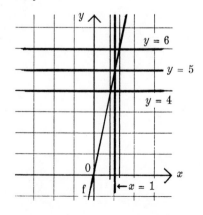

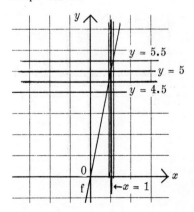

c Maximum width of
vertical strip: 0.04 in.

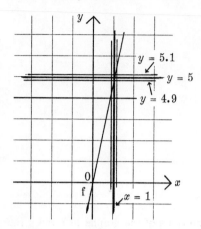

10 a Maximum width of vertical strip: 4 in.

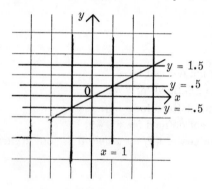

b Maximum width of vertical strip: 2 in.

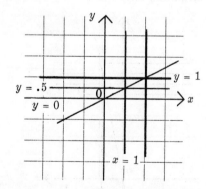

c Maximum width of vertical strip: 0.4 in.

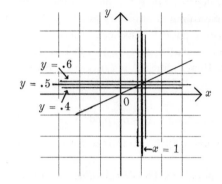

11 The smaller the absolute value of the slope, the greater the maximum width of the vertical strip. For these examples, the maximum width of the vertical strip is $\dfrac{2p}{|m|}$, where m is the slope of the line.

12 a No. $f(1) = 0$.
   b $f(0.9) = -1$; $f(0.99) = -1$; $f(0.999) = -1$; $f(0.9999) = -1$.
   c $f(1.1) = 1$; $f(1.01) = 1$; $f(1.001) = 1$; $f(1.0001) = 1$.
   d No. For values of x near $x = 1$, $f(x)$ is not close to $f(1) = 0$. For all $x \neq 1$, $|f(x) - f(1)| = 1$.

13 a (a) No. $f(1) = 0$. When $x \neq 1$, $f(x) = \dfrac{x(x-1)}{x-1} = x$.
      (b) $f(0.9) = 0.9$; $f(0.99) = 0.99$; $f(0.999) = 0.999$; $f(0.9999) = 0.9999$.
      (c) $f(1.1) = 1.1$; $f(1.01) = 1.01$; $f(1.001) = 1.001$; $f(1.0001) = 1.0001$.
      (d) No. For all values of x near 1, $f(x)$ is not close to $f(1) = 0$. For all $x \neq 1$ in the interval $.9 \leq x \leq 1.1$, $|f(x) - f(1)| \geq .9$.
   b (a) No. $f(1) = 1$. When $x \neq 1$, $f(x) = x$.
      (b) $f(0.9) = 0.9$; $f(0.99) = 0.99$; $f(0.999) = 0.999$; $f(0.9999) = 0.9999$.
      (c) $f(1.1) = 1.1$; $f(1.01) = 1.01$; $f(1.001) = 1.001$; $f(1.0001) = 1.0001$.
      (d) Yes. For all x sufficiently close to 1, $|f(x) - f(1)| < p$, where p is an arbitrarily small positive number.

14 a $f(3) = 6$.
   b $f(3) = 0$.
   c No possible value, since $f(x)$ gets smaller for x close to, but less than, 3; while $f(x)$ gets larger for x greater than 3.
   d $f(3) = 4$.

Page 231
1 (a) $d = 0.1$. (b) $d = 0.02$. (c) $d = 0.002$ (d) $d = 0.0002$.
2 (a) $d = 0.05$. (b) $d = 0.01$. (c) $d = 0.001$. (d) $d = 0.0001$.
3 (a) $d = 0.125$. (b) $d = 0.025$. (c) $d = 0.0025$. (d) $d = 0.00025$.
4 (a) $d = 0.75$. (b) $d = 0.15$. (c) $d = 0.015$. (d) $d = 0.0015$.
5 a $d = 0.2$. b 0.2 c 0.2 d 0.2.

1 Let $f(x) = a$ for all $x \in \Re$ define a constant function. Since f is defined for all real numbers, it is defined in an open interval containing an arbitrary point x_0. To show that f is continuous, we must show that, given a positive number p, there exists a positive number d such that $|x - x_0| < d$ implies that $|f(x) - f(x_0)| < p$. But $f(x) = a$ for all x, so that $|f(x) - f(x_0)| = |a - a| = 0$. Hence, for any $p > 0$, $|f(x) - f(x_0)| < p$. Thus, if $d = p$, for example, then $|x - x_0| < d$ implies that $|f(x) - f(x_0)| < p$. Therefore, f is a continuous function.

2 No. For example, if f is defined by $f(x) = x - 2$, then $1/f$ is defined by $\dfrac{1}{f(x)} = \dfrac{1}{x - 2}$. This function is not continuous at $x = 2$ because $f(x)$ is not defined for this value of x.

3 The function f/g would be continuous at all points in the common domain *except* at those points where $g(x) = 0$. If $g(x_0) = 0$, then f/g is not defined for $x = x_0$.

Chapter review
Pages 234-237

1 c	6 c	11 b	16 d
2 d	7 a	12 b	17 c
3 c	8 d	13 d	18 b
4 c	9 c	14 b	19 b
5 c	10 d	15 b	

Cumulative review
Pages 237-238

1 a

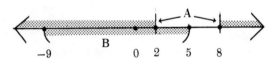

b See graph for part a. $A \cap B = \{x \mid -9 < x \leqq 2\}$.

c Greatest lower bound: -9; least upper bound: 2; least member does not exist; greatest member: 2.

2 a True. $f_1(x) + f_2(x) = (m_1 x + b_1) + (m_2 x + b_2)$
$$= (m_1 + m_2)x + (b_1 + b_2).$$
Since $m_1 + m_2 \in \Re$ and $b_1 + b_2 \in \Re$, $f_1 + f_2 \in S$.

b True. $\left(f_1(x) + f_2(x)\right) + f_3(x) = \left((m_1 + m_2)x + (b_1 + b_2)\right) + m_3 x + b_3$
$$= (m_1 + m_2 + m_3)x + (b_1 + b_2 + b_3)$$
$$= \left(m_1 + (m_2 + m_3)\right)x + \left(b_1 + (b_2 + b_3)\right)$$
$$= (m_1 x + b_1) + \left((m_2 + m_3))x + (b_2 + b_3)\right)$$
$$= f_1(x) + \left(f_2(x) + f_3(x)\right).$$
Hence, $(f_1 + f_2) + f_3 = f_1 + (f_2 + f_3)$.

c True. $f_1(x) + f_2(x) = (m_1 + m_2)x + (b_1 + b_2)$
$$= (m_2 + m_1)x + (b_2 + b_1)$$
$$= f_2(x) + f_1(x).$$

Hence, $f_1 + f_2 = f_2 + f_1$.

d True. Let $m = b = 0$. Then $f_0(x) = 0$. $f_0(x) + f(x) = 0 + mx + b = mx + b = f(x)$.
Hence, $f_0 + f = f$.

e True. Let $f_1(x) = m_1x + b_1$. Then $-f_1(x) = -m_1x - b_1$. $f_1(x) + \left(-f_1(x)\right) =$
$(m_1 - m_1)x + (b_1 - b_1) = 0 = f_0(x)$.

3 a True. $f(1 + i) = 1 + i + \dfrac{2}{1 + i} = \dfrac{1 + 2i - 1 + 2}{1 + i} = \dfrac{2(1 + i)}{1 + i} = 2.$

b True. The given equation is equivalent to $(x + 3)^2 + (y - 4)^2 = 25$.

c True. The distance from the line $y = -1$ to a point with coordinates of the

form $\left(x, \dfrac{x^2}{4}\right)$ is $\left|\dfrac{x^2}{4} + 1\right|$. The distance from such a point to the point $(0, 1)$

is $\sqrt{x^2 + \left(\dfrac{x^2}{4} - 1\right)^2} = \sqrt{x^2 + \left(\dfrac{x^4}{16} - \dfrac{x^2}{2} + 1\right)} = \sqrt{\dfrac{x^4}{16} + \dfrac{x^2}{2} + 1} = \left|\dfrac{x^2}{4} + 1\right|.$

d False. The equation for the line $3x + 4y + 5 = 0$ can be written as $y = -\frac{3}{4}x - \frac{5}{4}$.
The slope of this line is $-\frac{3}{4}$, so it is not parallel to the line with slope $-\frac{4}{3}$.

4 a

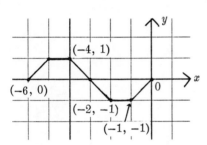

Domain: $\{x \mid -6 \leq x \leq 0\}$;
Range: $\{y \mid -1 \leq y \leq 1\}$.
Neither even nor odd

b

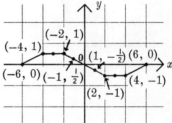

Domain: $\{x \mid -6 \leq x \leq 6\}$;
Range: $\{y \mid -1 \leq y \leq 1\}$.
An odd function

c

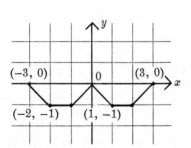

Domain: $\{x \mid -3 \leq x \leq 3\}$;
Range: $\{y \mid -1 \leq y \leq 0\}$.
An even function

d

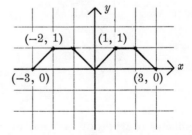

Domain: $\{x \mid -3 \leq x \leq 3\}$;
Range: $\{y \mid 0 \leq y \leq 1\}$.
An even function

5 a $\{x \mid x < 2\frac{1}{2} \text{ or } x > 6\}$

b $\dfrac{12}{f(\sqrt{3})} + \dfrac{13}{g(\sqrt{3})} = \dfrac{12}{3\sqrt{3} + 3} + \dfrac{13}{2\sqrt{3} - 5} = \dfrac{12(3\sqrt{3} - 3)}{18} + \dfrac{13(2\sqrt{3} + 5)}{-13} =$

$\dfrac{2(3\sqrt{3} - 3)}{3} - \dfrac{2\sqrt{3} + 5}{1} = \dfrac{6\sqrt{3} - 6 - 6\sqrt{3} - 15}{3} = -7.$

6 a

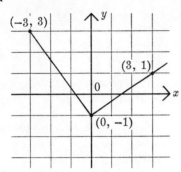

b

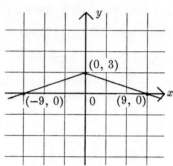

c

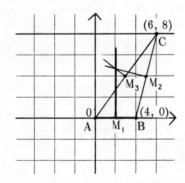

7

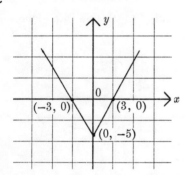

Coordinates of M_1: (2, 0); coordinates of M_2: (5, 4); coordinates of M_3: (3, 4). The equation for the perpendicular bisector of $\overline{AB}$ is $x = 2$. The equation for the perpendicular bisector of $\overline{BC}$ is $y = -\frac{1}{4}x + 5\frac{1}{4}$. The equation for the perpendicular bisector of $\overline{AC}$ is $y = -\frac{3}{4}x + 6\frac{1}{4}$. The intersection of $x = 2$ and $y = -\frac{1}{4}x + 5\frac{1}{4}$ is $(2, 4\frac{3}{4})$. Since $4\frac{3}{4} = -\frac{3}{4}(2) + 6\frac{1}{4}$, the point $(2, 4\frac{3}{4})$ is also on the line $y = -\frac{3}{4}x + 6\frac{1}{4}$. Hence, $(2, 4\frac{3}{4})$ is the common intersection point of the three lines.

8 a $m > 0$.
   b $m = 0$.
   c $m = b = 0$.
   d $b = 0$.
   e $m \neq 0$.
   f $m = 0$.

9 a

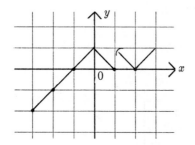

   b No. For values of x greater than 1 and sufficiently close to 1, $f(x_0)$ is not near $f(1) = 0$.

10 $d = 0.02$.

11 a Greatest lower bound: 4; Least upper bound: 5
    b $\{n \mid n > 4\};\ \{n \mid n > 9\};\ \{n \mid n > 10,000\}$.

Chapter 6
Quadratic functions

Page 247

1 a $\sqrt{(x_0)^2 + (y_0 - 4)^2}$

   b $|y_0 + 4|$

   c $\sqrt{(x_0)^2 + (y_0 - 4)^2} = |y_0 + 4|$.

   d $x_0^2 + y_0^2 - 8y_0 + 16 = y_0^2 + 8y_0 + 16$; $x_0^2 = 16y_0$. Since (x_0, y_0) is arbitrary, an equation for the parabola is $y = \dfrac{x^2}{16}$.

e

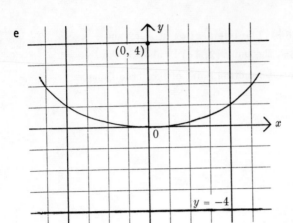

2 **a** $\sqrt{(x_0)^2 + (y_0 - 2)^2} = |y_0 + 2|$; $x_0^2 + y_0^2 - 4y_0 + 4 = y_0^2 + 4y_0 + 4$; $x_0^2 = 8y_0$. $y = \dfrac{x^2}{8}$.

See graph at left below.

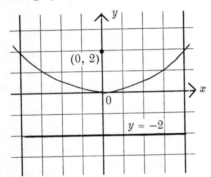

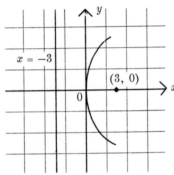

b $\sqrt{(x_0 - 3)^2 + y_0^2} = |x_0 + 3|$; $x_0^2 - 6x_0 + 9 + y_0^2 = x_0^2 + 6x_0 + 9$; $y_0^2 = 12x_0$. $x = \dfrac{y^2}{12}$.

[Notice that this equation does not define a function.] See graph at right above.

c $\sqrt{x_0^2 + (y_0 + 1)^2} = |y_0 - 1|$; $x_0^2 + y_0^2 + 2y_0 + 1 = y_0^2 - 2y_0 + 1$; $x_0^2 = -4y_0$. $y = \dfrac{-x^2}{4}$.

See graph at left below.

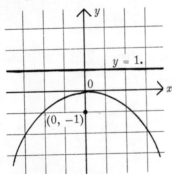

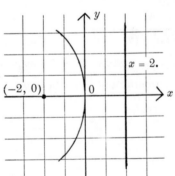

d $\sqrt{(x_0 + 2)^2 + y_0^2} = |x_0 - 2|$; $x_0^2 + 4x_0 + 4 + y_0^2 = x_0^2 - 4x_0 + 4$; $y_0^2 = -8x_0$. $x = \dfrac{-y^2}{8}$.

See graph at right above.

e $\sqrt{(x_0 - 2)^2 + (y_0 - \frac{1}{2})^2} = |y_0 + \frac{1}{2}|; \; x_0{}^2 - 4x_0 + 4 + y_0{}^2 - y_0 + \frac{1}{4} = y_0{}^2 + y_0 + \frac{1}{4};$

$x_0{}^2 - 4x_0 + 4 = 2y_0. \; y = \dfrac{(x - 2)^2}{2}.$

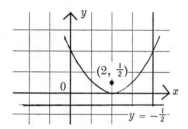

3 **a** For any point (x, y) on the parabola, the distance between (x, y) and the focus $(0, p)$ is $\sqrt{x^2 + (y - p)^2} = \sqrt{x^2 + y^2 - 2py + p^2}$. The distance from (x, y) to the directrix $y = -p$ is $|y + p|$. Since these two distances are equal for every point on the parabola, we have $\sqrt{x^2 + y^2 - 2py + p^2} = |y + p|$. If we square both sides and simplify, we obtain $x^2 = 4py$.

b Yes; each vertical line in the plane intersects the graph in just one point.

c If $p > 0$, the domain is $\Re$ and the range is $\{y \mid y \geq 0\}$. If $p < 0$, the domain is $\Re$ and the range is $\{y \mid y \leq 0\}$

4 **a** For any point (x, y) on the parabola, the distance between (x, y) and the focus $(p, 0)$ is $\sqrt{(x - p)^2 + y^2} = \sqrt{x^2 - 2px + p^2 + y^2}$. The distance from (x, y) to the directrix $x = -p$ is $|x + p|$. Since these two distances are equal for any two points on the parabola, we have $\sqrt{x^2 - 2px + p^2 + y^2} = |x + p|$. If we square both sides and simplify, we obtain $y^2 = 4px$.

b No. Yes

c If $p > 0$, the domain of g is $\{x \mid x \in \Re \text{ and } x \geq 0\}$ and the range of g is $\{y \mid y \in \Re \text{ and } y \geq 0\}$; the domain of $-$g is the same as the domain of g and the range of $-$g is $\{y \mid y \in \Re \text{ and } y \leq 0\}$. If $p < 0$, the domain of both g and $-$g is $\{x \mid x \in \Re \text{ and } x \leq 0\}$; the range of g is $\{y \mid y \in \Re \text{ and } y \geq 0\}$ and the range of $-$g is $\{y \mid y \in \Re \text{ and } y \leq 0\}$.

5 **a** Focus: $(0, 5)$; directrix: $y = -5$. See graph at left below.

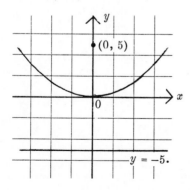

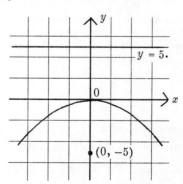

b Focus: $(0, -5)$; directrix: $y = 5$. See graph at right on the bottom of page 95.

c Focus: $(\frac{1}{2}, 0)$; directrix: $x = -\frac{1}{2}$. See graph at left below.

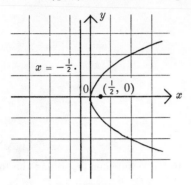
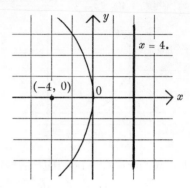

d Focus: $(-4, 0)$; directrix: $x = 4$. See graph at right above.

e Focus: $(0, \frac{1}{8})$; directrix: $y = -\frac{1}{8}$. See graph at left below.

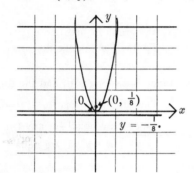
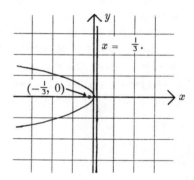

f Focus: $(-\frac{1}{3}, 0)$; directrix: $x = \frac{1}{3}$. See graph at right above.

6 a

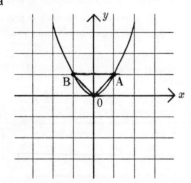

Coordinates of A: $(1, 1)$; coordinates of B: $(-1, 1)$

b $d(0, A) = d(0, B) = \sqrt{2}$; $d(A, B) = 2$.

c Area: $\frac{1}{2}d(0, A) \cdot d(0, A) = \frac{1}{2}\sqrt{2} \cdot \sqrt{2} = 1$.

7 The distance from a point (x_1, y_1) to the point $(0, \frac{1}{4})$ is $\sqrt{(x_1^2) + (y_1 - \frac{1}{4})^2}$. The distance from (x_1, y_1) to the line $h(x) = -\frac{1}{4}$ is $|y_1 + \frac{1}{4}|$. If these two distances are equal, then $\sqrt{x_1^2 + y_1^2 - \frac{1}{2}y_1 + \frac{1}{16}} = |y_1 + \frac{1}{4}|$ or $x_1^2 + y_1^2 - \frac{1}{2}y_1 + \frac{1}{16} = y_1^2 + \frac{1}{2}y_1 + \frac{1}{16}$. Hence, if these two distances are equal, then $x_1^2 = y_1$. Thus, $(x_1, y_1) = (x_1, x_1^2)$, which is a point on the graph of q.

Pages 249-251

1 a (0, 0) and (4, 16)

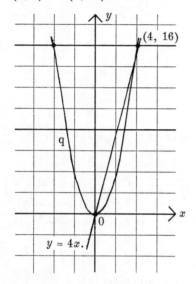

b (1, 1) and (−3, 9)

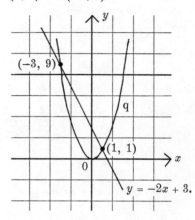

c $(2, 4)$ and $(-\frac{1}{3}, \frac{1}{9})$

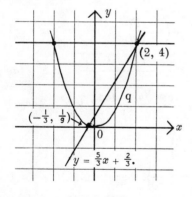

d (1, 1) and (−1, 1)

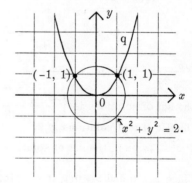

e $(\sqrt{3}, 3)$ and $(-\sqrt{3}, 3)$

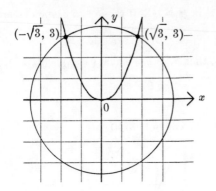

2 a $k = 9$.

c $k = 6\frac{1}{4}$.

e $k = \frac{1}{36}$.

b $k = 36a^2$.

d $k = 12\frac{1}{4}d^2$.

f $k = \frac{4}{25}c^2$.

3 a $\{3, 4\}$

c $\{-5, -1\}$

e $\{-1\frac{1}{3}, \frac{1}{3}\}$

g $\{-\frac{1}{3}, \frac{1}{2}\}$

b $\{-2, 5\}$

d $\{-\frac{1}{2}, 2\}$

f $\{-3, \frac{1}{2}\}$

h $\{-\frac{2}{5}, \frac{1}{4}\}$

4 a $x^2 + px + q = 0$. $x^2 + px = -q$. $x^2 + px + \frac{p^2}{4} = -q + \frac{p^2}{4}$. $(x + \frac{p}{2})^2 = \frac{-4q + p^2}{4}$; $|x + \frac{p}{2}| = \frac{\sqrt{p^2 - 4q}}{2}$. Hence, $x = \frac{-p}{2} - \frac{\sqrt{p^2 - 4q}}{2}$ or $x = \frac{-p}{2} + \frac{\sqrt{p^2 - 4q}}{2}$. If $p^2 - 4q \geq 0$, then the set of real-number solutions of $x^2 + px + q$ is $\{\frac{-p}{2} - \frac{\sqrt{p^2 - 4q}}{2}$, $\frac{-p}{2} + \frac{\sqrt{p^2 - 4q}}{2}\}$. If $p^2 - 4q < 0$, the set of real solutions is $\emptyset$.

b If $p^2 = 4q$, the set of solutions is $\{-\frac{p}{2}\}$.

5 a $x^2 + \frac{b}{a}x + \frac{c}{a} = 0$. $x^2 + \frac{b}{a}x + \frac{b^2}{4a^2} = -\frac{c}{a} + \frac{b^2}{4a^2}$. $(x + \frac{b}{2a})^2 = \frac{b^2 - 4ac}{4a^2}$. $|x + \frac{b}{2a}| = \frac{\sqrt{b^2 - 4ac}}{2a}$. Hence, $x = \frac{-b - \sqrt{b^2 - 4ac}}{2a}$ or $x = \frac{-b + \sqrt{b^2 - 4ac}}{2a}$. If $b^2 - 4ac \geq 0$, the set of solutions is $\{\frac{-b - \sqrt{b^2 - 4ac}}{2a}, \frac{-b + \sqrt{b^2 - 4ac}}{2a}\}$. If $b^2 - 4ac < 0$, then the set of real solutions is $\emptyset$.

b If $b^2 - 4ac = 0$, the set of solutions is $\{\frac{-b}{2a}\}$.

6 a Since $x_0 = 0$ and $p = 0.5$, if $d = \min\{1, \frac{p}{1 + 2|x_0|}\}$, then $d = 0.5$. If $|x - x_0| < 0.5$, then $|x| < 0.5$, or $-0.5 < x < 0.5$. Since $q(-0.5) = q(0.5) = 0.25$, it follows that $|q(x)| < 0.25$ whenever $|x| < 0.5$. Thus, if $|x - 0| < 0.5$, then $|q(x) - 0| < 0.5$.

Therefore, q is continuous at $x = 0$. See sketch at left below.

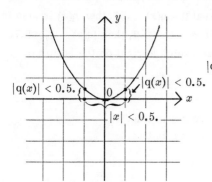

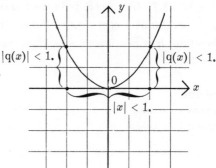

b Since $x_0 = 0$ and $p = 1$, if $d = \min\left\{1, \dfrac{p}{1 + 2 \, |x_0|}\right\}$, then $d = 1$. If $|x - x_0| < 1$, then

$|x| < 1$, or $-1 < x < 1$. Since $q(-1) = q(1) = 1$, it follows that $|q(x)| < 1$ whenever

$|x| < 0.5$. Thus, if $|x - 0| < 1$, then $|q(x) - 0| < 1$. Therefore, q is continuous

at $x = 0$. See sketch at right above.

c Since $x_0 = 2$ and $p = 1$, if $d = \min\left\{1, \dfrac{p}{1 + 2 \, |x_0|}\right\}$, then $d = 0.2$. If $|x - x_0| < 0.2$,

then $|x - 2| < 0.2$, or $1.8 < x < 2.2$. Since $q(1.8) = 3.24$ and $q(2.2) = 4.84$,

$3.24 < q(x) < 4.84$ whenever $1.8 < x < 2.2$. If $|q(x) - q(x_0)| < 1$, then

$|q(x) - 4| < 1$, or $3 < q(x) < 5$. But if $q(x)$ is in the interval $3 < q(x) < 5$, then

$q(x)$ is also in the interval $3.24 < q(x) < 4.84$. Hence, if $|x - 2| < 0.2$, then

$|q(x) - 4| < 1$, so q is continuous at $x = 2$. See sketch at left below.

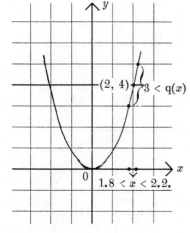

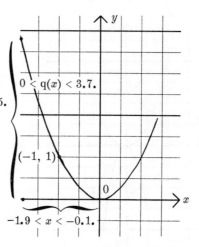

d Since $x_0 = -1$ and $p = 2.7$, if $d = \min\left\{1, \dfrac{p}{1 + 2 \, |x_0|}\right\}$, then $d = 0.9$. If $|x - x_0| < 0.9$,

then $|x + 1| < 0.9$ or $-1.9 < x < -0.1$. Since $q(-1.9) = 3.61$ and $q(-0.1) = 0.01$,

$0.01 < q(x) < 3.61$ whenever $-1.9 < x < -0.1$. If $|q(x) - q(x_0)| < 2.7$, then $|q(x) - 1| < 2.7$, or $-1.7 < q(x) < 3.7$, since $q(x) \geqq 0$, this requirement becomes $0 < q(x) < 3.7$. But if $q(x)$ is in the interval $0 < q(x) < 3.7$, then $q(x)$ is also in the interval $0.01 < q(x) < 3.61$. Hence, if $|x + 1| < 0.9$, then $|q(x) - 1| < 2.7$. Therefore, q is continuous at $x = -1$. See sketch at right on the bottom of page 99.

Pages 254-256

1 Statement c is true.

2 Statement b is true.

3 Statement a is true.

4 Statement e is true.

5 a

b

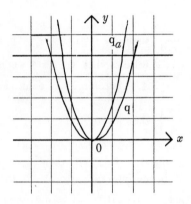

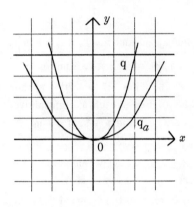

c

d

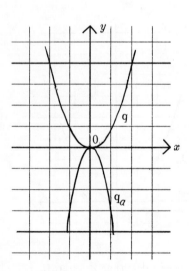

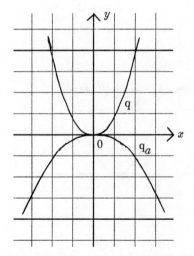

e

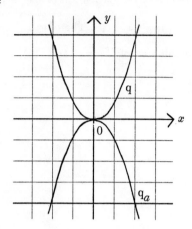

f

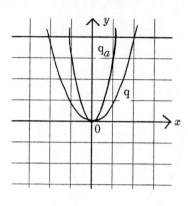

6 a $\{x \mid -6 < x < 6\}$

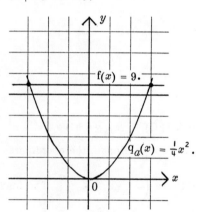

b $\{x \mid -\sqrt{3} < x < \sqrt{3}\}$

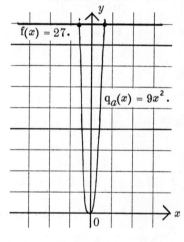

c $\{x \mid -3 < x < 1\}$

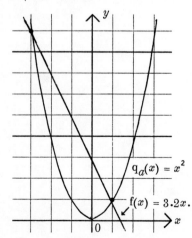

d $\{x \mid x < -2 \text{ or } x > 3\}$

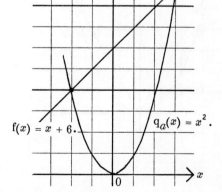

7 a Since $d(A, B) = d(B, C) = d(C, A)$ and since $d(B, C) = |2x|$, we have $\sqrt{x^2 + \frac{1}{16}x^4} =$

$|2x| \cdot \dfrac{\sqrt{16x^2 + x^4}}{4} = |2x|$. $16x^2 + x^4 = 64x^2$. $x^4 = 48x^2$. $x^2 = 48$. Therefore, $x = 4\sqrt{3}$.

The coordinates of B are $(4\sqrt{3}, 12)$; the coordinates of C are $(-4\sqrt{3}, 12)$.

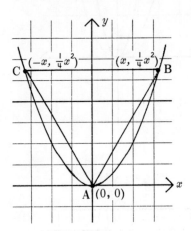

b $8\sqrt{3}$

c $\dfrac{12 \cdot 8\sqrt{3}}{2} = 48\sqrt{3}$.

8 Since $d(A, B) = d(B, C) = d(A, C)$ and since $d(B, C) = |2x|$, we have $\sqrt{x^2 + a^2x^4} =$

$|2x|$. $x^2 + a^2x^4 = 4x^2$. $a^2x^4 - 3x^2 = 0$. $a^2x^2 = 3$. $x = \dfrac{\sqrt{3}}{|a|}$. Hence, the coordinates of

B are $\left(\dfrac{1}{|a|}\sqrt{3}, \ 3 \cdot \dfrac{1}{|a|}\right)$ and the coordinates of C are $\left(-\dfrac{1}{|a|}\sqrt{3}, \ 3 \cdot \dfrac{1}{|a|}\right)$. The length

of each side is $\dfrac{2}{|a|}\sqrt{3}$. The area of the triangle is $\dfrac{1}{2} \cdot \dfrac{3}{|a|} \cdot \dfrac{2}{|a|}\sqrt{3} = \dfrac{3\sqrt{3}}{a^2}$.

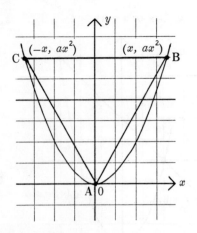

9 a Suppose that $\sqrt{x_0^2 + (ax_0^2 - k)^2} = |ax_0^2 - (-k)|$. Then $x_0^2 + (ax_0^2 - k)^2 = (ax_0^2 + k)^2 = a^2x_0^4 + 2akx_0^2 + k^2$. Hence, $x_0^2 + a^2x_0^4 - 2akx_0^2 + k^2 = a^2x_0^4 + 2akx_0^2 + k^2$, or $x_0^2 = 4akx_0^2$. Thus, $(1 - 4ak)x_0^2 = 0$. If this statement is to be true for all x, then $1 - 4ak = 0$, or $k = \dfrac{1}{4a}$.

b Suppose that $\sqrt{x_0^2 + (y_0 - \dfrac{1}{4a})^2} = |y_0 - (-\dfrac{1}{4a})|$. Then $x_0^2 + (y_0 - \dfrac{1}{4a})^2 = (y_0 + \dfrac{1}{4a})^2 = y_0^2 + \dfrac{1}{2a}y_0 + \dfrac{1}{16a^2}$. Hence, $x_0^2 + y_0^2 - \dfrac{1}{2a}y_0 + \dfrac{1}{16a^2} = y_0^2 + \dfrac{1}{2a}y_0 + \dfrac{1}{16a^2}$, or $x_0^2 = \dfrac{1}{a}y_0$. If this statement is to be true for all x, then it must be the case that $y_0 = ax_0^2$.

Pages 260-261

1 a

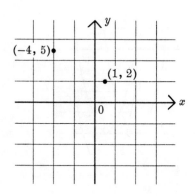

b

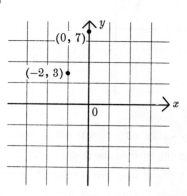

c

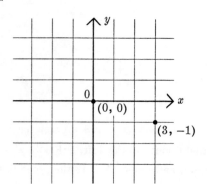

d

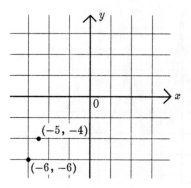

2 a g: $y = -3x + 9$. See diagram below. **b** h: $y = -3x + 6$. See graph for part a.

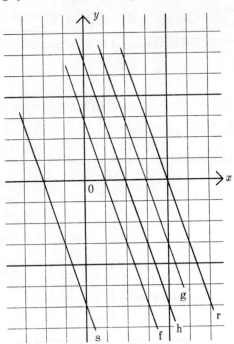

c r: $y = -3x + 12$. See graph for part a. **d** s: $y = -3x - 6$. See graph for part a.

3 The graph of F is the graph of q_a translated 5 units to the left. F:$F(x) = x^2 + 10x + 2$
The graph of G is the graph of F translated 2 units upward; it is the graph of q_a
translated 5 units to the left and 2 units upward. G: $G(x) = x^2 + 10x + 27$.
See diagram below at left.

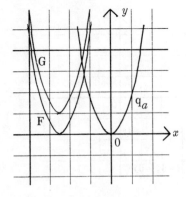 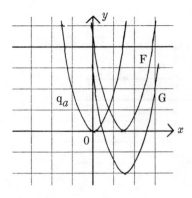

4 The graph of F is the graph of q_a translated 3 units to the right. F: $F(x) =$
$x^2 - 6x + 9$. The graph of G is the graph of F translated 4 units downward; it is
the graph of q_a translated 3 units to the right and 4 units downward. G: $G(x) =$
$x^2 - 6x + 5$. See diagram above at right.

5 The graph of F is the graph of q_a translated 6 units to the left. F: $F(x) = 2x^2 + 24x + 72$. The graph of G is the graph of F translated 3 units downward: it is the graph of q_a translated 6 units to the left and 3 units downward. G: $G(x) = 2x^2 + 24x + 69$. See diagram below at left.

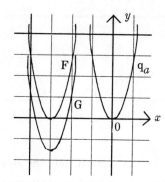
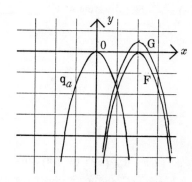

6 The graph of F is the graph of q_a translated 4 units to the right. F: $F(x) = -x^2 + 8x - 16$. The graph of G is the graph of F translated 1 unit upward; it is the graph of q_a translated 4 units to the right and 1 unit upward. G: $G(x) = -x^2 + 8x - 15$. See diagram above at right.

7 a $Q_{1, -2, 1}(x) = x^2 - 2x + 1 = (x^2 - 2x + 1) + 1 - 1 = (x - 1)^2$. Hence, the graph of Q is a 1 horizontal translate of the graph of $q(x) = x^2$. See diagram below.

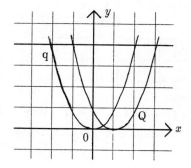

b $Q_{1, 4, 6}(x) = x^2 + 4x + 6 = (x^2 + 4x + 4) + 6 - 4 = (x + 2)^2 + 2$. Hence, the graph of Q is a -2 horizontal and a 2 vertical translate of the graph of $q(x) = x^2$. See diagram at right.

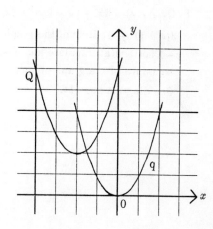

c $Q_{1,-4,-1}(x) = x^2 - 4x - 1 =$
$(x^2 - 4x + 4) - 1 - 4 = (x - 2)^2 - 5$.
Hence, the graph of Q is a 2 horizontal and a −5 vertical translate of the graph of $q(x) = x^2$. See diagram at right.

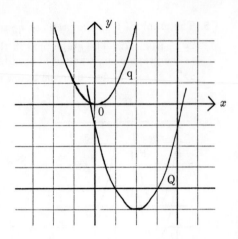

d $Q_{1,6,6}(x) = x^2 + 6x + 6 = (x^2 + 6x + 9) + 6 - 9 = (x + 3)^2 - 3$. Hence, the graph of Q is a −3 horizontal and a −3 vertical translate of the graph of $q(x) = x^2$. See diagram below at left.

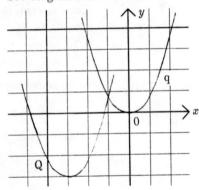

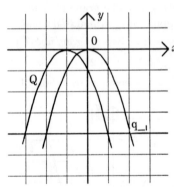

e $Q_{-1,-2,-1}(x) = -x^2 - 2x - 1 = -(x^2 + 2x + 1) - 1 + 1 = -(x + 1)^2$. Hence, the graph of Q is a −1 horizontal translate of the graph of $q_{-1}(x) = -x^2$. See diagram above at right.

f $Q_{3,6,0}(x) = 3x^2 + 6x = 3(x^2 + 2x + 1) - 3 =$
$3(x + 1)^2 - 3$. Hence, the graph of Q is a −1 horizontal translate and a −3 vertical translate of the graph of $q_3(x) = 3x^2$.
See diagram at right.

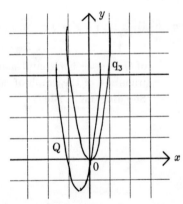

g $Q_{-1, -6, -8}(x) = x^2 - 6x - 8 = -(x^2 + 6x + 9) - 8 + 9 = -(x + 3)^2 + 1$. Hence, the graph of Q is a -3 horizontal and a 1 vertical translate of the graph $q_{-1}(x) = -x^2$.

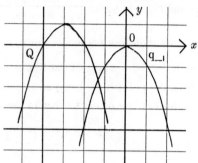

h $Q_{2, 4, 4}(x) = 2x^2 + 4x + 4 = 2(x^2 + 2x + 1) + 4 - 2 = 2(x + 1)^2 + 2$. Hence, the graph of Q is a -1 horizontal and a 2 vertical translate of the graph of $q_2(x) = 2x^2$.

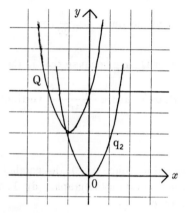

i $Q_{\frac{1}{2}, -1, -\frac{1}{2}}(x) = \frac{1}{2}x^2 - x - \frac{1}{2} = \frac{1}{2}(x^2 - 2x + 1) - \frac{1}{2} - \frac{1}{2} = \frac{1}{2}(x - 1)^2 - 1$. Hence, the graph of Q is a 1 horizontal and a -1 vertical translate of the graph of $q_{\frac{1}{2}}(x) = \frac{1}{2}x^2$.

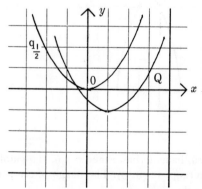

8 a The points are reflections of each other in the line $x = x_0$ if this line is the perpendicular bisector of the segment determined by the two points. The slope of the segment determined by $(x_0 - k, y_0)$ and $(x_0 + k, y_0)$ is $\dfrac{y_0 - y_0}{(x_0 - k) - (x_0 + k)} = \dfrac{0}{-2k} = 0$. Hence, the segment is horizontal and therefore perpendicular to the vertical line $x = x_0$. The distance from the point $(x_0 - k, y_0)$ to the line $x = x_0$ is $|x_0 - (x_0 - k)| = |k|$, and the distance from the point $(x_0 + k, y_0)$ to this line is $|(x_0 + k) - x_0| = |k|$. Hence, the points are reflections of each other in the line $x = x_0$.

b $Q_{a,b,c}\left(\dfrac{-b}{2a} + k\right) = a\left(\dfrac{-b}{2a} + k\right)^2 + b\left(\dfrac{-b}{2a} + k\right) + c = \dfrac{b^2 - 4abk}{4a} - \dfrac{-2k^2}{} - \dfrac{b^2 - 2abk}{2a} + c =$

$\dfrac{-b^2 + 4a^2k^2}{4a} + c$. $Q_{a,b,c}\left(\dfrac{-b}{2a} - k\right) = a\left(\dfrac{-b}{2a} - k\right)^2 + b\left(\dfrac{-b}{2a} - k\right) + c =$

$\dfrac{b^2 + 4abk + 4a^2k^2}{4a} - \dfrac{b^2 + 2abk}{2a} + c = \dfrac{-b^2 + 4a^2k^2}{4a} + c$.

c The graph of $Q_{a,b,c}$ is symmetric with respect to the line $x = -\dfrac{b}{2a}$.

9 The point $\left(-\dfrac{b}{2a}, \dfrac{4ac - b^2}{4a}\right)$ must lie on the graph of $Q_{a,b,c}$ because that is the point to which $(0, 0)$ is translated by a $-\dfrac{b}{2a}$ horizontal and a $\dfrac{4ac - b^2}{4a}$ vertical translation of the graph q_a.

Pages 266-268

1 a (a) $x = 2$. (b) $(2, -4)$ (c) -4 is a minimum value. Since $a > 0$, the parabola is concave upward so that the vertex is the lowest point on the graph. (d) The y-intercept is $(0, 0)$. The image of the y-intercept is $(4, 0)$.
(e) See diagram below at left.

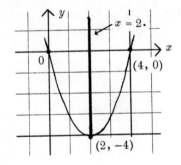
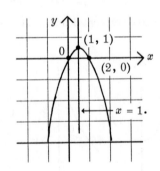

b (a) $x = 1$. (b) $(1, 1)$ (c) 1 is a maximum value. Since $a < 0$, the parabola is concave downward. (d) The y-intercept is $(0, 0)$. The image of the y-intercept is $(2, 0)$. (e) See diagram above at right.

c (a) $x = 3$. (b) $(3, 16)$ (c) 16 is a maximum value. Since $a < 0$ the parabola is concave downward. (d) The y-intercept is $(0, 7)$. The image of the y-intercept is $(6, 7)$. (e) See diagram below at left.

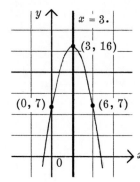
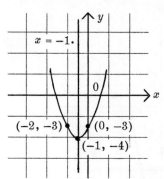

d (a) $x = -1$. (b) $(-1, -4)$. (c) -4 is a minimum value. Since $a > 0$, the parabola is concave upward. (d) The y-intercept is $(0, -3)$. The image of the y-intercept is $(-2, -3)$. (e) See diagram above at right.

e (a) $x = -2$. (b) $(-2, -13)$ (c) -13 is a minimum value because the parabola is concave upward. (d) The y-intercept is $(0, -5)$. The image of the y-intercept is $(-4, -5)$. (e) See diagram below at left.

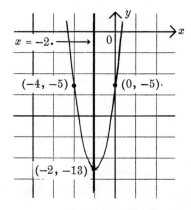
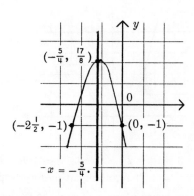

f (a) $x = -\frac{5}{4}$. (b) $\left(-\frac{5}{4}, \frac{17}{8}\right)$ (c) $\frac{17}{8}$ is a maximum value because the parabola is concave downward. (d) The y-intercept is $(0, -1)$. The image of the y-intercept is $\left(-2\frac{1}{2}, -1\right)$. (e) See diagram above at right.

2 a $0 = c$, $0 = 36a + 6b$, $9 = 9a + 3b$.
Hence, $a = -1$, $b = 6$, and $c = 0$.
Thus, an equation that defines
the parabola is $Q(x) = -x^2 + 6x$.
The axis of symmetry is $x = 3$.
The vertex is $(3, 9)$. See diagram
at right.

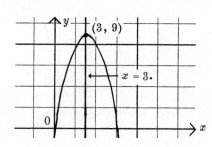

b $-12 = c$, $4 = 16a + 4b + c$, $-11 = a - b + c$. Hence, $a = 1$, $b = 0$ and $c = -12$. Thus, an equation that defines the parabola is $Q(x) = x^2 - 12$. The axis symmetry is $x = 0$, and the vertex is $(0, -12)$.

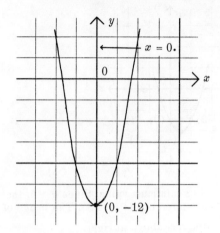

c $8 = 16a - 4b + c$, $2 = 4a - 2b + c$, $8 = 16a + 4b + c$. Hence, $a = \frac{1}{2}$, $b = 0$, and $c = 0$. Thus, an equation that defines the parabola is $Q(x) = \frac{1}{2}x^2$. The axis of symmetry is $x = 0$, and the vertex is $(0, 0)$.

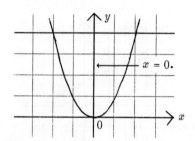

d $-3 = 4a - 2b + c$, $-3 = a - b + c$, $3 = a + b + c$. Hence, $a = 1$, $b = 3$, and $c = -1$. Thus, an equation for the parabola is $Q(x) = x^2 + 3x - 1$. The axis of symmetry is $x = -\frac{3}{2}$, and the vertex is $(-\frac{3}{2}, -\frac{13}{4})$.

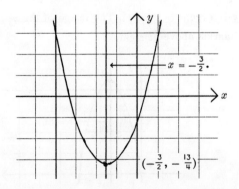

3 $x = y = 25.$

4 Since $A = xy$ and $2x + y = 400$, $A = x(400 - 2x) = 400x - 2x^2$. Hence, $A = -2(x^2 - 200x + 10,000) + 20,000 = -2(x - 100)^2 + 20,000$. Thus, the area will be maximum, 20,000 sq. ft., when $x = 100$ and $y = 200$.

5 $A = x^2 + (20 - x)^2 = x^2 + 400 - 40x + x^2 = 2(x^2 - 20x) + 400 = 2(x^2 - 20x + 100) + 200.$ Hence, the sum of the areas will be minimum, 200 sq. cm., when each piece is 10 cm. long.

6 $x = 10 \,'', y = 6''.$

7 Since $\big(d(0, P)\big)^2 = x^2 + y^2$ and $y = -2x + 10$, we have $\big(d(0, P)\big)^2 = x^2 + (-2x + 10)^2 = x^2 + 4x^2 - 40x + 100 = 5(x^2 - 8x) + 100 = 5(x^2 - 8x + 16) + 20 = 5(x - 4)^2 + 20.$ Hence, the distance will be a minimum, $2\sqrt{5}$, when $x = 4$ and $y = 2$.

8

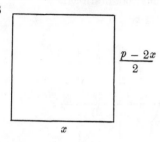

$$\frac{p - 2x}{2}$$

x

$$A = x\left(\frac{p - 2x}{2}\right) = \frac{px - 2x^2}{2} = -1\left(x^2 - \frac{px}{2}\right) = -1\left(x^2 - \frac{px}{2} + \frac{p^2}{16}\right) + \frac{p^2}{16} = -1\left(x - \frac{p}{4}\right)^2 + \frac{p^2}{16}.$$

Hence, the area will be maximum when $x = \frac{p}{4}$. But when $x = \frac{p}{4}$, each side of the rectangle is $\frac{p}{4}$; that is, the rectangle is a square.

9 a Since the perimeter of the equilateral triangle is x in., each side is $\frac{x}{3}$ in. long.

Hence, the area of the equilateral triangle is $\frac{\sqrt{3}}{4}\left(\frac{x}{3}\right)^2 = \frac{\sqrt{3}x^2}{36}$. Since the perimeter of the square is $(11 - x)$ in., each side is $\frac{11 - x}{4}$ in. Hence, the area of the square is $\left(\frac{11 - x}{4}\right)^2 = \frac{x^2 - 22x + 121}{16}$. Thus, the sum of the areas is

$$A(x) = \frac{\sqrt{3}x^2}{36} + \frac{x^2 - 22x + 121}{16} = \left(\frac{\sqrt{3}}{36} + \frac{1}{16}\right)x^2 - \frac{22}{16}x + \frac{121}{16}.$$

b The domain is $\{x \mid 0 \leq x \leq 11\}$.

c Since $a = \frac{\sqrt{3}}{36} + \frac{1}{16}$, the graph is concave upward.

d $A(x)$ is minimum when $x = \frac{-b}{2a} = \frac{22}{16}\bigg/\left(\frac{\sqrt{3}}{18} + \frac{1}{8}\right) = \frac{22}{16} \times \frac{72}{4\sqrt{3} + 9} = 11 \times \frac{9}{4\sqrt{3} + 9} = \frac{99}{4\sqrt{3} + 9} \times \frac{4\sqrt{3} - 9}{4\sqrt{3} - 9} = \frac{99(4\sqrt{3} - 9)}{-33} = 27 - 12\sqrt{3}.$

e The area will be maximum when $x = 0$; that is, when all of the wire is used for the square.

1 a $\{0.8, -3.8\}$ c $\{4.4, -0.4\}$ e $\{2.3, 0.2\}$

  b $\{1.4, -3.4\}$ d $\{0.8, -1.8\}$ f $\{0.2, -1.8\}$

2 a $b^2 - 4ac = 9$. Hence, there are two real solutions, both rational.

  b $b^2 - 4ac = 24$. Hence, there are two real solutions, both irrational.

  c $b^2 - 4ac = -7$. Hence, there are no real solutions.

  d $b^2 - 4ac = -71$. Hence, there are no real solutions.

  e $b^2 - 4ac = 57$. Hence, there are two real solutions, both irrational.

  f $b^2 - 4ac = 0$. Hence, there is one real solution.

  g $b^2 - 4ac = 44$. Hence, there are two real solutions, both irrational.

  h $b^2 - 4ac = 81$. Hence, there are two real solutions, both rational.

3 a $\{x \mid 2 < x < 4\}$ b $\{x \mid x < -4 \text{ or } x > -1\}$

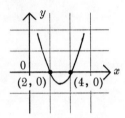

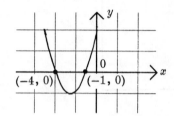

c $\{x \mid 1 \leqq x \leqq 3\}$ d $\{\tfrac{1}{2}\}$

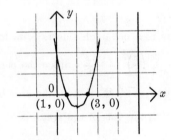

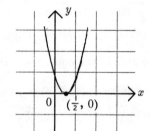

e $\{x \mid -\tfrac{1}{3} < x < 2\}$ f $\{x \mid x < \tfrac{2}{3} \text{ or } x > \tfrac{3}{2}\}$

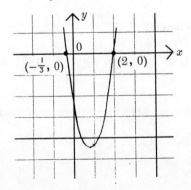

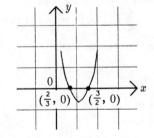

g $\{x \mid x \in \Re\}$

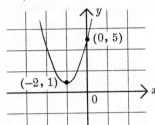

h $\{x \mid \dfrac{-1-\sqrt{5}}{2} \le x \le \dfrac{\sqrt{5}-1}{2}\}$

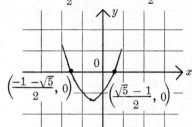

4 a The equation will have one real root if the discriminant is zero; that is, if $k^2 - 4 \cdot 36 = 0$. Hence, the equation will have one real root if $k = \pm 12$.

b The discriminant is zero if and only if $k^2 - 4(k+8) = 0$. Hence, the equation has just one real root if and only if $k = 8$ or $k = -4$.

c This equation has no real roots when $b^2 - 4ac = 16k^2 - 48k$ is less than zero. Hence, the equation has no real roots when $0 < k < 3$.

d This equation has two real roots when $144 - 4k^2 - 20k > 0$; hence, when $-9 < k < 4$.

5 a $6x^2 - 4x - 10 = 0.$ $\{\frac{5}{3}, -1\}$

b $x^2 - 9x + 20 = 0.$ $\{5, 4\}$

c $x^2 - 2x - 3 = 0.$ $\{3, -1\}$

d $z^2 - 17z + 16 = 0.$ $z = 16$ or $z = 1.$ $\{-4, 4, -1, 1\}$

e $4z^2 - 5z - 9 = 0.$ $z = \frac{9}{4}$ or $z = -1.$ $\{\frac{3}{2}, -\frac{3}{2}\}$

f $8x^2 - 6x + 1 = 0.$ $\{\frac{1}{4}, \frac{1}{2}\}$

6 a Let $r_1 = \dfrac{-b + \sqrt{b^2 - 4ac}}{2a}$ and let $r_2 = \dfrac{-b - \sqrt{b^2 - 4ac}}{2a}$. Then $r_1 + r_2 = \dfrac{-2b}{2a} = \dfrac{-b}{a}$.

$$r_1 \cdot r_2 = \left(\dfrac{-b + \sqrt{b^2 - 4ac}}{2a}\right)\left(\dfrac{-b - \sqrt{b^2 - 4ac}}{2a}\right) = \dfrac{b^2 - (b^2 - 4ac)}{4a^2} = \dfrac{4ac}{4a^2} = \dfrac{c}{a}.$$

b If the quadratic equation $x^2 + px + q = 0$ has two real roots, r_1 and r_2, then $r_1 + r_2 = -p$ and $r_1 \cdot r_2 = q.$

7 Suppose that an equation has roots kr_1 and kr_2. Then $kr_1 + kr_2 = k(r_1 + r_2)$ and $kr_1 \cdot kr_2 = k^2(r_1 r_2)$. But, from exercise 6, $r_1 + r_2 = \dfrac{-b}{a}$ and $r_1 \cdot r_2 = \dfrac{c}{a}$. Hence,

$k(r_1 + r_2) = k\left(\dfrac{-b}{a}\right)$ and $k(r_1 \cdot r_2) = k^2 \dfrac{c}{a}$. Thus, the equation with roots kr_1 and kr_2 must have the form $ax^2 + kbx + k^2c = 0.$

8 Suppose that an equation has roots $r_1 + k$ and $r_2 + k$. Then $(r_1 + k) + (r_2 + k) = (r_1 + r_2) + 2k$ and $(r_1 + k)(r_2 + k) = r_1 r_2 + k(r_1 + r_2) + k^2$. By exercise 6, $r_1 + r_2 = \dfrac{-b}{a}$ and $r_1 \cdot r_2 = \dfrac{c}{a}$. Hence, $(r_1 + r_2) + 2k = \dfrac{-b}{a} + 2k = \dfrac{-b + 2ak}{a}$ and $r_1 r_2 + k(r_1 + r_2) + k^2 = \dfrac{c}{a} + k\left(-\dfrac{b}{a}\right) + k^2 = \dfrac{c - kb + k^2 a}{a}$. Thus, the equation with roots $r_1 + k$ and $r_2 + k$ must have the form $ax^2 + (b - 2ak)x + (c - kb + k^2 a) = 0.$

1 **a** 49 ft.   **b** 100 ft.   **c** 1369 ft.   **d** 1849 ft.

2 **a** $\frac{3}{4}$ sec.   **b** $1\frac{1}{4}$ sec.   **c** 5 sec.   **d** 30 sec.

3 **a** $h(t) = 48t - 16t^2$.

     b $\{t \mid 0 \leq t \leq 3\}$

     c $h(t) = -16(t^2 - 3t) = -16(t^2 - 3t + \frac{9}{4}) + 36 = -16(t - \frac{3}{2})^2 + 36$. $h(t)$ is maximum

     when $t = \frac{3}{2}$, and the maximum height of the ball is 36 ft.

4 **a** $h(t) = 80t - 16t^2$. Domain: $\{t \mid 0 \leq t \leq 5\}$. $h(t) = -16(t^2 - 5t) = -16(t - \frac{5}{2})^2 + 100$.

     Hence, the maximum height is 100 ft. after $2\frac{1}{2}$ sec.

     b $h(t) = 56t - 16t^2$. Domain: $\{t \mid 0 \leq t \leq 3\frac{1}{2}\}$.

     $h(t) = -16(t^2 - \frac{7}{2}t) = -16(t^2 - \frac{7}{2}t + \frac{49}{16}) + 49 = -16(t^2 - \frac{7}{4})^2 + 49$. Hence, the

     maximum height is 49 ft. after $1\frac{3}{4}$ sec.

     c $h(t) = 44t - 16t^2$. Domain $\{t \mid 0 \leq t \leq 2\frac{3}{4}\}$.

     $h(t) = -16(t^2 - \frac{11}{4}t) = -16(t^2 - \frac{11}{4}t + \frac{121}{4} = -16(t - \frac{11}{8})^2 + \frac{121}{4}$. Hence, the

     maximum height is $30\frac{1}{4}$ ft. after $1\frac{3}{8}$ sec.

     d $h(t) = v_0 t - 16t^2$. Domain: $\{t \mid 0 \leq t \leq \frac{v_0}{16}\}$. $h(t) = -16\left(t^2 - \frac{v_0}{16}t + (\frac{v_0}{32})^2\right) + \frac{v_0^2}{64} = $

     $-16(t - \frac{v_0}{32})^2 + \frac{v_0^2}{64}$. Hence, the maximum height is $\frac{v_0^2}{64}$ ft. after $\frac{v_0}{32}$ sec.

5 **a** 16 ft. per sec., 48 ft. per sec., 80 ft. per sec., 112 ft. per sec., 144 ft. per sec.

     b $144 + 32 = 176$ ft. per sec.

     c 32 ft. per sec.

     d Average velocity in the interval $k + 1 \leq t \leq k + 2$ is $\dfrac{16(k + 2)^2 - 16(k + 1)^2}{k + 2 - (k + 1)} = $

     $32k + 48$ ft. per sec. Average velocity in the interval $k \leq t \leq k + 1$ is

     $\dfrac{16(k + 1)^2 - 16k^2}{k + 1 - k} = 32k + 16$ ft. per sec. Hence, the average velocity in the

     interval $k + 1 \leq t \leq k + 2$ is greater by 32 ft. per sec. than the average velocity

     over the interval $k \leq t \leq k + 1$.

6 **a** 0 ft. per sec., 32 ft. per sec.; 64 ft. per sec.; 96 ft. per sec.

     b $V(t) = 32t$.

7 **a** $1600 = 16t^2$; hence; $t = 10$.

     b $V(t) = 32(10) = 320$ ft. per sec., which is equivalent to $218\frac{2}{11}$ miles per hour.

8 **a** Average velocity in the interval $k + 1 \leq t \leq k + 2$ is

     $\dfrac{128(k + 2) - 16(k + 2)^2 - \left(128(k + 1) - 16(k + 1)^2\right)}{k + 2 - (k + 1)} = -32k + 80$ ft. per sec.

     Average velocity in the interval $k \leq t \leq k + 1$ is

     $\dfrac{128(k + 1) - 16(k + 1)^2 - (128k - 16k^2)}{k + 1 - k} = -32k + 112$ ft. per sec.

     Hence, the average velocity over the interval $k + 1 \leq t \leq k + 2$ is less by

32 ft. per sec. than the average velocity over the interval $k \leq t \leq k + 1$.

b 128 ft. per sec., 96 ft. per sec., 64 ft. per sec., 32 ft. per sec.

c $V(t) = 128 - 32t$.

d $h(t) = -16(t^2 - 8t) = -16(t^2 - 8t + 16) + 256 = -16(t - 4)^2 + 256$. Hence, the object reaches its maximum height of 256 ft. after 4 seconds. $V(4) = 128 - 32 \cdot 4 = 0$. Thus, the velocity is 0 when the object reaches its maximum height.

e $0 = 128t - 16t^2 = 16t(8 - t)$; therefore, the object hits the ground after 8 seconds. $V(8) = 128 - 32(8) = -128$ ft. per sec. The velocity is negative because the object is falling back to earth, in the opposite direction from that of its initial velocity.

9 a $h(t) = v_0 t - 16t^2$.

b $V(t) = v_0 - 32t$.

c $h(t) = -16(t^2 - \frac{v_0}{16}t) = -16(t^2 - \frac{v_0}{16}t + \frac{v_0^2}{1024}) + \frac{v_0^2}{64} = -16(t - \frac{v_0}{32})^2 + \frac{v_0^2}{64}$. Hence,

the object reaches its maximum height of $\frac{v_0^2}{16}$ ft. after $\frac{v_0}{32}$ sec. $V(\frac{v_0}{32}) = v_0 - 32(\frac{v_0}{32}) = 0$.
Thus, the velocity is 0 when the object reaches its maximum height.

d $0 = 16t(\frac{v_0}{16} - t)$. Therefore, the object strikes the ground after $\frac{v_0}{16}$ sec. $V(\frac{v_0}{16}) =$

$v_0 - 32(\frac{v_0}{16}) = -v_0$.

Pages 282-283

1 a

t	(x, y)
0	(1, 0)
1	(0, 1)
−1	(2, 1)
2	(−1, 4)
−2	(3, 4)

Since $t = 1 - x$, $y = (1 - x)^2$.
See diagram at right.

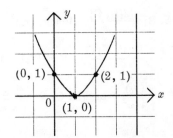

b

t	(x, y)
0	(0, 0)
1	(3, 5)
−1	(−3, −7)
2	(6, 8)
$\frac{1}{2}$	$(\frac{3}{2}, \frac{11}{4})$
−2	(−6, −16)

Since $t = \frac{x}{3}$, $y = 2x - \frac{x^2}{9}$.
See diagram at right.

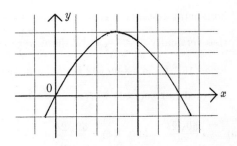

c

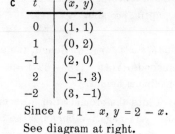

t	(x, y)
0	$(1, 1)$
1	$(0, 2)$
-1	$(2, 0)$
2	$(-1, 3)$
-2	$(3, -1)$

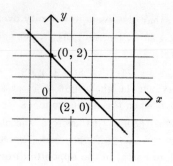

Since $t = 1 - x$, $y = 2 - x$.
See diagram at right.

2 a

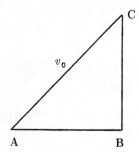

Since $\triangle ABC$ is a right triangle, $(v_0)^2 = \big(d(A, B)\big)^2 + \big(d(B, C)\big)^2$. Since the slope m of AC is equal to the tangent of $\angle CAB$ (see exercise 8, page 185), $m = \dfrac{d(B, C)}{d(A, B)}$; that is, $d(A, B) = \dfrac{d(B, C)}{m}$. Hence, $(v_0)^2 = \left(\dfrac{d(B, C)}{m}\right)^2 + \big(d(B, C)\big)^2 = $

$\dfrac{\big(d(B, C)\big)^2 + m^2\big(d(B, C)\big)^2}{m^2}$, or $m^2(v_0)^2 = (1 + m^2)\big(d(B, C)\big)^2$. Therefore,

$\big(d(B, C)\big)^2 = \dfrac{m^2(v_0)^2}{1 + m^2}$, or $d(B, C) = \dfrac{mv_0}{\sqrt{1 + m^2}}$. Since $d(A, B) = \dfrac{d(B, C)}{m}$,

$d(A, B) = \dfrac{v_0}{\sqrt{1 + m^2}}$.

b Since gravity does not affect the horizontal component, in t seconds the horizontal distance traveled is $x = \dfrac{v_0 t}{\sqrt{1 + m^2}}$ ft. In t seconds, the ball would rise vertically $\dfrac{mv_0 t}{\sqrt{1 + m^2}}$ ft. if there were no gravity. However, because the ball loses $16t^2$ ft. in t seconds because of the effect of gravity, the vertical distance traveled in t seconds is $f(x) = \dfrac{mv_0 t}{\sqrt{1 + m^2}} - 16t^2$ ft.

3 (a) $x = \dfrac{50\sqrt{2}t}{\sqrt{2}} = 50t$; $f(x) = \dfrac{50\sqrt{2}t}{\sqrt{2}} - 16t^2 = 50t - 16t^2$.

(b) Since $t = \dfrac{x}{50}$, $f(x) = x - \dfrac{16x^2}{2500} = x - \dfrac{4}{625}x^2$. Domain: $\{x \mid 0 \leq x \leq \dfrac{625}{4}\}$

(c)

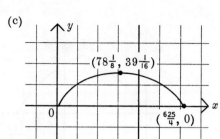

(d) Maximum height: $39\frac{1}{16}$ ft.

Horizontal distance: $156\frac{1}{4}$ ft.

4 (a) $x = \dfrac{78t}{\sqrt{\frac{169}{144}}} = \dfrac{78t}{\frac{13}{12}} = 72t;\ \ f(x) = \dfrac{\frac{5}{12} \cdot 78t}{\sqrt{\frac{169}{144}}} - 16t^2 = \dfrac{\frac{130}{4}t}{\frac{13}{12}} - 16t^2 = 30t - 16t^2.$

(b) Since $t = \dfrac{x}{72}$, $f(x) = \dfrac{30x}{72} - 16\left(\dfrac{x}{72}\right)^2$

$= \dfrac{5}{12}x - \dfrac{1}{324}x^2.$

Domain: $\{x \mid 0 \le x \le 135\}$

(c) See diagram at right.

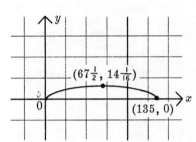

(d) Maximum height: $14\frac{1}{16}$ ft.

Horizontal distance: 135 ft.

5 (a) $x = \dfrac{68t}{\frac{17}{15}} = 60t;\ \ f(x) = \dfrac{\frac{8}{15} \cdot 68t}{\frac{17}{15}} - 16t^2 = 32t - 16t^2.$

(b) Since $t = \dfrac{x}{60}$, $f(x) = \dfrac{8}{15}x - \dfrac{1}{225}x^2.$

Domain: $\{x \mid 0 \le x \le 120\}$

(c) See diagram at right.

(d) Maximum height: 16 ft.

Horizontal distance: 120 ft.

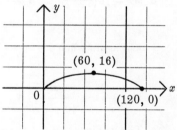

6 (a) $x = \dfrac{75t}{\frac{25}{7}} = 21t;$

$f(x) = \dfrac{\frac{24}{7} \cdot 75t}{\frac{25}{7}} - 16t^2 = 72t - 16t^2.$

(b) Since $t = \dfrac{x}{21}$, $f(x) = \dfrac{24}{7}x - \dfrac{16}{441}x^2.$

Domain: $\{x \mid 0 \le x \le 94\frac{1}{2}\}$

(c) See diagram at right.

(d) Maximum height: 81 ft.

Horizontal distance: $94\frac{1}{2}$ ft.

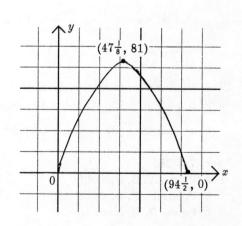

7 (a) $x = 30t$; $f(x) = 30\sqrt{3}t - 16t^2$.

(b) Since $t = \dfrac{x}{30}$, $f(x) = \sqrt{3}x - \dfrac{4}{225}x^2$.

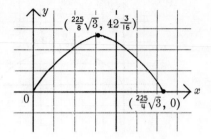

Domain: $\{x \mid 0 \le x \le \frac{225}{4}\sqrt{3}\}$

(c) See diagram at right.

(d) Maximum height: $42\frac{3}{16}$ ft.

Horizontal distance: 96.43 ft. (approx.)

8 (a) $x = 25\sqrt{3}t$; $f(x) = 25t - 16t^2$.

(b) Since $t = \dfrac{x}{25\sqrt{3}}$, $f(x) = \dfrac{\sqrt{3}}{3}x - \dfrac{16}{1875}x^2$.

Domain: $\{x \mid 0 \le x \le \frac{625}{16}\sqrt{3}\}$

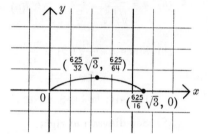

(c) See diagram at right.

(d) Maximum height: $9\frac{49}{64}$ ft.

Horizontal distance: 67.5 ft. (approx.)

9 a Since $t = \dfrac{x(\sqrt{1 + m^2})}{v_0}$, $f(x) = \dfrac{mv_0\left(\dfrac{x\sqrt{1 + m^2}}{v_0}\right)}{\sqrt{1 + m^2}} - 16\left(\dfrac{x^2(1 + m^2)}{v_0^2}\right) = mx - \dfrac{16(1 + m^2)}{v_0^2}x^2$.

b $mx - 16\left(\dfrac{1 + m^2}{v_0^2}\right)x^2 = \dfrac{16(1 + m^2)}{v_0^2}x\left(\dfrac{mv_0^2}{16(1 + m^2)} - x\right)$. Hence, $f(x) = 0$ when $x = 0$

and again when $x = \dfrac{mv_0^2}{16(1 + m^2)}$. Therefore, the domain of the function is

$\{x \mid 0 \le x \le \dfrac{mv_0^2}{16(1 + m^2)}\}$.

c The maximum height is reached after $\frac{1}{2}$ the horizontal distance is traveled;

that is, when $x = \dfrac{mv_0^2}{32(1 + m^2)}$. Hence, the maximum height is $\dfrac{m^2v_0^2}{32(1 + m^2)} - \dfrac{m^2v_0^2}{64(1 + m^2)} =$

$\dfrac{m^2v_0^2}{64(1 + m^2)}$.

10 a $m = \tan 45 = 1$. Hence, $x = 100t$; $f(x) = 100t - 16t^2$.

b $m = \tan 30 = \dfrac{\sqrt{3}}{3}$. Hence, $x = 60\sqrt{3}t$; $f(x) = 60t - 16t^2$.

c $m = \tan 60 = \sqrt{3}$. Hence, $x = 30\sqrt{3}t$; $f(x) = 90t - 16t^2$.

Pages 287-288

1 a Points A, B, C, and I

b Points E, F, G, and K

c Points D, H, J and L

2 a Points B and I; point C; point A
  b Points F and G; point E; point K
  c Concave downward; concave upward; concave upward; concave upward, concave downward; concave downward
3 a Near points D and H
  b Near point J
  c Near points A, B, C, and I
  d Near points E, F, and G, and K
4 Near point L

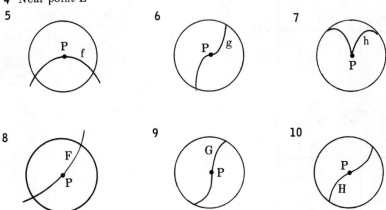

5   6   7

8   9   10

11 Let P be an arbitrary point in the shaded region. Through P, construct lines perpendicular to ℓ and ℓ', intersecting ℓ and ℓ' in points A and A', respectively. Through P, construct a line perpendicular to the boundary (ℓ_1 or ℓ_2) on the same side of ℓ as P and that intersects the boundary in point C. Through C, construct lines perpendicular to ℓ and ℓ', intersecting ℓ and ℓ' in points B and B', respectively. Now $\overline{B'C} \cong \overline{BC}$ and $\overline{A'P} > \overline{B'C}$; so $\overline{A'P} > \overline{BC}$. However, $\overline{BC} > \overline{AP}$. Therefore, $\overline{A'P} > \overline{AP}$. Hence, P is closer to ℓ than it is to ℓ'.

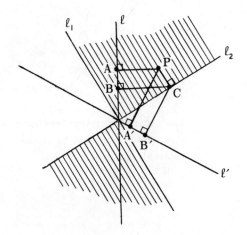

1 Radius: $\frac{3}{4}\sqrt{5}$

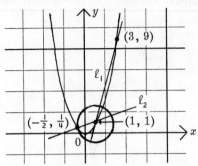

2 Radius: $\sqrt{10}$

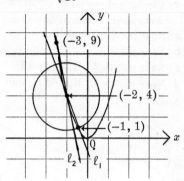

3 Radius: $\sqrt{m^2 + m^4} = |m|\sqrt{1 + m^2}$

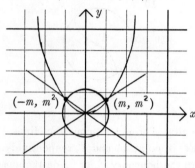

4 a

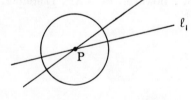

The slope of any line bracketed by this sector pair must be in the interval $0 < m_1 < m < m_2$.

b

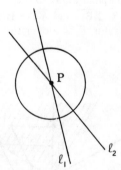

The slope of any line bracketed by this sector pair must be in the interval $m_1 < m < m_2 < 0$.

c

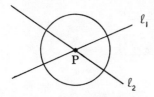

The slope of any line bracketed by this sector pair must be in the interval $-1 < m < 1$.

d

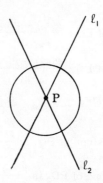

The slope of any line bracketed by this sector pair must satisfy the inequality $|m| > 1$, which is equivalent to $m < -1$ or $m > 1$, or the line is vertical and m does not exist.

e

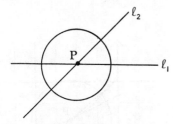

The slope of any line bracketed by this sector pair must satisfy the inequality $0 < m < m_2$

f

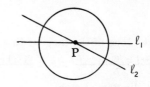

The slope of any line bracketed by this sector pair must satisfy the inequality $m_2 < m < 0$.

g

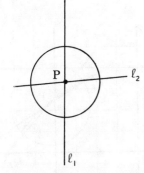

The slope of any line bracketed by this sector pair must satisfy the inequality $m > m_2 > 0$.

h

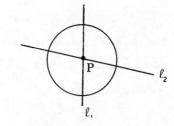

The slope of any line bracketed by this sector pair must satisfy the inequality $m < m_2$.

5 a Yes

b Slope of PQ_2: $\dfrac{g(x_0) - g(x_0 + h)}{x_0 - (x_0 + h)} = \dfrac{g(x_0) - g(x_0 + h)}{-h}$.

Slope of PQ_1: $\dfrac{g(x_0) - g(x_0 - h)}{x_0 - (x_0 - h)} = \dfrac{g(x_0) - g(x_0 - h)}{h}$.

c $\dfrac{g(x_0) - g(x_0 - h)}{h} < m < \dfrac{g(x_0) - g(x_0 + h)}{-h}$

6 Since the slope of PQ_1 is $\dfrac{g(x_0) - g(x_0 - h)}{h}$

and the slope of PQ_2 is $\dfrac{g(x_0) - g(x_0 + h)}{-h}$,

the slope of the tangent line must satisfy

$\dfrac{g(x_0) - g(x_0 + h)}{-h} < m < \dfrac{g(x_0) - g(x_0 - h)}{h}$.

See diagram at right.

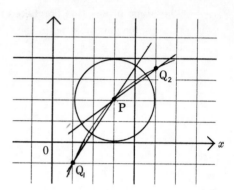

7 a The slope of the tangent line must satisfy

$\dfrac{g(x_0) - g(x_0 - h)}{h} < m < \dfrac{g(x_0) - g(x_0 + h)}{-h}$.

See diagram at right.

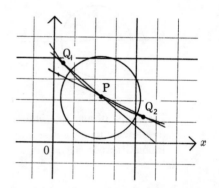

b The slope of the tangent line must satisfy

$\dfrac{g(x_0) - g(x_0 + h)}{-h} < m < \dfrac{g(x_0) - g(x_0 - h)}{h}$.

See diagram at right.

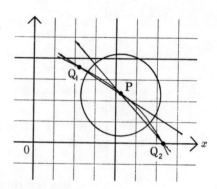

8 a $2 - h < m < 2 + h$. **9 a** $-2 - h < m < -2 + h$.

b $-4 - h < m < -4 + h$. **b** $4 - h < m < 4 + h$.

c $2x_0 - h < m < 2x_0 + h$. **c** $-2x_0 - h < m < -2x_0 + h$.

1 The graph of g has the x-axis as a tangent at $(0, 0)$.

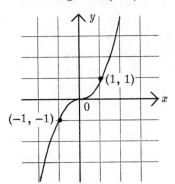

2 The graph of g has no tangent at $(0, 0)$.

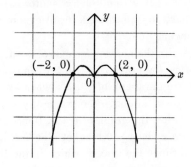

3 The graph of g has no tangent at $(0, 0)$.

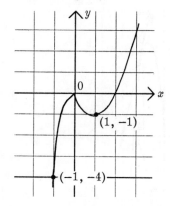

4 The graph of g has no tangent at $(0, 0)$.

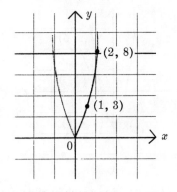

5 a The difference in ordinates for points on the graphs of $g(x) = x^3$ and $y = h^2x$ which have the same abscissa is given by $x^3 - h^2x = x(x^2 - h^2)$. When $x(x^2 - h^2)$ is positive, the graph of $g(x) = x^3$ is above the graph of $y = h^2x$; when $x(x^2 - h^2)$ is negative, the graph of $g(x) = x^3$ is below the graph of $y = h^2x$. Now when $0 < x < h$, $x > 0$ and $x^2 - h^2 < 0$; so $x(x^2 - h^2) < 0$ and the graph of $g(x) = x^3$ is below the graph of $y = h^2x$. When $-h < x < 0$, $x < 0$, and $x^2 - h^2 < 0$; so $x(x^2 - h^2) > 0$ and the graph of $g(x) = x^3$ is above the graph of $y = h^2x$. If we consider $g(x) = x^3$ and $y = -h^2x$, by a similar analysis we can arrive at the following conclusions:

When $-h < x < 0$, the graph of $g(x) = x^3$ is below the graph of $y = -h^2x$.

When $0 < x < h$, the graph of $g(x) = x^3$ is above the graph of $y = -h^2x$.

Thus, circle C, $y = h^2x$, and $y = -h^2x$ define a sector pair that brackets the graph of $g(x) = x^3$ at $(0, 0)$.

b Any line through the origin having slope m, where $|m| > h^2$, will not be bracketed by the sector pair in part a. Since we can choose h^2 as small as we wish, for any line through the origin having slope m, $m \neq 0$, we can construct a sector pair which brackets the graph of g and the x-axis at the origin, but does not bracket this line. Such a sector pair, of course, will not bracket the y-axis. Thus, no line through $(0, 0)$ except the x-axis can satisfy the definition of a tangent line.

c Yes. In the answer for exercise 5a, it was shown that the graph of $g(x) = x^3$ is below the graph of $y = h^2 x$ when $0 < x < h$ and that the graph of $g(x) = x^3$ is above the graph of $y = h^2 x$ when $-h < x < 0$. Also, if $0 < x$, then the graph of $g(x) = x^3$ is above the graph of $y = 0$; and if $x < 0$, then the graph of $g(x) = x^3$ is below the graph of $y = 0$. Hence, the circle C and the sector pair formed by $y = h^2 x$ and $y = 0$ bracket g at $(0, 0)$.

d No. Since the x-axis, which is the line $y = 0$, is the tangent line to g at $(0, 0)$, the sector pair determined by the x-axis and the line $y = h^2 x$ does not bracket the tangent at $(0, 0)$.

Pages 306-307

1 a $y = 2x - \frac{7}{2}$. See graph at left below.

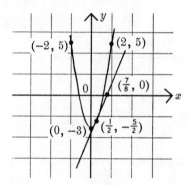 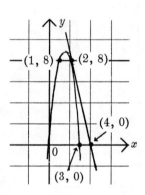

b $y = -4x + 16$. See graph at right above.

c $y = 9x + 10$. See graph at left below.

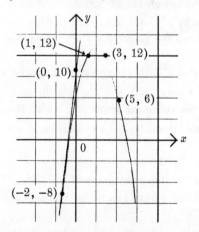 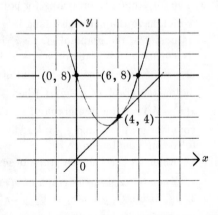

d $y = x$. See graph at right above.

2 a (−2, 1). See graph at left below.

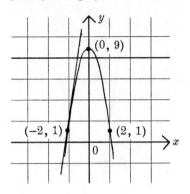 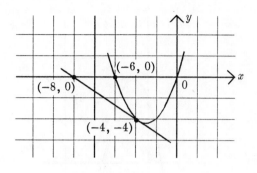

b (−4, −4). See graph at right above.
c (3, 6). See graph at left below.

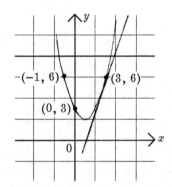 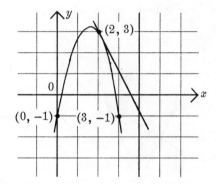

d (2, 3). See graph at right above.

3 a (2, 0) and (−2, 0). $y = -4x - 8$; $y = 4x - 8$. See graph at left below.

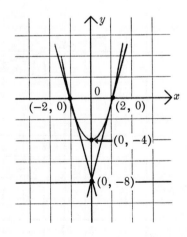 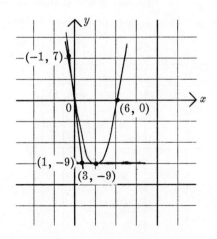

b (3, −9) and (−1, 7). $y = -9$ and $y = -8x - 1$. See graph at right above.

c $(5, -9)$ and $(3, -1)$. $y = -2x + 5$ and $y = -6x + 21$. See graph at left below.

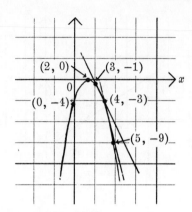 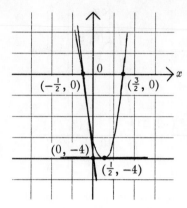

d $(\frac{1}{2}, -4)$ and $(-\frac{1}{2}, 0)$. $y = -4$ and $y = -8x - 4$. See graph at right above.

4 a $y = \frac{1}{2}x - 1$. See graph at left below.

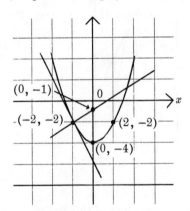 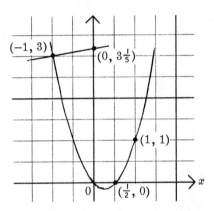

b $y = \frac{1}{5}x + 3\frac{1}{5}$. See graph at right above.

c $y = \frac{1}{2}x - 4$. See graph at left below.

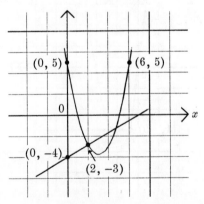 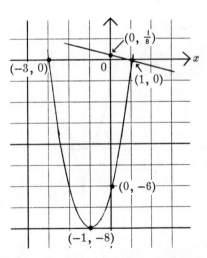

d $y = -\frac{1}{8}x + \frac{1}{8}$. See graph at right above.

1 a Since $-\dfrac{b}{2a} = 0$, the graph is rising for $\{x \mid x > 0\}$, and the graph is falling for $\{x \mid x < 0\}$. See graph at left below.

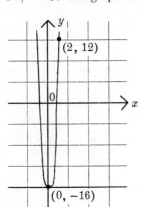

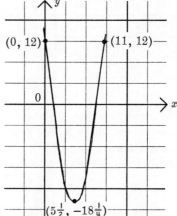

b Rising: $\{x \mid x > 5\frac{1}{2}\}$; falling: $\{x \mid x < 5\frac{1}{2}\}$. See graph at right above.

c Rising: $\{x \mid x < 1\frac{1}{4}\}$; falling: $\{x \mid x > 1\frac{1}{4}\}$. See graph at left below.

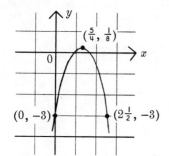

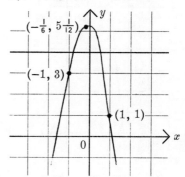

d Rising: $\{x \mid x < -\frac{1}{6}\}$; falling: $\{x \mid x > -\frac{1}{6}\}$. See graph at right above.

e Rising: $\{x \mid x > 6\}$; falling: $\{x \mid x < 6\}$. See graph at left below.

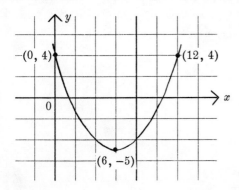

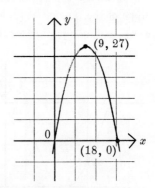

f Rising: $\{x \mid x < 9\}$; falling: $\{x \mid x > 9\}$. See graph at right above.

2 a The minimum value is −6 at $x = 4$, which is the same as the minimum value when the domain is $\Re$. See graph at left below.

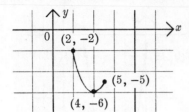 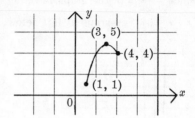

b The maximum value is 5 at $x = 3$, which is the same as the maximum value when the domain is $\Re$. See graph at right above.

c The minimum value is 1 at $x = 2$. The minimum value is −1 at $x = 1$ when the domain is $\Re$. See graph at left below.

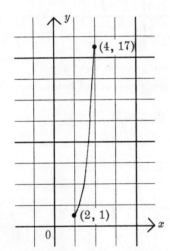 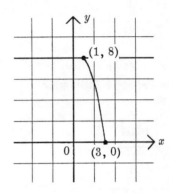

d The maximum value is 8 at $x = 1$. The maximum value is 9 at $x = 0$ when the domain is $\Re$. See graph at right above.

3 a Substituting $(0, -3)$ and $(3, 0)$ into $Q(x) = ax^2 + bx + c$, we have $-3 = a \cdot 0 + b \cdot 0 + c$, or $c = -3$, and $0 = 9a + 3b - 3$, or $1 = 3a + b$. Since the slope of the tangent at $(0, -3)$ is −2, we have $-2 = 2a \cdot 0 + b$, or $b = -2$. Hence, $a = 1$, and an equation for the function is $Q(x) = x^2 - 2x - 3$.

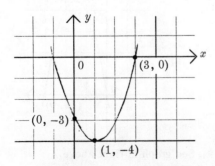

b $Q(x) = -x^2 + 4x + 2$.

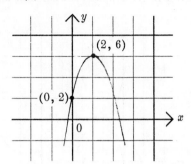

(2, 6)

(0, 2)

c $Q(x) = \frac{3}{4}x^2 - 3x$.

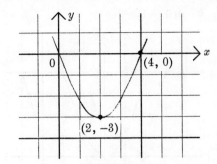

(4, 0)

(2, −3)

d $Q(x) = -\frac{1}{9}x^2 - \frac{4}{9}x - 4\frac{4}{9}$.

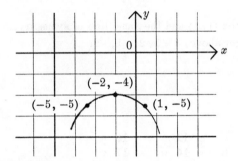

(−2, −4)

(−5, −5)   (1, −5)

4 An equation for the function is $Q(x) = 2x^2 - 7x + 6$. Hence, the slope of the tangent at (2, 0) is 1.

5 $Q'(x) = 2ax + b$. $Q'(x_0 + k) = 2a(x_0 + k) + b = 2ax_0 + 2ak + b$.
$Q'(x_0) = 2ax_0 + b$. $Q'(x_0 + k) - Q'(x_0) = 2ak$.

6 a All parabolas have y-intercept (0, 3). In the graphs shown at left below, $k = 1, 4, 0,$ and -4.

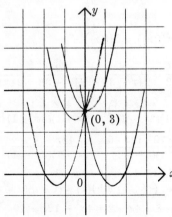

(0, 3)

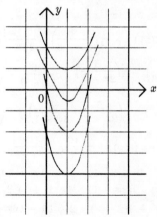

b All parabolas have the same line of symmetry, $x = 2$. In the graphs shown at right above, $k = 4, 2, 0, -4$.

c All parabolas have their vertex on the x-axis. In the graphs shown at left below, $k = 0, 1, -1, -3$.

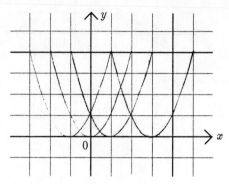
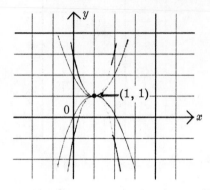

d All parabolas have the same vertex $(1, 1)$ and the same line of symmetry, $x = 1$. In the graphs shown at right above, $k = 1, 2, -1, -2$.

7 $Q(x) = kx^2 + 4x + 3$.

Chapter review
Pages 312-314

1 d	4 b and c	7 c	10 b	13 a	16 c
2 d	5 d	8 a	11 b	14 c	17 c
3 c	6 c	9 b	12 a	15 d	18 b

Cumulative review
Pages 314-315

1 a Example: $\mathcal{S} = \{x \mid x \ \Re \text{ and } -3 < x < 25\}$
 b Example: $\mathcal{S} = \{x \mid x \in \Re \text{ and } x \leqq 2\pi\}$
 c Example: $\mathcal{S} = \{x \mid x \in \Re \text{ and } -2\frac{1}{2} < x\}$
 d Example: $\mathcal{S} = \{x \mid x < -1 \text{ or } x > \frac{1}{3}\}$

2 a $(a + b)\big(f(x)\big) = -\frac{1}{12}\left(\dfrac{1}{2x - 3}\right) = \dfrac{-1}{24x - 36}$. $a\big(f(x)\big) + b\big(f(x)\big) =$

$\dfrac{2}{3}\left(\dfrac{1}{2x - 3}\right) - \dfrac{3}{4}\left(\dfrac{1}{2x - 3}\right) = \dfrac{2}{6x - 9} - \dfrac{3}{8x - 12} = \dfrac{8}{24x - 36} - \dfrac{9}{24x - 36} = \dfrac{-1}{24x - 36}$.

b $a(f + g)(x) = 2\left(\dfrac{5}{2x + 1} + \dfrac{3}{3x - 1}\right) = 2\left(\dfrac{15x - 5 + 6x + 3}{(2x + 1)(3x - 1)}\right) = \dfrac{42x - 4}{(2x + 1)(3x - 1)}$.

$a\big(f(x)\big) + a\big(g(x)\big) = \dfrac{10}{2x + 1} + \dfrac{6}{3x - 1} = \dfrac{30x - 10 + 12x + 6}{(2x + 1)(3x - 1)} = \dfrac{42x - 4}{(2x + 1)(3x - 1)}$.

3 a $a < 0$. **b** $a < -1$. **c** $0 < a < 1$. **d** $a > 1$. **e** $a < -1$.

4 a $(f \circ g)(x) = f(2x - 1) = 4x^2 - 4x + 2$. Hence, $\big((f \circ g) \circ h\big)(x) = (f \circ g)(2 - x) =$
$4(2 - x)^2 - 4(2 - x) + 2 = 16 - 16x + 4x^2 - 8 + 4x + 2 = 4x^2 - 12x + 10$.
$(g \circ h)(x) = g(2 - x) = -2x + 3$. Hence, $\big(f \circ (g \circ h)(x)\big) = f(-2x + 3) =$
$(-2x + 3)^2 + 1 = 4x^2 - 12x + 10$.

b The graph of f ∘ g ∘ h is the graph of q translated $\frac{3}{2}$ units to the right and 1 unit upward.

5 Since the slope of the tangent line is 8, the slope of the parallel line is 8, and the slope of the perpendicular line is $-\frac{1}{8}$. Hence, an equation for the parallel line is $y = 8x - 20$, and an equation for the perpendicular line is $y = -\frac{1}{8}x + 4\frac{3}{8}$.

6 **a** $x = \frac{5}{2}$.   **b** $(\frac{5}{2}, -2\frac{1}{4})$; a minimum value

c x-intercepts: $(1, 0)$ and $(4, 0)$; y-intercept: $(0, 4)$

d

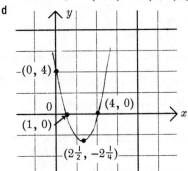

7 **a** $-\frac{5}{32} + \sqrt{\frac{345}{32}}$ and $-\frac{5}{32} - \sqrt{\frac{345}{32}}$.

b To the nearest tenth, the roots are 0.4 and -0.7.

8 **a** $k = \frac{3}{2}$.   **b** $-\frac{3}{2} < k < 0$.   **c** $k > \frac{3}{2}$.

9 Slope of $\overline{AC}$: $\dfrac{y_0 - \frac{1}{4}}{x_0 - \frac{1}{2}} = \dfrac{4y_0 - 1}{4x_0 - 2}$. Slope of $\overline{BC}$: $\dfrac{y_0 - \frac{1}{4}}{x_0 + \frac{1}{2}} = \dfrac{4y_0 - 1}{4x_0 + 2}$.

If $\dfrac{4y_0 - 1}{4x_0 - 2} = \dfrac{4y_0 - 1}{4x_0 + 2} + 1$, then $\dfrac{4y_0 - 1}{4x_0 - 2} = \dfrac{4y_0 + 4x_0 + 1}{4x_0 + 2}$, or $16x_0y_0 - 4x_0 + 8y_0 - 2 =$

$16x_0y_0 + 16x_0^2 - 4x_0 - 8y_0 - 2$. This last equation simplifies to $16y_0 = 16x_0^2$. Hence, if the slope of $\overline{AC}$ exceeds the slope of $\overline{BC}$ by 1, then it must be the case that $y_0 = x_0^2$.

10 *Closure*:
   1) Since $\mathcal{I}$ is closed under addition, $(a + c) \in \mathcal{I}$ and $(b + d) \in \mathcal{I}$. Hence,
      $(a, b) \oplus (c, d) = (a + c, b + d) \in \mathcal{S}$.
   2) Since $\mathcal{I}$ is closed under multiplication, $ac \in \mathcal{I}$ and $bd \in \mathcal{I}$. Hence,
      $(a, b) \otimes (c, d) = (ac, bd) \in \mathcal{S}$.
Commutative:
   3) Since addition is commutative on $\mathcal{I}$, $a + c = c + a$ and $b + d = d + b$. Hence,
      $(a, b) \oplus (c, d) = (a + c, b + d) = (c + a, d + b) = (c, d) \oplus (a, b)$.
   4) Since multiplication is commutative on $\mathcal{I}$, $ac = ca$ and $bd = db$. Hence,
      $(a, b) \otimes (c, d) = (ac, bd) = (ca, db) = (c, d) \otimes (a, b)$.
Associative:
   5) Since addition is associative on $\mathcal{I}$, $(a + c) + e = a + (c + e)$ and $(b + d) + f = b + (d + f)$. Hence, $\big((a, b) \oplus (c, d)\big) \oplus (e, f) = \big((a + c) + e, (b + d) + f\big) =$

$$\big(a + (c + e),\ b + (d + f)\big) = (a,\ b) \oplus \big((c,\ d) \oplus (e,\ f)\big).$$

6) Since multiplication is associative on $\mathcal{I}$, $(ac)e = a(ce)$ and $(bd)f = b(df)$. Hence, $\big((a,\ b) \otimes (c,\ d)\big) \otimes (e,\ f) = \big((ac)e,\ (bd)f\big) = \big(a(ce),\ b(df)\big) = (a,\ b) \otimes \big((c,\ d) \otimes (e,\ f)\big).$

Identity:

7) Since $0 \in \mathcal{I}$, $(0,\ 0) \in \mathcal{S}$ and $(a,\ b) \oplus (0,\ 0) = (a + 0,\ b + 0) = (a,\ b) = (0,\ 0) \oplus (a,\ b).$

8) Since $1 \in \mathcal{I}$, $(1,\ 1) \in \mathcal{S}$ and $(a,\ b) \otimes (1,\ 1) = (a,\ b) = (1,\ 1) \otimes (a,\ b).$

Inverse:

9) For each $a \in \mathcal{I}$, $-a \in \mathcal{I}$. Hence, for each $(a,\ b) \in \mathcal{S}$, $(-a,\ -b) \in \mathcal{S}$ and $(a,\ b) \oplus (-a,\ -b) = (0,\ 0) = (-a,\ -b) \oplus (a,\ b).$

10) It is not the case that for each $a \in \mathcal{I}$, where $a \neq 0$, $\frac{1}{a} \in \mathcal{I}$. Hence, it is not the case that for each $(a,\ b) \in \mathcal{S}$ where $(a,\ b) \neq (0,\ 0)$, $(\frac{1}{a}, \frac{1}{b}) \in \mathcal{S}$. For example, $(3,\ 4) \in \mathcal{S}$, but $(3,\ 4)$ does not have a multiplicative inverse in $\mathcal{S}$.

11) *Distributive*:

Since multiplication distributes over addition in $\mathcal{I}$, $a(c + e) = ac + ae$ and $b(d + f) = bd + bf$. Hence, $(a,\ b) \otimes \big((c,\ d) \oplus (e,\ f)\big) = \big(a(c + e),\ b(d + f)\big) = (ac + ae,\ bd + bf) = \big((a,\ b) \otimes (c,\ d)\big) \oplus \big((a,\ b) \otimes (e,\ f)\big).$

11 a If f is an even function, then $(x_0,\ y_0) \in$ f implies that $(-x_0,\ y_0) \in$ f. But this means that $a(x_0)^2 + b(x_0) + c = a(-x_0)^2 + b(-x_0) + c$, or $ax_0{}^2 + bx_0 + c = ax_0{}^2 - bx_0 + c$ which implies that $bx_0 = -bx_0$. If x_0 is any real number different from 0, then $bx_0 = -bx_0$ only if $b = -b = 0$. Thus, if f is an even function, $b = 0$. If $b = 0$, then $f(x) = ax^2 + c$. Hence, $(x_0,\ y_0) \in$ f implies that $(-x_0,\ y_0) \in$ f, since $a(x_0)^2 + c = a(-x_0)^2 + c$. Thus, if $b = 0$, f is an even function.

b If f is an odd function, then $(x_0,\ y_0) \in$ f implies that $(-x_0,\ -y_0) \in$ f. This is true if and only if $ax_0{}^2 + bx_0 + c = -\big(a(-x_0)^2 + b(-x_0) + c\big)$, or $ax_0{}^2 + bx_0 + c = -ax_0{}^2 + bx_0 - c$, which implies that $a = -a$. But $a = -a$ only if $a = 0$, in which case the function would not be a quadratic function. Hence, no quadratic function is an odd function.

Chapter 7
Polynomial functions

Pages 320-321

1 a Yes. Function f is of degree 11.

b Yes. Function g is of degree 0.

c No. The term $-2\sqrt{x} = -2x^{\frac{1}{2}}$ has a fractional exponent.

d No. The term $\frac{1}{x} = x^{-1}$ has a negative exponent.

2 a $g(-2) = -33.$

b $F(\frac{1}{2}) = \frac{7}{8}.$

c $G(2.5) = 25.75.$

d $H(-\sqrt{2}) = 0.$

3 a $(f + g)(x) = 3x^3 + x^2 - x + 6$; $(f \cdot g)(x) = 3x^5 - 9x^4 + 17x^3 - 5x^2 + 7x + 5$.
Degree of f is 3; degree of g is 2; degree of f + g is 3; and degree of f · g is 5.

b $(f + g)(x) = \frac{2}{3}x$; $(f \cdot g)(x) = -\frac{1}{4}x^8 - \frac{1}{3}x^7 - \frac{1}{9}x^6 - \frac{1}{3}x^5 - \frac{2}{9}x^4$. Degree of f is 4; degree of g is 4; degree of f + g is 1; and degree of f · g is 8.

4 a $a = 6$ and $b = 0$.

b $a = 9$ and $b = 2$.

c $a = 3$ and $b = 2$ or $a = -2$ and $b = -3$.

5 a $\dfrac{P_1}{P_2}(x) = 2x - 1$.

b The quotient is not a polynomial

c $\dfrac{P_1}{P_2}(x) = 4x^2 + 3x$.

d $\dfrac{P_1}{P_2}(x) = x^4 - 2x^3 + 4x^2 - 8x + 16$.

e The quotient is not a polynomial.

f $\dfrac{P_1}{P_2}(x) = x^{n-1} + ax^{n-2} + a^2 x^{n-3} + \ldots + a^{n-2}x + a^{n-1}$.

6 a 3   **b** $-1, -\frac{2}{3}, \frac{2}{3}$ **c** $-3, -\frac{1}{2}, 5$ **d** $-\frac{3}{2}, \frac{2}{3}, 1$

7 a $P(x) = (x)(x - 2)(x + 2)$. $-2, 0, 2$

b $P(x) = (x)(x - 1)(x - 2)$. $0, 1, 2$

c $P(x) = (x)(2x - 3)(x + 2)$. $-2, 0, \frac{3}{2}$

d $P(x) = (x^2 + 9)(x - 3)(x + 3)$. $-3, 3$

e $P(x) = (x - 3)(x + 3)(x - 1)(x + 1)$. $-3, -1, 1, 3$

f $P(x) = (x - 2)(x^2 + 2x + 4)$. 2

g $P(x) = (x - 1)(x^2 + x + 1)(x + 1)(x^2 - x + 1)$. $-1, 1$

h $P(x) = (x - 1)(x^2 + x + 1)(x - 2)(x^2 + 2x + 4)$. $1, 2$

8 a Since P is a polynomial function, it is defined by an equation of the form
$P(x) = b_n x^n + b_{n-1} x^{n-1} + \ldots + b_1 x + b_0$. Hence, if $a \neq 0$, aP is defined by
$aP(x) = a \cdot b_n x^n + a \cdot b_{n-1} x^{n-1} + \ldots + a \cdot b_1 x + a \cdot b_0$. Since $a \cdot b_n$, $a \cdot b_{n-1}$, $\ldots$, $a \cdot b_0$ are real numbers, aP is a polynomial function. If $a = 0$, $aP(x) = 0$, so that aP is the zero polynomial.

b Suppose that P is of degree n, then its term of greatest degree is of the form $b_n x^n$, where $b_n \neq 0$. The term of greatest degree of aP is of the form $a \cdot b_n x^n$. Since $a \neq 0$ and $b_n \neq 0$, $a \cdot b_n \neq 0$; hence, aP is also of degree n.

c The zeros of P are the solutions of $P(x) = 0$. The zeros of aP are the solutions of $aP(x) = 0$. But by the properties of real numbers, if $a \neq 0$, $aP(x) = 0$ is equivalent to $P(x) = 0$. Thus, the zeros of P are also the zeros of aP. Conversely, if r_1 is a zero of aP, then $aP(r_1) = 0$. Since $a \neq 0$, it follows that $P(r_1) = 0$. Hence, r_1 is a zero of P. Hence, the functions have the same zeros.

9 a Let P_1 be defined by $P_1(x) = a_n x^n + a_{n-1} x^{n-1} + \ldots + a_1 x + a_0$ and let P_2 be defined by $P_2(x) = b_m x^m + b_{m-1} x^{m-1} + \ldots + b_1 x + b_0$. Then $(P_1 \cdot P_2)(x) = a_n b_m x^{m+n} +$

$(a_{n-1}b_m + a_n b_{m-1})\, x^{m+n-1} + \ldots + (a_1 b_0 + a_0 b_1)x + a_0 b_0$. Since the coefficients of each term in the product is a real number and since $m + n$ is an integer, $P_1 \cdot P_2$ is a polynomial function.

b As shown in part a, if P_1 is of degree n and P_2 is of degree m, then $P_1 \cdot P_2$ is of degree $m + n$.

c Suppose that $P_1(x) = (x - r_1)(x - r_2)(x - r_3) \cdot \ldots \cdot (x - r_n) = 0$, so that r_1, r_2, $\ldots$, r_n are the zeros of P_1. Suppose also that $P_2(x) = (x - s_1)(x - s_2) \cdot \ldots \cdot (x - s_m) = 0$, so that s_1, s_2, $\ldots$, s_m are the zeros of P_2. Then $(P_1 \cdot P_2)(x) = (x - r_1)(x - r_2) \cdot \ldots \cdot (x - r_n)(x - s_1)(x - s_2) \cdot \ldots \cdot (x - s_m) = 0$, so that the zeros of $P_1 \cdot P_2$ are r_1, r_2, $\ldots$, r_n, s_1, s_2, $\ldots$ s_m. Hence, the set of zeros of $P_1 \cdot P_2$ is the union of the set of zeros of P_1 and the set of zeros of P_2.

10 a Let P_1 be defined by $P_1(x) = a_n x^n + a_{n-1}x^{n-1} + \ldots + a_1 x + a_0$ and let P_2 be defined by $P_2(x) = b_m x^m + b_{m-1}x^{m-1} + \ldots + b_1 x + b_0$, where $m \geq n$. Then $P_1 + P_2$ is defined by $(P_1 + P_2)(x) = b_m x^m + \ldots + b_{n+1}x^{n+1} + (a_n + b_n)x^n + \ldots + (a_1 + b_1)x + (a_0 + b_0)$. Since the coefficients of $P_1 + P_2$ are real numbers, $P_1 + P_2$ is a polynomial function.

b As the equation for $P_1 + P_2$ given in part a shows, the sum is found by adding the coefficients of terms of the same degree. If one of the polynomials has terms of greater degree than the other, then those terms occur in the sum with the coefficients they have in the given polynomial. Hence, the polynomial $P_1 + P_2$, as described in part a, has degree m since $m > n$.

c Let P_1 be defined by $P_1(x) = a_n x^n + a_{n-1}x^{n-1} + \ldots + a_1 x + a_0$ and let P_2 be defined by $P_2(x) = b_n x^n + b_{n-1}x^{n-1} + \ldots + b_1 x + b_0$. Then $P_1 + P_2$ is defined by $(P_1 + P_2)(x) = (a_n + b_n)x^n + (a_{n-1} + b_{n-1})\, x^{n-1} + \ldots + (a_1 + b_1)x + (a_0 + b_0)$. If b_n is not the additive inverse of a_n, then $a_n + b_n \neq 0$, and the degree of $P_1 + P_2$ is n. However, if $b_n = -a_n$, then $a_n + b_n = 0$ and the degree of $P_1 + P_2$ is less than n. Since $P_1 \neq -P_2$, there will be at least one pair of coefficients, a_j and b_j such that $b_j \neq -a_j$. Hence, $a_j + b_j \neq 0$, and the degree of $P_1 + P_2$ will be j, since the coefficient of x^j will be different from zero.

Pages 325-327

1 a The domain is $\Re$. No.

b The range is $\Re$.

c $x = -2$, $x = 0$, or $x = 2$. $\{x \mid -2 < x < 0$ or $x > 2\}$. $\{x \mid x < -2$ or $0 < x < 2\}$.

d As x becomes large, $\mid f(x) \mid$ becomes large, but $f(x) < 0$. As $\mid x \mid$ becomes large, but $x < 0$, $f(x)$ becomes large.

e $f'(x) = 0$ for $x = -1$ or $x = 1$. $f'(x) < 0$ for $\{x \mid x < -1$ or $x > 1\}$. $f'(x) > 0$ for $\{x \mid -1 < x < 1\}$.

2 (a) The domain is $\Re$. No. (b) The range is $\{y \mid y > 0\}$. (c) $f(x)$ is never zero. $f(x)$ is never less than zero. $f(x) > 0$ for all x in $\Re$. (d) As x becomes large, $f(x)$ becomes large. As $|x|$ becomes large, but $x < 0$, $f(x)$ becomes small, but $f(x) > 0$. (e) $f'(x)$ is never zero. $f'(x)$ is never less than zero. $f'(x) > 0$ for all x in $\Re$.

3 (a) The domain is $\{x \mid x \in \Re$ and $x \neq 1$ or $x \neq -1\}$. f is discontinuous at $x = 1$ or $x = -1$. (b) The range is $\Re$. (c) $x = 0$. $\{x \mid x < -1$ or $0 < x < 1\}$. $\{x \mid -1 < x < 0$ or $x > 1\}$. (d) As x becomes large, $f(x)$ becomes small, but $f(x) > 0$. As $|x|$ becomes large, but $x < 0$, $|f(x)|$ becomes small, but $f(x) < 0$. (e) $f'(x) = 0$ for $x = 0$. $f'(x) < 0$ for $\{x \mid x \in \Re$ and $x \neq -1$ or $x \neq 0$ or $x \neq 1\}$. $f'(x)$ is never greater than zero.

4 (a) The domain is $\Re$. No. (b) The range is $\{y \mid y \leqq 3\}$. (c) $x = -4$ or $x = 4$. $\{x \mid x < -4$ or $x > 4\}$. $\{x \mid -4 < x < 4\}$. (d) As x becomes large, $|f(x)|$ becomes large, but $f(x) < 0$. As $|x|$ becomes large, but $x < 0$, $|f(x)|$ becomes large, but $f(x) < 0$. (e) $x = -2$, $x = 0$, or $x = 2$. $\{x \mid x > 2$ or $-2 < x < 0\}$. $\{x \mid 0 < x < 2$ or $x < -2\}$.

5 (a) The domain is $\{x \mid x \in \Re$ and $x \neq -2$ or $x \neq 2\}$. f is discontinuous at $x = -2$ or $x = 2$. (b) The range is $\{y \mid y \leqq -2$ or $y > 0\}$. (c) $f(x)$ is never zero. $\{x \mid -2 < x < 2\}$. $\{x \mid x < -2$ or $x > 2\}$. (d) As x becomes large, $f(x)$ becomes small, but $f(x) > 0$. As $|x|$ becomes large, but $x < 0$, $f(x)$ becomes small, but $f(x) > 0$. (e) $x = 0$. $\{x \mid 0 < x < 2$ or $x > 2\}$. $\{x \mid x < -2$ or $-2 < x < 0\}$.

6 The graph of one function fulfilling these requirements is shown at left below.

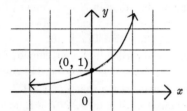

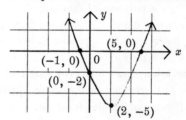

7 The graph of one function fulfilling these requirements is shown at right above.

8 The graph of a function fulfilling these requirements is shown below.

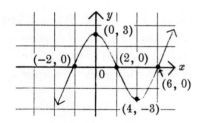

9 **a** As x becomes large, $P(x)$ becomes large. As $|x|$ becomes large, but $x < 0$, $|P(x)|$ becomes large, but $P(x) < 0$.

b As x becomes large, $|P(x)|$ becomes large, but $P(x) < 0$. As $|x|$ becomes large, but $x < 0$, $|P(x)|$ becomes large, but $P(x) < 0$.

c As x becomes large, $|P(x)|$ becomes large, but $P(x) < 0$. As $|x|$ becomes large, but $x < 0$, $P(x)$ becomes large.

d As x becomes large, $P(x)$ becomes large. As $|x|$ becomes large, but $x < 0$, $P(x)$ becomes large.

10 a As x becomes large, $f(x)$ becomes large. As $|x|$ becomes large, but $x < 0$, $f(x)$ becomes large.

b As x becomes large, $f(x)$ becomes large. As $|x|$ becomes large, but $x < 0$, $|f(x)|$ becomes large, but $f(x) < 0$.

c As x becomes large, $|f(x)|$ becomes large, but $f(x) < 0$. As $|x|$ becomes large, but $x < 0$, $|f(x)|$ becomes large, but $f(x) < 0$.

d As x becomes large, $|f(x)|$ becomes large, but $f(x) < 0$. As $|x|$ becomes large, but $x < 0$, $f(x)$ becomes large.

11 If $P(x) = a_n x^n \left(1 + \dfrac{a_{n-1}}{a_n} \cdot \dfrac{1}{x} + \dots + \dfrac{a_1}{a_n} \cdot \dfrac{1}{x^{n-1}} + \dfrac{a_0}{a_n} \cdot \dfrac{1}{x^n} \right)$ and $P(x) = f(x)g(x)$, where

$f(x) = a_n x^n$, then $g(x) = 1 + \dfrac{a_{n-1}}{a_n} \cdot \dfrac{1}{x} + \dots + \dfrac{a_1}{a_n} \cdot \dfrac{1}{x^{n-1}} + \dfrac{a_0}{a_n} \cdot \dfrac{1}{x^n}$. As $|x|$ increases,

every term of this expression except the constant term 1 gets closer and closer to 0. Hence, the value of $g(x)$ gets closer and closer to 1 as $|x|$ increases.

Pages 330-332

1 a Since P is a polynomial function, it is continuous for all x in $\Re$ and, hence, for all x between 1 and 2. $P(1) = -2$ and $P(2) = 5$. Since 0 is a number between -2 and 5, there must be a number x_0 between 1 and 2 such that $P(x_0) = 0$.

b Since P is a polynomial function, it is continuous for all x in $\Re$ and, hence, for all x between 0 and 1. $P(0) = -2$ and $P(1) = 3$. Since 0 is a number between -2 and 3, there must be a number x_0 between 0 and 1 such that $P(x_0) = 0$.

c Since P is a polynomial function, it is continuous for all x in $\Re$ and, hence, for all x between 0 and -1. $P(0) = -1$ and $P(-1) = 2$. Since 0 is a number between 2 and -1, there must be a number x_0 between -1 and 0 such that $P(x_0) = 0$.

d Since P is a polynomial function, it is continuous for all x in $\Re$. $P(0) = a_0$ and, for large positive values of x, $P(x)$ has the same sign as a_n. Therefore, if a_0 and a_n have opposite signs, there must be at least one positive number x_0 such that $P(x_0) = 0$.

e Since P is a polynomial function, it is continuous for all x in $\Re$. $P(0) = a_0$ and for negative values of x whose absolute value is large, $P(x)$ has the opposite sign from a_n. Hence, if $|x|$ is large, but $x < 0$, $P(0)$ and $P(x)$ have opposite signs. From this it follows that there must be at least one negative number x_0 such that $P(x_0) = 0$.

2 a The graph of P has at least one x-intercept to the right of the origin if a_0 and a_n have opposite signs.

b The graph of P has at least one x-intercept to the left of the origin if n is odd and a_0 and a_n have the same sign.

3 a The slope of the segment determined by $\big(a, f(a)\big)$ and $\big(b, f(b)\big)$ is $\dfrac{f(b) - f(a)}{b - a}$.

By the point-slope form of the linear equation $y - f(a) = \dfrac{f(b) - f(a)}{b - a}(x - a)$ is

an equation for the line containing this segment. Therefore, an equation for the segment is $y = f(a) + \dfrac{f(b) - f(a)}{b - a}(x - a)$, $a \leqq x \leqq b$.

b The intersection of the segment $y = f(a) + \dfrac{f(b) - f(a)}{b - a}(x - a)$, $a \leqq x \leqq b$, and the line $y = k$ is the point (x_1, k). Substituting these coordinates into the equation for the segment, we have $k = f(a) + \dfrac{f(b) - f(a)}{b - a}(x_1 - a)$, which is equivalent to $\dfrac{k - f(a)}{f(b) - f(a)} = \dfrac{x_1 - a}{b - a}$.

4 a Since $(17)^2 = 289$ and $(18)^2 = 324$, x must be between 17 and 18. $310 - 289 = 21$ and $324 - 289 = 35$; hence, $x = 17 + \frac{21}{35} = 17.6$.

b Since $(26)^2 = 676$ and $(27)^2 = 729$, x must be between 26 and 27. $713 - 676 = 37$ and $729 - 676 = 53$; hence, $x = 26 + \frac{37}{53} \approx 26.7$.

c $(97)^2 = 9409$ and $(98)^2 = 9604$. $9565 - 9409 = 156$ and $9604 - 9409 = 195$. Hence, $x = 97 + \frac{156}{195} = 97.8$.

d $5^3 = 125$ and $6^3 = 216$. $190 - 125 = 65$ and $216 - 125 = 91$. Hence, $x = 5 + \frac{65}{91} \approx 5.7$.

e $7^3 = 343$ and $8^3 = 512$. $495 - 343 = 152$ and $512 - 343 = 169$. Hence, $x = 7 + \frac{152}{169} \approx 7.9$.

f $9^3 = 729$ and $10^3 = 1000$. $946 - 729 = 217$ and $1000 - 729 = 271$. Hence, $x = 9 + \frac{217}{271} \approx 9.8$.

5 a $x_0 > x_1$.

b $x_0 < x_1$.

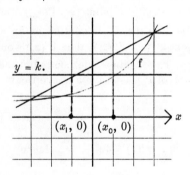

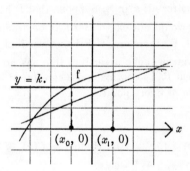

c $x_0 < x_1$.

d $x_0 < x_1$.

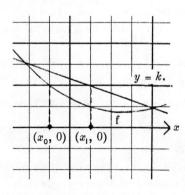

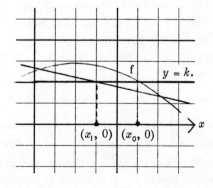

1 a $P'(x) = 6x^2 - 1$.

   b $P'(x) = -3x^2 + 2x$.

   c $P'(x) = 2x^3 - 3x^2$.

   d $P'(x) = 42x^6 - 22$.

   e $P'(x) = -3x^3 + x^2 - 5x$.

   f $P'(x) = 3 \cdot 2x^7 + 15x^5 - 6x^4$.

2 a $m = 2(3) - 1 = 5$. $y = 5x - 9$.

   b $m = 4(-2)^3 + 2(-2) = -36$. $y = -36x - 62$.

   c $m = -6(-1)^2 - 18(-1) = 12$. $y = 12x + 10$.

   d $m = -20$. $y = -20x + 25$.

3 a $(1, -1)$ and $(-1, 3)$ b $(0, 0)$

4 a $y = 1$.   b $y = 2$.

   c Since ℓ_a is defined by $y = 1$, $2\ell_a$ is defined by $y = 2$, which is the equation that defines ℓ_b. Hence, $\ell_b = 2\ell_a$.

5 a $y = -29x - 56$.   b $y = -14\frac{1}{2}x - 28$.

   c Since ℓ_a is defined by $y = -29x - 56$, $\frac{1}{2}\ell_a$ is defined by $y = -14\frac{1}{2}x - 28$, which is the equation that defines ℓ_b. Hence, $\ell_b = \frac{1}{2}\ell_a$.

6 a $y = 51x - 145$.   b $y = -3x + 22$.   c $y = 48x - 123$.

   d $\ell_a(x) + \ell_b(x) = (51x - 145) + (-3x + 22) = 48x - 123 = \ell_c(x)$. Hence, $\ell_c = \ell_a + \ell_b$.

7 (a) ℓ_a: $y = 5x + 7$.   (b) ℓ_b: $y = 7x + 7$.   (c) $(f + g)(x) = x^5 + 3x^3 - 2x + 4$. Hence, ℓ_c: $y = 12x + 14$.   (d) $\ell_a(x) + \ell_b(x) = (5x + 7) + (7x + 7) = 12x + 14 = \ell_c(x)$.

8 Since P is a polynomial function, P' is a polynomial function. Hence, P' is continuous for all x in $\Re$. Suppose that P has no tangent at a point $(x_0, P(x_0))$; then $P'(x_0)$ would not exist. But this contradicts the fact that P' is continuous for all x in $\Re$. Furthermore, if P has a vertical tangent at $(x_0, P(x_0))$, then $P'(x_0)$ would not exist because a vertical line has no slope. This again would contradict the fact that P' is continuous. Therefore, the graph of P must have a nonvertical tangent at every point.

Page 341

1 a $f'(x) = 45x^2 - 30x$. Hence, $\frac{1}{5}f'(x) = 9x^2 - 6x$. $\frac{1}{5}f(x) = 3x^3 - 3x^2$. Hence $(\frac{1}{5}f)'(x) = 9x^2 - 6x$.

   b $f'(x) = -30x^4 + 9x^2 - 6$. Hence, $-3(f'(x)) = 90x^4 - 27x^2 + 18$. $(-3)f(x) = 18x^5 - 9x^3 + 18x$. Hence, $(-3f)'(x) = 90x^4 - 27x^2 + 18$.

2 a $f'(x) = 3$ and $g'(x) = 14x - 3$. Hence, $f'(x) + g'(x) = 14x$. $(f + g)(x) = 7x^2 + 11$. Hence, $(f + g)'(x) = 14x$.

   b $f'(x) = 9x^2 - 12x$ and $g'(x) = 8x^3 + 7$. Hence, $f'(x) + g'(x) = 8x^3 + 9x^2 - 12x + 7$. $(f + g)(x) = 2x^4 + 3x^3 - 6x^2 + 7x + 4$. Hence, $(f + g)'(x) = 8x^3 + 9x^2 - 12x + 7$.

3 $\frac{1}{4}f(x) = \frac{3}{2}x^4 + \frac{1}{4}x^3 - x^2 + 2x - 8$. Hence, $(\frac{1}{4}f)'(x) = 6x^3 + \frac{3}{4}x^2 - 2x + 2$. Thus, the slope of the tangent line at $x = -2$ is $6(-2)^3 + \frac{3}{4}(-2)^2 - 2(-2) + 2 = -39$, and an equation for the tangent line is $y = -39x - 72$.

4 $(f + g)(x) = 4x^3 - 3x^2 + 1$. Hence, $(f + g)'(x) = 12x^2 - 6x$. Thus the slope of the tangent line at $x = 1$ is 6, and an equation of the tangent line is $y = 6x - 4$.

5 a $(2f)'(x) = 18x^2$.   c $2f'(x) + 3g'(x) = 18x^2 + 42x$.

   b $(3g)'(x) = 42x$.   d $(2f + 3g)'(x) = 18x^2 + 42x$.

6 a $(2f)'(x) = 16x^3 + 4x$.   c $2f'(x) + 3g'(x) = 16x^3 + 9x^2 - 2x$.

   b $(3g)'(x) = 9x^2 - 6x$.   d $(2f + 3g)'(x) = 16x^3 + 9x^2 - 2x$.

7 a Since $p'(x) = 2x + 5$, a polynomial p must have the terms x^2 and $5x$. Since $p(0) = 3$, the constant term must be 3. Hence, p must be defined by $p(x) = x^2 + 5x + 3$.

   b Polynomial p must have the term x^3, and since $p(1) = 1$, p must be defined by $p(x) = x^3$.

   c Polynomial p must have the terms $2x^3$ and $2x^2$. Since $p(0) = 2$, the constant term must be 2. Hence, p is defined by $p(x) = 2x^3 + 2x^2 + 2$.

   d Polynomial p must have the terms $-3x^4$ and $5x$. Since $p(0) = -1$, the constant term must be -1. Hence, p is defined by $p(x) = -3x^4 + 5x - 1$.

Pages 344-346

1 a $-2f(x) = -6x^2 - 12x + 14$ and $3g(x) = -12x^2 - 6x + 9$. Hence, $(-2f + 3g)'(x) = -36x - 18$. $(-2f)'(x) = -12x - 12$ and $(3g)'(x) = -24x - 6$. Hence, $(-2f)'(x) + (3g)'(x) = -36x - 18$.

   b $2f(x) = 2x^3 - 12x^2$ and $-\frac{1}{2}g(x) = x^2 - 2x + 3$. Hence, $(2f - \frac{1}{2}g)'(x) = 6x^2 - 22x - 2$. $(2f)'(x) = 6x^2 - 24x$ and $(-\frac{1}{2}g)'(x) = 2x - 2$. Hence, $(2f)'(x) + (-\frac{1}{2}g)'(x) = 6x^2 - 22x - 2$.

   c $\frac{1}{3}f(x) = x^4 + x^2 + 5$ and $-3g(x) = 3x^3 + 48x$. Hence, $(\frac{1}{3}f - 3g)'(x) = 4x^3 + 9x^2 + 2x + 48$. $(\frac{1}{3}f)'(x) = 4x^3 + 2x$ and $(-3g)'(x) = 9x^2 + 48$. Hence, $(\frac{1}{3}f)'(x) + (-3g)'(x) = 4x^3 + 9x^2 + 2x + 48$.

   d $-\frac{1}{4}f(x) = -\frac{3}{2}x^5 + \frac{3}{4}x^3 - \frac{7}{4}x$ and $\frac{1}{2}g(x) = \frac{5}{2}x^4 - \frac{11}{2}$. Hence, $(-\frac{1}{4}f + \frac{1}{2}g)(x) = -\frac{15}{2}x^4 + 10x^3 + \frac{9}{4}x^2 - \frac{7}{4}$. $(-\frac{1}{4}f)'(x) = -\frac{15}{2}x^4 + \frac{9}{4}x^2 - \frac{7}{4}$ and $(\frac{1}{2}g)'(x) = 10x^3$. Hence, $(\frac{1}{4}f)'(x) + (\frac{1}{2}g)'(x) = -\frac{15}{2}x^4 + 10x^3 + \frac{9}{4}x^2 - \frac{7}{4}$.

2 a If $n > 1$, then $f'(x) = nx^{n-1}$; therefore the slope of the tangent line to f at $(0, 0)$ is $n(0)^{n-1} = 0$. Hence, since $f(0) = 0$, the tangent line at $(0, 0)$ is $y = 0$, which is an equation of the x-axis.

   b If n is even, then $x^n \geq 0$ for all x in $\Re$; so that $f(x) \geq 0$ for all x. $f(x) = 0$ only for $x = 0$; therefore, $(0, 0)$ must be a minimum point on the graph of f.

   c If n is odd, then $x^n \geq 0$ for all $x \geq 0$ and $x^n < 0$ for all $x < 0$. Hence, $(0, 0)$ is neither a maximum nor a minimum point on the graph.

3 a The slope of the tangent line to the graph of f at the point $P(x_0, f(x_0))$ is $f'(x_0)$. Hence, an equation of the tangent line is $\ell(x) - f(x_0) = (f'(x_0))(x - x_0)$, or $\ell(x) = (f'(x_0))(x - x_0) + f(x_0)$.

   b Substituting $x_0 - h$ for x in the equation of the tangent line, we have $\ell(x_0 - h) = (f'(x_0))(x_0 - h - x_0) + f(x_0) = (f'(x_0))(-h) + f(x_0) = (-f'(x_0))(h) + f(x_0)$. Substituting $x_0 + h$ for x in the equation for the tangent line, we have $\ell(x_0 + h) = (f'(x_0))(x_0 + h - x_0) + f(x_0) = (f'(x_0))(h) + f(x_0)$.

4 a $\ell(10 + 0.1) = (2 \cdot 10)(0.1) + (10)^2 = 102.$

b $(10.1)^2 = 102.01.$ The error in the approximation is $0.01.$

5 a $\ell(10 - 0.1) = (-3 \cdot 100)(0.1) + (10)^3 = 970.$

b $(9.9)^3 = 970.299;$ hence, the error in the approximation is $0.299.$

6 a $\ell(100 - 0.001) = (-4\pi(100)^2(0.001) + \frac{4}{3}\pi(100)^3 = -40\pi + \frac{4000000}{3}\pi = 3,999,880\pi.$

Hence, the volume of the gas is approximately $\frac{3,999,880}{3}\pi$ c.c.,

b Since the volume of the sphere is $\frac{4}{3}\pi r^3 = \frac{4000000}{3}\pi$ c.c., the volume of the plastic

is approximately $\frac{4,000,000}{3}\pi - \frac{3,999,880}{3}\pi = \frac{120}{3}\pi = 40\pi$ c.c.

7 a y is multiplied by 4. **b** y is divided by 9.

c y is multiplied by $\frac{1}{9}$; that is, y is divided by 9.

d y is divided by 0.01; that is, y is multiplied by 100.

8 a y is multiplied by 8. **b** y is divided by 27.

c y is multiplied by $\frac{1}{27}$; that is, y is divided by 27.

d y is divided by 0.001; that is, y is multiplied by 1000.

9 3750 gallons per minute

10 $\frac{125}{8}p$ pounds

Pages 351-353

1 a $f'(x) = 3x + 6$; hence, the graph of f is rising for $\{x \mid x > -3\}$ and falling for $\{x \mid x < -3\}$. See graph at left below.

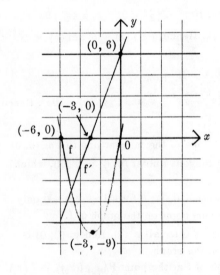 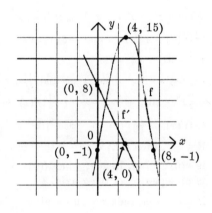

b Since $f'(x) = -2x + 8$, the graph of f is rising for $\{x \mid x < 4\}$ and falling for $\{x \mid x > 4\}$. See graph at right above.

c Rising: $\{x \mid x > 0\}$; falling: $\{x \mid x < 0\}$.

d The graph is rising for $\{x \mid x \in \Re$ and $x \neq 0\}$, since $f'(x) = nx^{n-1}$ is greater than 0 for all values of x different from 0.

2 **a** $g'(x) = 9x^2 - 4 = (3x - 2)(3x + 2)$.

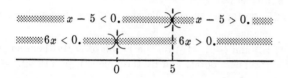

Hence, the graph of g is rising for $\{x \mid x < -\frac{2}{3}$ or $x > \frac{2}{3}\}$, and the graph is falling for $\{x \mid -\frac{2}{3} < x < \frac{2}{3}\}$.

b $g'(x) = 6x^2 - 30x = 6x(x - 5)$.

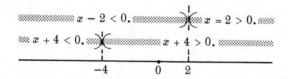

Hence, the graph of g is rising for $\{x \mid x < 0$ or $x > 5\}$, and the graph is falling for $\{x \mid 0 < x < 5\}$.

c $g'(x) = -3x^2 - 6x + 24 = -3(x + 4)(x - 2)$.

Since the constant factor is negative, the product of all three factors is positive only when the two linear factors have opposite sign. Hence, the graph of g is rising for $\{x \mid -4 < x < 2\}$, and the graph is falling for $\{x \mid x < -4$ or $x > 2\}$.

d $g'(x) = 3x^2 - 8x - 3 = (3x + 1)(x - 3)$.

Hence, the graph of g is rising for $\{x \mid x < -\frac{1}{3}$ or $x > 3\}$, and the graph is falling for $\{x \mid -\frac{1}{3} < x < 3\}$.

3 **a** $f'(x) = 3x^2 - 75 = 3(x - 5)(x + 5)$. Therefore, the graph of f is rising when $3(x - 5)(x + 5) > 0$; that is, for $\{x \mid x < -5$ or $x > 5\}$. The graph of f is falling when $3(x - 5)(x + 5) < 0$; that is, for $\{x \mid -5 < x < 5\}$.

b Rising: $\{x \mid 0 < x < 7\}$; falling: $\{x \mid x < 0$ or $x > 7\}$.

c Rising: $\{x \mid x < -5$ or $x > 1\}$; falling: $\{x \mid -5 < x < 1\}$.

d Rising: $\{x \mid -\frac{7}{3} < x < 1\}$; falling: $\{x \mid x < -\frac{7}{3}$ or $x > 1\}$.

4 a $x = -1$.   **b** $\{x \mid x \neq -1\}$ **c** $\emptyset$

    d Neither. If $(-1, 0)$ were a relative maximum or a relative minimum, $f(x)$ must be increasing on one side of point $(-1, 0)$ and decreasing on the other. However, the answers to parts b and c indicate that $f(x)$ is increasing on both sides of this point.

5 a Increase. $f'(x_0 - h) > 0$.   **b** Decrease. $f'(x_0 + h) < 0$.

    c $f'(x_0 - h) < 0$ and $f'(x_0 + h) > 0$.

    d $f'(x_0 - h)$ and $f'(x_0 + h)$ will have the same sign.

    e $\big(x_0, f(x_0)\big)$ is a relative maximum point on the graph of f. $\big(x_0, f(x_0)\big)$ is a relative minimum point on the graph of f. $\big(x_0, f(x_0)\big)$ is neither a relative maximum nor a relative minimum point on the graph of f.

6 a $f'(x) = 0$ at the point $(3, 27)$ on the graph of f. By theorem (1) of exercise 5e, $(3, 27)$ is a relative maximum point.

    b $f'(x) = 0$ at the points $(2, 16)$ and $(-2, -16)$ on the graph of f. By theorem (1), point $(2, 16)$ is a relative maximum point, and by theorem (2), point $(-2, -16)$ is a relative minimum point.

    c $f'(x) = 0$ at the points $(0, 5)$ and $(2, 1)$ on the graph of f. By theorem (1), point $(0, 5)$ is a relative maximum point; and by theorem (2), point $(2, 1)$ is a relative minimum point.

    d $f'(x) = 0$ at the points $(-3, 13\frac{1}{2})$ and $(2, -7\frac{1}{3})$. By theorem (1), point $(-3, 13\frac{1}{2})$ is a relative maximum point, and by theorem (2), point $(2, -7\frac{1}{3})$ is a relative minimum point.

Pages 358-359

1 Concave upward: $\{x \mid x \in \Re\}$. The graph is never concave downward.

2 Concave upward: $\{x \mid x > \frac{2}{3}\}$; concave downward: $\{x \mid x < \frac{2}{3}\}$

3 Concave upward: $\{x \mid x < \frac{3}{5}\}$; concave downward: $\{x \mid x > \frac{3}{5}\}$

4 Concave upward: $\{x \mid x < -1 \text{ or } x > 1\}$; concave downward: $\{x \mid -1 < x < 1\}$

5 Concave upward: $\{x \mid x < -\frac{3}{4} \text{ or } x > \frac{4}{3}\}$; concave downward: $\{x \mid -\frac{3}{4} < x < \frac{4}{3}\}$

6 Concave upward: $\{x \mid x \in \Re\}$. The graph is never concave downward.

7 a $f'(x) = 0$ for $x = 1$ and $x = -1$. Since $f'(x) > 0$ for $x < -1$ and $f'(x) < 0$ for $x > -1$, f has a relative maximum at $x = -1$. Since $f'(x) < 0$ for $x < 1$ and $f'(x) > 0$ for $x > 1$, f has a relative minimum at $x = 1$.

    b $f'(x) = 0$ for $x = 0$ and $x = 2$. f has a relative maximum at $x = 0$; and f has a relative minimum at $x = 2$.

    c $f'(x) = 0$ when $x = 3$ and $x = -9$. f has a relative minimum at $x = 3$; and f has a relative maximum at $x = -9$.

    d $f'(x) = 0$ at $x = 0$. f has neither a relative maximum nor a relative minimum at $x = 0$.

8 a $f''(x) = 0$ at $x = 0$. Since $f''(x) < 0$ for $x > 0$ and $f''(x) > 0$ for $x < 0$, $(0, 11)$ is a point at which the graph changes concavity.

    b $f''(x) = 0$ at $x = 3$. The point $(3, -32)$ is a point at which the graph changes concavity.

c $f''(x) = 0$ at $x = \frac{1}{2}$. The point $(\frac{1}{2}, 10\frac{3}{8})$ is not a point at which the graph changes concavity.

d $f''(x) = 0$ at $x = 1$ and $x = 2$. The points $(1, -7)$ and $(2, -16)$ are both points at which the graph of f changes concavity.

Pages 365-367

1 a Positive: $\{x \mid -2 < x < 0 \text{ or } x > 3\}$; negative: $\{x \mid x < -2 \text{ or } 0 < x < 3\}$.

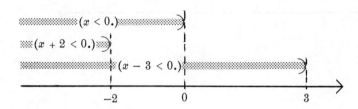

b Positive: $\{x \mid -2\frac{1}{2} < x < 1 \text{ or } x > 7\}$; negative: $\{x \mid x < -2\frac{1}{2} \text{ or } 1 < x < 7\}$.

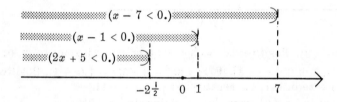

c Positive: $\{x \mid -5 < x < 0 \text{ or } x > 2\frac{2}{3}\}$; negative: $\{x \mid x < -5 \text{ or } 0 < x < 2\frac{2}{3}\}$.

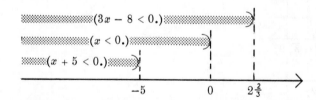

d Positive: $\{x \mid -2\frac{2}{5} < x < 0 \text{ or } x > 2\frac{2}{5}\}$; negative: $\{x \mid x < -2\frac{2}{5} \text{ or } 0 < x < 2\frac{2}{5}\}$.

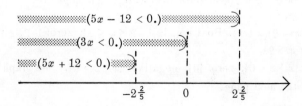

e Positive: $\{x \mid x < -4$ or $-\frac{7}{2} < x < 0$ or $x > 5\}$; negative: $\{x \mid -4 < x < -\frac{7}{2}$ or $0 < x < 5\}$.

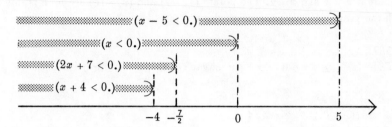

f Positive: $\{x \mid x < -2$ or $-1 < x < 1$ or $x > 2\}$; negative: $\{x \mid -2 < x < -1$ or $1 < x < 2\}$.

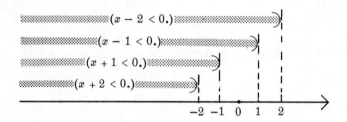

2 $P(x) = x(x + \sqrt{3})(x - \sqrt{3})$. Positive: $\{x \mid -\sqrt{3} < x < 0$ or $x > \sqrt{3}\}$; zero: $\{-\sqrt{3}, 0, \sqrt{3}\}$; negative: $\{x \mid x < -\sqrt{3}$ or $0 < x < \sqrt{3}\}$. $P'(x) = 3x^2 - 3 = 3(x - 1)(x + 1)$. Positive: $\{x \mid x < -1$ or $x > 1\}$; zero: $\{-1, 1\}$; negative: $\{x \mid -1 < x < 1\}$.
$P''(x) = 6x$. Positive: $\{x \mid x > 0\}$; zero: $\{0\}$; negative: $\{x \mid x < 0\}$.

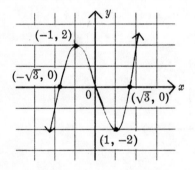

3 $P(x) = -x(x - 2\sqrt{3})(x + 2\sqrt{3})$.
Positive: $\{x \mid x < -2\sqrt{3}$ or $0 < x < 2\sqrt{3}\}$; zero: $\{-2\sqrt{3}, 0, 2\sqrt{3}\}$; negative: $\{x \mid -2\sqrt{3} < x < 0$ or $x > 2\sqrt{3}\}$.
$P'(x) = -3x^2 + 12 = -3(x - 2)(x + 2)$. Positive: $\{x \mid -2 < x < 2\}$; zero: $\{-2, 2\}$; negative: $\{x \mid x < -2$ or $x > 2\}$.
$P''(x) = -6x$. Positive: $\{x \mid x < 0\}$; zero: $\{0\}$; negative: $\{x \mid x > 0\}$. See graph on the left at the top of the next page.

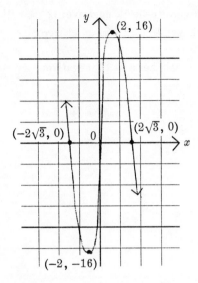

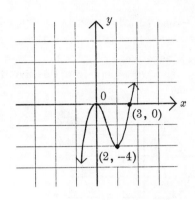

4 $P(x) = (x)(x)(x - 3)$. Positive: $\{x \mid x > 3\}$; zero: $\{0, 3\}$; negative: $\{x \mid x < 3, x \neq 0\}$
$P'(x) = 3x^2 - 6x = 3x(x - 2)$. Positive: $\{x \mid x < 0 \text{ or } x > 2\}$; zero: $\{0, 2\}$;
negative: $\{x \mid 0 < x < 2\}$.
$P''(x) = 6x - 6$. Positive: $\{x \mid x > 1\}$; zero: $\{1\}$; negative: $\{x \mid x < 1\}$. See
graph above at the right.

5 $P(x) = x^2(x + 6)$. Positive: $\{x \mid x > -6, x \neq 0\}$; zero: $\{-6, 0\}$; negative: $\{x \mid x < -6\}$.
$P'(x) = 3x^2 + 12x = 3x(x + 4)$. Positive: $\{x \mid x < -4 \text{ or } x > 0\}$; zero: $\{-4, 0\}$;
negative: $\{x \mid -4 < x < 0\}$.
$P''(x) = 6x + 12 = 6(x + 2)$. Positive: $\{x \mid x > -2\}$; zero: $\{-2\}$; negative: $\{x \mid x < -2\}$.
See graph below at the left.

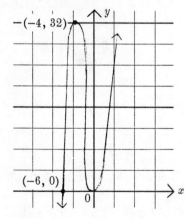

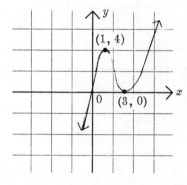

6 $P(x) = x(x - 3)^2$. Positive: $\{x \mid x > 0, x \neq 3\}$; zero: $\{0, 3\}$; negative: $\{x \mid x < 0\}$.
$P'(x) = 3x^2 - 12x + 9 = 3(x - 1)(x - 3)$. Positive: $\{x \mid x < 1 \text{ or } x > 3\}$; zero: $\{1, 3\}$;
negative: $\{x \mid 1 < x < 3\}$.
$P''(x) = 6x - 12 = 6(x - 2)$. Positive: $\{x \mid x > 2\}$; zero: $\{2\}$; negative: $\{x \mid x < 2\}$.
See graph above at the right.

7 $P(x) = -x(x + 3)^2$. Positive: $\{x \mid x < 0,\ x \neq -3\}$; zero: $\{-3, 0\}$; negative: $\{x \mid x > 0\}$.
   $P'(x) = -3x^2 - 12x - 9 = -3(x + 1)(x + 3)$. Positive: $\{x \mid -3 < x < -1\}$; zero:
   $\{-3, -1\}$; negative: $\{x \mid x < -3 \text{ or } x > -1\}$.
   $P''(x) = -6x - 12 = -6(x + 2)$. Positive: $\{x \mid x < -2\}$; zero: $\{-2\}$; negative:
   $\{x \mid x > -2\}$.

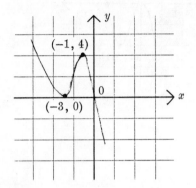

8 $P(x) = x^3(x - 4)$. Positive: $\{x \mid x < 0 \text{ or } x > 4\}$; zero: $\{0, 4\}$; negative: $\{x \mid 0 < x < 4\}$.
   $P'(x) = 4x^3 - 12x^2 = 4x^2(x - 3)$. Positive: $\{x \mid x > 3\}$; zero: $\{0, 3\}$; negative:
   $\{x \mid x < 3,\ x \neq 0\}$.
   $P''(x) = 12x^2 - 24x = 12x(x - 2)$. Positive: $\{x \mid x < 0 \text{ or } x > 2\}$; zero: $\{0, 2\}$;
   negative: $\{x \mid 0 < x < 2\}$.

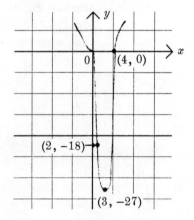

9 $P(x) = x^2(x - \sqrt{6})(x + \sqrt{6})$. Positive: $\{x \mid x < -\sqrt{6} \text{ or } x > \sqrt{6}\}$; zero: $\{-\sqrt{6}, 0, \sqrt{6}\}$;
   negative: $\{x \mid -\sqrt{6} < x < \sqrt{6}\}$.
   $P'(x) = 4x^3 - 12x = 4x(x - \sqrt{3})(x + \sqrt{3})$. Positive: $\{x \mid -\sqrt{3} < x < 0 \text{ or } x > \sqrt{3}\}$;
   zero: $\{-\sqrt{3}, 0, \sqrt{3}\}$; negative: $\{x \mid x < -\sqrt{3} \text{ or } 0 < x < \sqrt{3}\}$.
   $P''(x) = 12x^2 - 12 = 12(x - 1)(x + 1)$. Positive: $\{x \mid x > 1 \text{ or } x < -1\}$; zero: $\{1, -1\}$;
   negative: $\{x \mid -1 < x < 1\}$. See graph at the top of the next page.

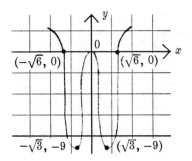

10 Assume that a product of two or more nonzero real numbers contains an even number of negative factors that can be grouped in pairs. The product of each pair of negative factors will be positive, and, together with any positive factors in the original product, the product of all factors will be positive. Hence, if the original product contains an even number of negative factors, the product of all factors is positive.

Now assume that the product of two or more nonzero real numbers is positive but that the product contains an odd number of negative factors. If the negative factors are grouped by pairs, there will be one unpaired negative factor. The product of all the pairs of negative factors and any positive factors in the original product will be positive. And the product of this number with the one remaining negative factor will be negative. Hence, if there is an odd number of negative factors, the final product will be negative; but this contradicts the assumption that the product is positive. Hence, if the product is positive, it must contain an even number of negative factors.

11 a Two. $x > 0$ and $x + 3 < 0$ and $x - 2 > 0$; $x > 0$ and $x + 3 > 0$ and $x - 2 < 0$.

b $x < 0$ and $x + 3 < 0$ and $x - 2 < 0$.

c The set of solutions for $x < 0$ and $x + 3 > 0$ and $x - 2 > 0$ is $\emptyset$.

The set of solutions for $x > 0$ and $x + 3 < 0$ and $x - 2 > 0$ is $\emptyset$.

The set of solutions for $x > 0$ and $x + 3 > 0$ and $x - 2 < 0$ is $\{x \mid 0 < x < 2\}$.

The set of solutions for $x < 0$ and $x + 3 > 0$ and $x - 2 < 0$ is $\{x \mid x < -3\}$.

The set of solutions of $x^3 + x^2 - 6x < 0$ is the union of these four sets. $\{x \mid x < -3 \text{ or } 0 < x < 2\}$.

12 a $x < 0$ and $x - 1 > 0$ and $x - 2 > 0$ and $x - 3 > 0$.

$x > 0$ and $x - 1 < 0$ and $x - 2 > 0$ and $x - 3 > 0$.

$x > 0$ and $x - 1 > 0$ and $x - 2 < 0$ and $x - 3 > 0$.

$x > 0$ and $x - 1 > 0$ and $x - 2 > 0$ and $x - 3 < 0$.

$x < 0$ and $x - 1 < 0$ and $x - 2 < 0$ and $x - 3 > 0$.

$x < 0$ and $x - 1 < 0$ and $x - 2 > 0$ and $x - 3 < 0$.

$x < 0$ and $x - 1 > 0$ and $x - 2 < 0$ and $x - 3 < 0$.

$x > 0$ and $x - 1 < 0$ and $x - 2 < 0$ and $x - 3 < 0$.

b Sixteen conditions must be considered. The pattern of positive and negative factors is indicated in the following chart. In each row, any factor that is not designated as less than zero is to be taken as greater than or equal to zero. This chart is shown on the following page.

x	$x-1$	$x-2$	$x-3$	$x-4$
<0				
	<0			
		<0		
			<0	
				<0
<0	<0	<0		
<0	<0		<0	
<0	<0			<0
<0		<0	<0	
<0		<0		<0
<0			<0	<0
	<0	<0	<0	
	<0	<0		<0
	<0		<0	<0
		<0	<0	<0
<0	<0	<0	<0	<0

c 2^{n-1}; n.

Pages 370-371

1 a $P(x) = (x - 3)(3x^2 + 5x + 17) + 36$.
   b $P(x) = (x + 2)(x^3 - 2x^2 + 4x - 8) + 32$.
   c $P(x) = (x - \frac{1}{2})(4x^2 - x + 4\frac{1}{2}) + \frac{1}{4}$.

2 a $k = -6$.   b $k = -4$.   c $k = -5$.

3 a $P(x) = (x - 5)(x + 4)(x + 3)$; $\{-4, -3, 5\}$
   b $P(x) = (x + 3)(2x - 1)(x - 4)$; $\{-3, \frac{1}{2}, 4\}$
   c $P(x) = (x + \frac{1}{2})(3x + 4)(2x - 3)$; $\{-\frac{4}{3}, -\frac{1}{2}, \frac{3}{2}\}$

4 a $P(x) = (x - 1)(x - 3)(x + 3)$; $\{-3, 1, 3\}$
   b $P(x) = (x + 1)(2x - 5)(x + 4)$; $\{-4, -1, \frac{5}{2}\}$
   c $P(x) = (x + 2)(x + \sqrt{3})(x - \sqrt{3})$; $\{-2, -\sqrt{3}, \sqrt{3}\}$

5 a False. If $P(x) = x^n + c^n$, then $P(c) = c^n + c^n = 2c^n$ and $2c^n \neq 0$ whenever $c \neq 0$.
      Hence, $x - c$ is not a factor of $x^n + c^n$.

   b True. If $P(x) = x^n - c^n$ and n is even, then $P(-c) = (-c)^n - c^n = c^n - c^n = 0$, so
      $(x - (-c)) = (x + c)$ is a factor of $P(x)$.

c False. If $P(x) = x^n - c^n$ and n is odd, then $P(-c) = -(c^n) - c^n = -2c^n$.

d False. If $P(x) = x^n + c^n$ and n is even, then $P(-c) = (-c)^n + c^n = 2c^n$.

e True. If $P(x) = x^n + c^n$ and n is odd, then $P(-c) = -(c^n) + c^n = 0$.

6 Let $P(x) - P(c) = a_n(x^n - c^n) + a_{n-1}(x^{n-1} - c^{n-1}) + \ldots + a_1(x - c)$. Since $x^k - c^k = (x - c)(x^{k-1} + cx^{k-2} + \ldots + c^{k-2}x + c^{k-1})$, it follows that $(x - c)$ is a factor of each term of $P(x) - P(c)$. That is, the first term of $P(x) - P(c)$ can be expressed as $a_n(x - c)(x^{n-1} + cx^{n-2} + \ldots + c^{n-2}x + c^{n-1})$; the second term can be expressed as $a_{n-1}(x - c)(x^{n-2} + cx^{n-3} + \ldots + c^{n-3}x + c^{n-2})$; and so on, to the last term, which is given as $a_1(x - c)$. Thus, if we factor $(x - c)$ out of $P(x) - P(c)$, we obtain

$$P(x) - P(c) = (x - c)\,[a_n(x^{n-1} + cx^{n-2} + \ldots + c^{n-2}x + c^{n-1}) + a_{n-1}(x^{n-2} + cx^{n-3} + \ldots + c^{n-3}x + c^{n-2}) + \ldots + a_1]$$

$$= (x - c)\,[a_n x^{n-1} + (a_{n-1} + c)x^{n-2} + \ldots + (a_n c^{n-1} + a_{n-1}c^{n-2} + \ldots + a_1)].$$

Now let $a_n x^{n-1} + (a_{n-1} + c)x^{n-2} + \ldots + (a_n c^{n-1} + a_{n-1}c^{n-2} + \ldots + a_1) = Q(x)$, which is a polynomial of degree $n - 1$. Then $P(x) - P(c) = (x - c)Q(x)$ or $P(x) = (x - c)Q(x) + P(c)$.

7 Assume that the degree of $R(x)$ is m. This means that $R(x) = b_m x^m + b_{m-1}x^{m-1} + \ldots + b_1 x + b_0$. Then $(x - c)\,R(x) = b_m x^{m+1} + (b_{m-1} - cb_m)x^m + \ldots + (b_0 - cb_1)x - cb_0$. Now, if $P(x) = a_n x^n + a_{n-1}x^{n-1} + \ldots + a_1 x + a_0$ and $P(x) = (x - c)\,R(x)$, it follows that $a_n x^n = b_m x^{m+1}$, so that $a_n = b_m$ and $n = m + 1$. Hence, $m = n - 1$, and the degree of $R(x)$ is $n - 1$.

8 Since $x - c$ is a factor of $P_1(x)$, it follows that $P_1(x) = (x - c)Q_1(x)$, where $Q_1(x)$ is a polynomial whose degree is one less than the degree of P_1. Similarly, since $x - c$ is a factor of $P_2(x)$, it follows that $P_2(x) = (x - c)Q_2(x)$, where $Q_2(x)$ is a polynomial whose degree is one less than the degree of $P_2(x)$. Hence, $P_1(x) + P_2(x) = (x - c)Q_1(x) + (x - c)Q_2(x) = (x - c)\big(Q_1(x) + Q_2(x)\big)$, which establishes that $x - c$ is a factor of $P_1(x) + P_2(x)$.

9 If $x - c_1$ is a factor of $P(x)$, then $P(x) = (x - c)Q(x)$, where $Q(x)$ is a polynomial whose degree is one less than the degree of $P(x)$. If $x - c_2$ is a factor of $P(x)$, then it must also be a factor of $(x - c_1)Q(x) = P(x)$. If $c_2 \neq c_1$, then $x - c_2$ is not a factor of $x - c_1$ and therefore must be a factor of $Q(x)$. Hence, $Q(x) = (x - c_2)R(x)$, where $R(x)$ is a polynomial whose degree is one less than the degree of $Q(x)$. Thus, $P(x) = (x - c_1)(x - c_2)R(x)$, which implies that $(x - c_1)(x - c_2) = x^2 - (c_1 + c_2)x + c_1 c_2$ is a factor of $P(x)$.

Page 375

1 **a** $P(x) = (x - 2i)(x^2 + 2ix)$.

b $P(x) = (x + 2i)(x^3 - 2ix^2 - 4x + 8i)$.

c $P(x) = (x - i)\big(x^2 + (1 + i)x + i\big)$.

2 a $P(x) = (x + 2)\big(x - (1 + i)\big)\big(x - (1 - i)\big)$; $\{2, 1 + i, 1 - i\}$

b $P(x) = (x + 3)(x - 4i)(x + 4i)$; $\{-3, 4i, -4i\}$

c $P(x) = (x - i)(x + i)(x - 1)(x - 1)$; $\{i, -i, 1\}$

3 a $P(x) = (x + 1)(x - \frac{1}{2} - \frac{\sqrt{3}}{2}i)(x - \frac{1}{2} + \frac{\sqrt{3}}{2}i)$; $\{-1, \frac{1}{2} + \frac{\sqrt{3}}{2}i, \frac{1}{2} - \frac{\sqrt{3}}{2}i\}$

b $P(x) = (x - 1)(x + \frac{1}{2} - \frac{\sqrt{3}}{2}i)(x + \frac{1}{2} + \frac{\sqrt{3}}{2}i)$; $\{1, -\frac{1}{2} + \frac{\sqrt{3}}{2}i, -\frac{1}{2} - \frac{\sqrt{3}}{2}i\}$

c $P(x) = (x - 1)(x - 2 - i)(x - 2 + i)$; $\{1, 2 + i, 2 - i\}$

4 Suppose that all of the coefficients of $Q(x)$ were real; that is, suppose that

$Q(x) = b_{n-1}x^{n-1} + b_{n-2}x^{n-2} + \cdots + b_1 x + b_0$, where b_{n-1}, b_{n-2}, $\ldots$, b_0 are elements

of $\Re$. Then $P(x) = (x - c)Q(x) = b_{n-1}x^n + (b_{n-2} - cb_{n-1})x^{n-1} + \cdots + (b_0 - cb_1)x - cb_0$.

Since $b_{n-1} \neq 0$, $-cb_{n-1}$ is a nonreal complex number; and since cb_{n-1} cannot be the

additive inverse of the real number b_{n-2}, the coefficient $b_{n-2} - cb_{n-1}$ of x^{n-1} is a

nonreal complex number. But $P(x)$ has only real coefficients, so the assumption that

the coefficients of $Q(x)$ were all real has led to a contradiction. Hence, at least one

of the coefficients of $Q(x)$ must be nonreal.

5 a Since $P(x)$ is of degree 3, by Theorem 34/7, c_1, c_2 and c_3 are all of the zeros of

$P(x)$. Hence,

$P(x) = (x - c_1)(x - c_2)(x - c_3) = x^3 - (c_1 + c_2 + c_3)x^2 + (c_1c_2 + c_1c_3 + c_2c_3)x - c_1c_2c_3$.

Equating the two expressions for $P(x)$, we have $x^3 + px^2 + qx + r = x^3 -$

$(c_1 + c_2 + c_3)x^2 + (c_1c_2 + c_1c_3 + c_2c_3)x - c_1c_2c_3$. Since two polynomials are equal

if and only if their corresponding coefficients are equal, it must be the case

that $-(c_1 + c_2 + c_3) = p$.

b From the equality in part a, it follows that $c_1c_2 + c_1c_3 + c_2c_3 = q$.

c From the answer for part a, it follows that $-c_1c_2c_3 = r$.

Pages 378-379

1 a $P(x) = (x - i)(x + i)(x - 3)$; $\{i, -i, 3\}$

b $P(x) = (x + 2i)(x - 2i)(x + 1)$; $\{-2i, 2i, -1\}$

c $P(x) = \big(x - (2 - i)\big)\big(x - (2 + i)\big)(x - 1)$; $\{2 - i, 2 + i, 1\}$

2 a $P(x) = x^2 - 4x + 5$.

b $P(x) = x^3 + 2x^2 + 9x + 18$.

c $P(x) = x^3 - 3x^2 + 25x - 75$.

d $P(x) = x^3 - 4x^2 + 6x - 4$.

e $P(x) = x^4 + 3x^2 - 4$.

f $P(x) = x^4 + 7x^3 + 3x^2 - 65x - 102$.

3 a $P(x) = (x - \sqrt{3})(x + \sqrt{3})(x + 6)$; $\{\sqrt{3}, -\sqrt{3}, -6\}$

b $P(x) = (x + \sqrt{5})(x - \sqrt{5})(x - i)(x + i)$; $\{-\sqrt{5}, \sqrt{5}, i, -i\}$

c $P(x) = \big(x - (2 - \sqrt{3})\big)\big(x - (2 + \sqrt{3})\big)(x - 2i)(x + 2i)$; $\{2 - \sqrt{3}, 2 + \sqrt{3}, 2i, -2i\}$

4 a $P(x) = x^4 - x^2 - 2$.

b $P(x) = x^4 - 6x^3 + 5x^2 - 24x + 4$.

c $P(x) = x^4 - 6x^3 - 6x^2 + 42x - 7$.

d $P(x) = x^4 - 4x^3 + 4x^2 - 4$.

5 a $(a + bi) + (a - bi) = (a + a) + (b - b)i = 2a + 0i$, which is a real number.

  b $(a + bi) - (a - bi) = (a - a) + (b + b)i = 0 + 2bi$, which is a pure imaginary number.

  c $(a + bi)(c + di) = (ac - bd) + (ad + bc)i$. The product of the conjugates is $(a - bi)(c - di) = (ac - bd) - (ad + bc)i$, which is the conjugate of $(ac - bd) + (ad + bc)i$.

6 Let $P(x) = a_n x^n + a_{n-1} x^{n-1} + \ldots + a_1 x + a_0$. Then

$$P(C) = a_n C^n + a_{n-1} C^{n-1} + \ldots + a_1 C + a_0.$$ Hence,

$$\overline{P(C)} = \overline{a_n C^n + a_{n-1} C^{n-1} + \ldots + a_1 C + a_0}$$

$$= \overline{a_n C^n} + \overline{a_{n-1} C^{n-1}} + \ldots + \overline{a_1 C} + \overline{a_0}.$$

[Conjugate of a sum equals the sum of the conjugates.]

$$= \overline{a_n}\ \overline{C^n} + \overline{a_{n-1}}\ \overline{C^{n-1}} + \ldots + \overline{a_1}\ \overline{C} + \overline{a_0}$$

[Conjugate of a product equals the product of the conjugates.]

$$= a_n \overline{C^n} + a_{n-1}\overline{C^{n-1}} + \ldots + a_1\overline{C} + a_0$$

[Conjugate of a given real number is the given number.]

$$= a_n(\overline{C})^n + a_{n-1}(\overline{C})^{n-1} + \ldots + a_1(\overline{C}) + a_0$$

[Special case of property 4, page 377.]

$$= P(\overline{C}).$$

Pages 385-387

1 Expressions a and c are irreducible quadratic expressions.

2 a Negative: $\{x \mid x < 3\}$; zero: $\{3\}$; positive: $\{x \mid x > 3\}$. See diagram at left below; the graph must be contained in the shaded regions.

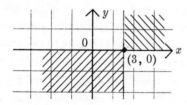 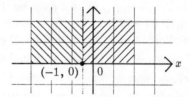

  b Negative: $\emptyset$; zero: $\{-1\}$; positive: $\{x \mid x \neq -1\}$. See diagram at right above; the graph must be contained in the shaded regions.

  c Negative: $\{x \mid x < 2\}$; zero: $\{2\}$; positive: $\{x \mid x > 2\}$. See diagram at left below; the graph must be contained in the shaded regions.

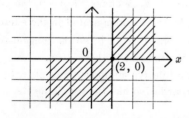 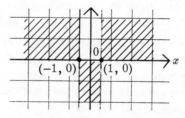

  d Negative: $\{x \mid -1 < x < 1\}$; zero: $\{-1, 1\}$; positive: $\{x \mid x < -1 \text{ or } x > 1\}$. See diagram at right above; the graph must be contained in the shaded regions.

e Negative: $\{x \mid x > -5 \text{ and } x \neq 0\}$; zero: $\{-5, 0\}$; positive: $\{x \mid x < -5\}$. See diagram at left below; the graph must be contained in the shaded regions.

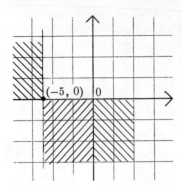 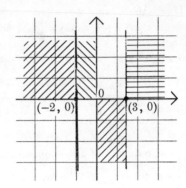

f Negative: $\{x \mid 0 < x < 3\}$; zero: $\{-2, 0, 3\}$; positive: $\{x \mid x < 0 \text{ and } x \neq -2 \text{ or } x > 3\}$. See diagram at right above; the graph must be contained in the shaded regions.

3 a $a = 25; \; b = -9$.

b $a = 1; \; b = -1$.

4 a If $k_1 = 1$, then $(x - r_1)$ is a linear factor of $P(x)$. Since $\big((r_1 - h) - r_1\big) = -h$ is less than zero and $\big((r_1 + h) - r_1\big) = h$ is greater than zero, the linear factor $(x - r_1)$ changes sign as x increases from $r_1 - h$ to $r_1 + h$. Since none of the other factors of $P(x)$ changes sign in this interval, $P(x)$ must change sign as x increases from $r_1 - h$ to $r_1 + h$. Hence, the graph of P must intersect the x-axis at $(r_1, 0)$, where $P(x) = 0$.

b Since $P(r_2) = 0$, $(r_2, 0)$ is a point on the graph of P. Because r_2 is a zero of multiplicity 2 of $P(x)$, by the theorem stated in the exercise, it is a zero of multiplicity 1 of $P'(x)$. Therefore, $P'(r_2) = 0$, and the tangent line to the graph of P at $(r_2, 0)$ is a horizontal line. Also, since r_2 is a zero of multiplicity 1 of $P'(x)$, the argument given in exercise 4a establishes that $P'(r_2 - h)$ and $P'(r_2 + h)$ are of opposite signs. Hence, the point $(r_2, 0)$ is either a relative maximum or a relative minimum point on the graph of P.

c By the argument given in exercise 4a, $(x - r_3)$ changes sign as x increases from $r_3 - h$ to $r_3 + h$; hence, $(x - r_3)^3$ changes sign in this interval. Since none of the other linear factors of $P(x)$ changes sign in this interval, this means that $P(x)$ changes signs as x increases from $r_3 - h$ to $r_3 + h$. Because $P(r_3) = 0$, the graph of P intersects the x-axis at $(r_3, 0)$. Also, by the theorem stated in the exercise, r_3 is a zero of multiplicity 2 of $P'(x)$. Therefore, $P'(r_3) = 0$; so the tangent to the graph of P at $(r_3, 0)$ is horizontal. Hence, the tangent is the x-axis.

5 a The graph of P has a relative maximum or a relative minimum point at $(r, 0)$.

b The graph of P crosses the x-axis at $(r, 0)$ and also has the x-axis as its tangent line at this point.

6 **a**

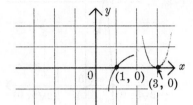

b

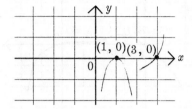

c

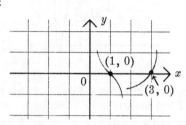

d

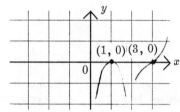

7 **a** P(x) negative: $\{x \mid |x| < \sqrt{7}\}$; P($x$) zero: $\{-\sqrt{7}, \sqrt{7}\}$; P(x) positive: $\{x \mid |x| > \sqrt{7}\}$. P′($x$) negative: $\{x \mid x < -\sqrt{3}$ or $0 < x < \sqrt{3}\}$; P′(x) zero: $\{-\sqrt{3}, 0, \sqrt{3}\}$; P′($x$) positive: $\{x \mid -\sqrt{3} < x < 0$ or $x > \sqrt{3}\}$. P″(x) negative: $\{x \mid |x| < 1\}$; P″(x) zero: $\{-1, 1\}$; P″(x) positive: $\{x \mid |x| > 1\}$. See diagram at left below.

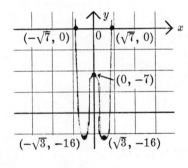

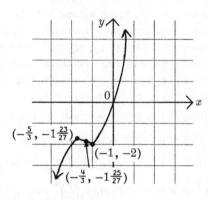

b P(x) negative: $\{x \mid x < 0\}$; P(x) zero: $\{0\}$; P(x) positive: $\{x \mid x > 0\}$. P′(x) negative: $\{x \mid -\frac{5}{3} < x < -1\}$; P′($x$) zero: $\{-\frac{5}{3}, -1\}$; P′(x) positive: $\{x \mid x < -\frac{5}{3}$ or $x > -1\}$. P″(x) negative; $\{x \mid x < -\frac{4}{3}\}$; P″($x$) zero: $\{-\frac{4}{3}\}$; P″(x) positive: $\{x \mid x > -\frac{4}{3}\}$. See diagram at right above.

c P(x) negative: $\{x \mid x < -1$ or $x > 0\}$; P(x) zero: $\{-1, 0\}$. P(x) positive: $\{x \mid -1 < x < 0\}$. P′(x) negative: $\{x \mid x > -\frac{3}{4}, x \neq 0\}$. P′($x$) zero: $\{-\frac{3}{4}, 0\}$; P′(x) positive: $\{x \mid x < -\frac{3}{4}\}$. P″($x$) negative: $\{x \mid x < -\frac{1}{2}$ or $x > 0\}$; P″(x) zero: $\{-\frac{1}{2}, 0\}$; P″(x) positive: $\{x \mid -\frac{1}{2} < x < 0\}$. See diagram on the left at the top of the next page.

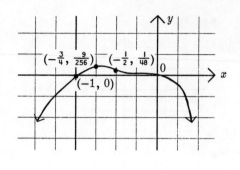 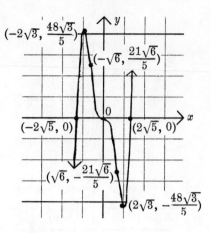

d P(x) negative: $\{x \mid x < -2\sqrt{5} \text{ or } 0 < x < 2\sqrt{5}\}$; P(x) zero: $\{-2\sqrt{5}, 0, 2\sqrt{5}\}$; P(x) positive: $\{x \mid -2\sqrt{5} < x < 0 \text{ or } x > 2\sqrt{5}\}$. P′(x) negative: $\{x \mid -2\sqrt{3} < x < 2\sqrt{3}\}$; P(x) zero: $\{-2\sqrt{3}, 0, 2\sqrt{3}\}$; P′(x) positive: $\{x \mid x < -2\sqrt{3} \text{ or } x > 2\sqrt{3}\}$. P″(x) negative: $\{x \mid x < -\sqrt{6} \text{ or } 0 < x < \sqrt{6}\}$; P″(x) zero: $\{-\sqrt{6}, 0, \sqrt{6}\}$. P″(x) positive: $\{x \mid -\sqrt{6} < x < 0 \text{ or } x > \sqrt{6}\}$. See diagram at the right above.

Page 392

1. Possible: $\{-1, 1\}$; actual: $\{-1, 1\}$

2. Possible: $\{-2, -1, 1, 2\}$; actual: $\{-1, 2\}$

3. Possible: $\{\pm 6, \pm 3, \pm 2, \pm 1\}$; actual: $\{-1, 6\}$

4. Possible: $\{\pm 12, \pm 6, \pm 4, \pm 3, \pm 2, \pm 1\}$ actual: $\{-3, -2, 2\}$

5. Possible: $\{\pm 14, \pm 7, \pm 2, \pm 1\}$; actual: $\{-2, 1\}$

6. Possible: $\{\pm 6, \pm 3, \pm 2, \pm 1\}$; actual: $\{-3, 1\}$

7. Possible: $\{-1, -\frac{1}{2}, \frac{1}{2}, 1\}$; actual: $\{-\frac{1}{2}\}$

8. Possible: $\{\pm 4, \pm 2, \pm\frac{4}{3}, \pm 1, \pm\frac{2}{3}, \pm\frac{1}{3}\}$; actual: $\{\frac{4}{3}\}$

9. Possible: $\{\pm 1, \pm\frac{1}{2},\}$; actual: $\{-1, \frac{1}{2}, 1\}$

10. Possible: $\{\pm 15, \pm 5, \pm 3, \pm\frac{5}{3}, \pm 1, \pm\frac{1}{3}\}$; actual: $\{-3, \frac{5}{3}\}$

11. Since $\frac{p}{q}$ is a zero of P(x), $a_n\left(\frac{p}{q}\right)^n + a_{n-1}\left(\frac{p}{q}\right)^{n-1} + \ldots + a_1\frac{p}{q} + a_0 = 0$. Multiplying

    through by q^n, we get $a_n p^n + a_{n-1}p^{n-1}q + \ldots + a_1 pq^{n-1} + a_0 q^n = 0$, or

    $a_0 q^n = -\left(a_n p^n + a_{n-1}p^{n-1}q + \ldots + a_1 pq^{n-1}\right) = -p\left(a_n p^{n-1} + a_{n-1}p^{n-2}q + \ldots + a_1 q^{n-1}\right)$.

    Since p is a factor of the right side of this equation, it must also be a factor of

    $a_0 q^n$. Since p and q have no common integral factors, q^n cannot be divisible by p; hence, a_0 must be divisible by p.

12. **a** Since P is not a constant function, P(x) must be different from 0 for some values of x between a and b. If P(x) > 0 for some values of x between a and b, then P(x) must have a maximum value for some x between a and b. If P(x) < 0 for some values of x between a and b, then P(x) must have a minimum value for some x between a and b. In either case, the graph of P must have a horizontal tangent

at some point between $(a, 0)$ and $(b, 0)$. Hence, for some value of x, say x_0, between a and b, $P'(x_0) = 0$.

b Horizontal tangent to the graph of P.

13 a ℓ: $\ell(x) = \dfrac{P(b) - P(a)}{b - a} (x - a) + P(a)$.

b $P - \ell$: $(P - \ell)(x) = P(x) - \dfrac{P(b) - P(a)}{b - a} (x - a) - P(a)$.

Since P and ℓ are polynomial functions, $-1 \cdot \ell = -\ell$ and $P - \ell$ are polynomial functions. Also, because P is of degree n, where $n > 1$, and ℓ is of degree 1,

$P - \ell$ is of degree n. Finally, $(P - \ell)(a) = P(a) - \dfrac{P(b) - P(a)}{b - a} (a - a) - P(a) = 0$

and $(P - \ell)(b) = P(b) - \dfrac{P(b) - P(a)}{b - a} (b - a) - P(a) = 0$. Therefore, $P - \ell$ does satisfy the conditions stated in the hypothesis of the theorem.

c By the theorem stated in exercise 12a, there is a number x_0 between a and b

such that $(P - \ell)'(x_0) = 0$. Now $(P - \ell)'(x_0) = P'(x_0) - \dfrac{P(b) - P(a)}{b - a} = 0$. Hence,

$P'(x_0) = \dfrac{P(b) - P(a)}{b - a}$, which is the slope of the line through $(a, P(a))$ and

$(b, P(b))$. Therefore, the tangent to the graph of P at the point $(x_0, P(x_0))$ is parallel to this line.

Pages 394-395

1 The possible rational zeros are $\{\pm 4, \pm 2, \pm 1\}$. By Theorem 39/7, the possible rational zeros are $\{4, 2, 1\}$. There are no actual rational zeros.

2 Possible rational zeros: $\{\pm 1\}$; by Theorem 38/7: $\{-1\}$; actual rational zeros: $\{-1\}$.

3 Possible rational zeros: $\{\pm 6, \pm 3, \pm 2, \pm 1\}$; by Theorem 38/7: $\{-6, -3, -2, -1\}$; actual rational zeros: $\{-3, -2, -1\}$.

4 Possible rational zeros: $\{\pm 2, \pm 1, \pm\frac{1}{2}\}$; by Theorem 39/7: $\{2, 1, \frac{1}{2}\}$; actual rational zeros: $\{2, 1, \frac{1}{2}\}$.

5 Possible rational zeros: $\{\pm 3, \pm\frac{3}{2}, \pm 1, \pm\frac{1}{2}\}$; by Theorem 39/7: $\{3, \frac{3}{2}, 1, \frac{1}{2}\}$; actual rational zeros: $\{\frac{1}{2}\}$.

6 Possible rational zeros: $\{\pm 2, \pm 1, \pm\frac{1}{2}\}$; by Theorem 39/7: $\{2, 1, \frac{1}{2}\}$; actual rational zeros: $\{2, \frac{1}{2}\}$.

7 Possible rational zeros: $\{\pm 3, \pm\frac{3}{2}, \pm 1, \pm\frac{3}{4}, \pm\frac{1}{2}, \pm\frac{1}{4}\}$; by Theorem 38/7: $\{-3, -\frac{3}{2}, -1, -\frac{3}{4}, -\frac{1}{2}, -\frac{1}{4}\}$; actual rational zeros: $\{-\frac{1}{2}\}$.

8 Possible rational zeros: $\{\pm 4, \pm 2, \pm\frac{4}{3}, \pm 1, \pm\frac{2}{3}, \pm\frac{1}{2}, \pm\frac{1}{3}, \pm\frac{1}{6}\}$; by Theorem 38/7: $\{-4, -2, -\frac{4}{3}, -1, -\frac{2}{3}, -\frac{1}{2}, -\frac{1}{3}, -\frac{1}{6}\}$; actual rational zeros: $\{-2, -1\}$

9 If the coefficients of $P(x)$ are all negative and $x_0 > 0$, then $P(x_0) < 0$. Hence, P has no positive zeros when all the coefficients of $P(x)$ are all negative.

10 a $P(c_i) = (c_i - c)Q(c_i) + P(c)$. Since $c_i > c > 0$, $c_i - c > 0$ and since all the coefficients of $Q(x)$ are positive, $Q(c_i) > 0$. Hence $(c_i - c)Q(c_i) > 0$. Finally, since $P(c) > 0$ by assumption, $(c_i - c)Q(c_i) + P(c) > 0$. Hence, $P(c_i) > 0$.

b Since all the coefficients of $Q(x)$ are negative and $c_i > 0$, $Q(c_i) < 0$; and since

$(c_1 - c) > 0$, $(c_1 - c)Q(c_1) < 0$. Further, since $P(c)$ is less than zero, $(c_1 - c)Q(c_1) + P(c) < 0$. Since $P(c_1) = (c_1 - c)Q(c_1) + P(c)$, $P(c_1) < 0$.

c No. By part a, if $P(c)$ and the coefficients of $Q(x)$ are positive, $P(c_1) < 0$ for any positive number c_1 greater than c. By part b, if $P(c)$ and the coefficients of $Q(x)$ are negative, $P(c_1) < 0$ for any positive number c_1 greater than c.

d Carry out the divisions of $P(x)$ by $x - 1$, $x - 2$, $x - 3$, and so on, until you obtain a quotient and a remainder which have the property that the coefficients of the quotient and the remainder have the same sign. The integer a in the divisor $(x - a)$ which produces this quotient and remainder is then the least positive integer that is an upper bound for the set of positive zeros of $P(x)$.

11 a Suppose that $c_1 < c < 0$. First of all, $P(c_1) = (c_1 - c) Q(c_1) + P(c)$. Since $c_1 < c < 0$, $(c_1 - c) < 0$. Now suppose that the coefficients of the even powers of $Q(x)$ are positive and that the coefficients of the odd powers of $Q(x)$ and $P(c)$ are negative. Then $Q(c_1) > 0$ so that $(c_1 - c)Q(c_1) + P(c) < 0$. Hence, $P(c_1) < 0$. If the coefficients of the even powers of $Q(x)$ are negative and the coefficients of the odd powers of $Q(x)$ are positive, then $Q(c_1) < 0$. Further, since in this case $P(c) > 0$, $(c_1 - c)Q(c_1) + P(c) > 0$. Hence, $P(c_1) > 0$. These cases show that if $c_1 < c < 0$, $P(c_1)$ is either less than zero or greater than zero, so that P has no zeros less than c.

b Carry out the divisions of $P(x)$ by $x + 1$, $x + 2$, $x + 3$, and so on, until you obtain a quotient and a remainder which exhibit an alternation of signs from term to term. The integer a in the divisor $x - a$ which produces this quotient and remainder is then the greatest integer that is a lower bound for the set of negative zeros of $P(x)$.

12 a Upper bound: 2; lower bound: −3
   b Upper bound: 2; lower bound: −4
   c Upper bound: 3; lower bound: −2
   d Upper bound: 2; lower bound: −3

Pages 397-399

1 a $P(-3) = -1$ and $P(-4) = 13$. Therefore, $P(-4) P(-3) < 0$ and, by Theorem 40/7, there is at least one real number x_0 in the interval $-4 < x_0 < -3$ such that $P(x_0) = 0$. The only possible rational zeros of P are $\{\pm 5, \pm 1\}$; thus, the zero of P between -4 and -3 must be irrational.

b $P(1) = -2$ and $P(2) = 3$. Therefore, $P(1) P(2) < 0$ and, by Theorem 40/7, there is at least one real number x_0 in the interval $1 < x_0 < 2$ such that $P(x_0) = 0$. The only possible rational zeros of P are $\{\pm 3, \pm 1\}$; thus, the zero of P between 1 and 2 must be irrational.

2 a Between 1 and 2; irrational
   b Between 0 and 1; rational, $\frac{1}{2}$
   c Between 2 and 3; rational, $\frac{5}{2}$
   d Between −1 and 0; rational, $-\frac{1}{2}$

3 a P(x) has a zero between −2 and −1, which is closer to −2 than to −1; a zero between −1 and 0, which is closer to 0 than to −1; and a zero between 1 and 2, which is closer to 2 than to 1.
b P(x) has a zero between 2 and 3, which is closer to 2 than to 3.
c P(x) has a zero between 0 and 1, which is closer to 1 than to 0.
d P(x) has a zero between −2 and −1 that is closer to −2 than to −1 and a zero between 1 and 2 that is closer to 2 than to 1.
4 The graph of P($-x$) is the reflection in the y-axis of the graph of P(x). Thus, any negative zeros of P(x) will be positive zeros of P($-x$). By the theorem stated in the exercise, if P($-x$) contains n variations in sign, then P($-x$) has $n - 2k$ positive roots, where k is a nonnegative integer. Hence, P(x) has $n - 2k$ negative zeros.

	Number of positive zeros	Number of negative zeros	Number of nonreal zeros
5 a	2	1	0
	0	1	2
b	0	1	2
c	1	3	0
	1	1	2
d	2	1	4
	0	1	6

Chapter review
Pages 399-401

1	c	5	d	9	c	13	d	17	d	21 d
2	c	6	b	10	b	14	c	18	b	22 d
3	d	7	b	11	c	15	a	19	c	23 b
4	d	8	d	12	d	16	b	20	c	24 a

Cumulative review
Pages 401-403

1 a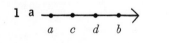

c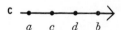

b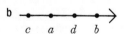

d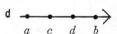

2 a (a) The set is a function because every replacement for x corresponds to exactly one image, y. (b) The graph is symmetric with respect to the y-axis. (c) The domain of the function is $\Re$; the range is the set of all nonnegative real numbers.
b (a) The set is a function because every replacement for x corresponds to

exactly one image, y. (b) The graph has no symmetries. (c) The domain is
$\{x \mid x \in \Re$ and $x \neq 0\}$; the range is $\{y \mid y \in \Re$ and $y \neq 1\}$.

c (a) The set is not a function because each x is mapped onto two different
values, y. (b) The graph is symmetric with respect to both axes and the
origin.

d (a) The set is a function because each x is mapped onto exactly one image,
y. (b) The graph is symmetric with respect to the y-axis. (c) The domain is
$\{x \mid |x| \leq \frac{5}{4}\}$; the range is $\{y \mid 0 \leq y \leq 5\}$.

3 The slope of the tangent to the graph of q at point A is -1 and the slope of the
tangent at point B is 1. Hence, the two tangents, which intersect at point C, are
perpendicular because the product of their slopes is -1.

An equation of the tangent to the graph of q at point A is $y = -x - \frac{1}{4}$. An
equation of the tangent at point B is $y = x - \frac{1}{4}$. Hence, point C has coordinates
$(0, -\frac{1}{4})$. Therefore, $[d(A, B)]^2 = 1$; $[d(A, C)]^2 = \frac{1}{4} + \frac{1}{4} = \frac{1}{2}$; and $[d(B, C)]^2 = \frac{1}{4} + \frac{1}{4} = \frac{1}{2}$.
Hence, $[d(A, B)]^2 = [d(A, C)]^2 + [d(B, C)]^2$, and $\triangle ABC$ is a right triangle.

4 a

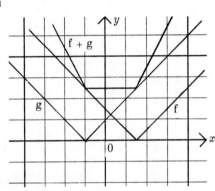

b

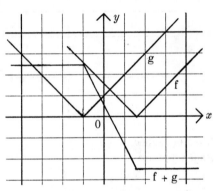

5 a The discriminant of this quadratic equation, $b^2 - 4ac = 64 - 100 = -36$, is
less than zero. Thus, the equation has no real roots.

b $(4 - 3i)^2 - 8(4 - 3i) + 25 = (16 - 9 - 24i) - 32 + 24i + 25 = 0$.

c The other root is $4 + 3i$. For every nonreal complex root of a polynomial equation,
the conjugate of that number is also a root of the equation.

6 a $f_1(x) = x^2 - 8x + 16$.

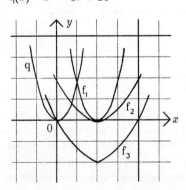

b $f_2(x) = \frac{1}{4}x^2 - 2x + 4$. See graph for part a.

c $f_3(x) = \frac{1}{4}x^2 - 2x$. See graph for part a.

7 a $\ell(x) = -\frac{1}{4}x + 1$.

b $\ell^{-1}(x) = -4x + 4$

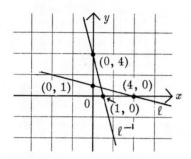

8 a $h(t) = 30t - 16t^2$; $d(t) = 72t$.

b 135 ft.   **c** $14\frac{1}{16}$ ft.   **d** $f(x) = \frac{5}{12} - \frac{x^2}{324}$.

9 a $f(x) < 0$ for $x < 3$ and $x \neq -3$. $f(x) = 0$ for $x = 3$ and $x = -3$; $f(x) > 0$ for $x > 3$. The graph is below the x-axis for $x < 3$, except for $x = -3$; the graph has x-intercepts for $x = -3$ and for $x = 3$; the graph is above the x-axis for $x > 3$.

b $f'(x) = 3x^2 + 6x - 9 = 3(x^2 + 2x - 3)$. Hence, $f'(x) < 0$ for x in the interval $-3 < x < 1$; $f'(x) = 0$ for $x = -3$ and for $x = 1$; $f'(x) > 0$ for $x < -3$ and for $x > 1$. The graph is decreasing in the interval $-3 < x < 1$; the graph has horizontal tangents at $x = -3$ and at $x = 1$; the graph is increasing for $x < -3$ and $x > 1$.

c $f''(x) = 6x + 6 = 6(x + 1)$. Hence, $f''(x) < 0$ for $x < -1$, $f''(x) = 0$ for $x = -1$, $f''(x) > 0$ for $x > -1$. The graph is concave downward for $x < -1$; the graph has an inflection point at $x = -1$; and the graph is concave upward for $x > -1$.

d

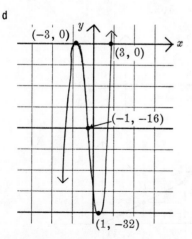

10 The height should be 2.

Page 411

1 a $|C| = 10.$

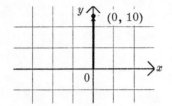

b $|C| = 6.$

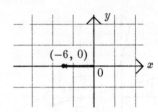

c $|C| = 8\sqrt{2}.$

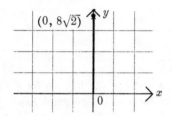

d $|C| = \frac{9}{5}.$

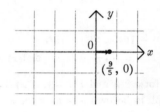

e $|C| = 2\sqrt{5}.$

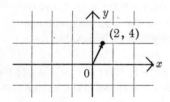

f $|C| = \sqrt{34}.$

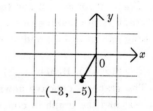

g $|C| = \sqrt{10}.$

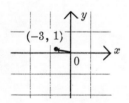

h $|C| = 5\sqrt{2}.$

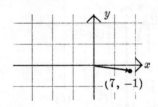

2 a $|C| = 2\sqrt{5};\ C = -4 + 2i.$
$|2C| = 4\sqrt{5};\ 2C = -8 + 4i.$
$|\frac{1}{2}C| = \sqrt{5};\ \frac{1}{2}C = -2 + i.$

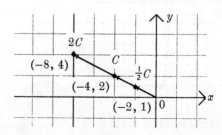

b $|C| = \sqrt{13};\ C = 2 + 3i.$

$|2C| = 2\sqrt{13};\ 2C = 4 + 6i.$

$|\frac{1}{2}C| = \frac{\sqrt{13}}{2};\ C = 1 + \frac{3}{2}i.$

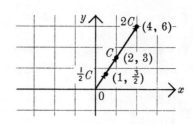

c $|C| = \sqrt{26};\ C = -5 - i.$

$|2C| = 2\sqrt{26};\ 2C = -10 - 2i.$

$|\frac{1}{2}C| = \frac{\sqrt{26}}{2};\ \frac{1}{2}C = -\frac{5}{2} - \frac{1}{2}i.$

d $|C| = 4;\ C = -4 + 0i.$

$|2C| = 8;\ 2C = -8 + 0i.$

$|\frac{1}{2}C| = 2;\ \frac{1}{2}C = -2 + 0i.$

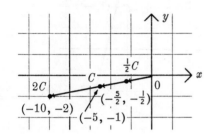

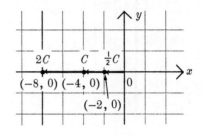

3 a $|C| = 3\sqrt{2};\ C = -3 - 3i.$

$|-C| = 3\sqrt{2};\ -C = 3 + 3i.$

$|-3C| = 9\sqrt{2};\ -3C = 9 + 9i.$

$|-\frac{1}{3}C| = \sqrt{2};\ -\frac{1}{3}C = 1 + i.$

b $|C| = 2\sqrt{5};\ C = 2 - 4i.$

$|-C| = 2\sqrt{5};\ -C = -2 + 4i.$

$|-3C| = 6\sqrt{5};\ -3C = -6 + 12i.$

$|-\frac{1}{3}C| = \frac{2\sqrt{5}}{3};\ -\frac{1}{3}C = -\frac{2}{3} + \frac{4}{3}i$

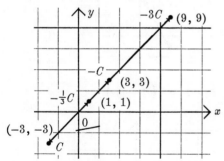

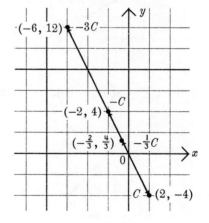

c $|C| = 3\sqrt{2};\ C = 0 - 3\sqrt{2}i.$
    $|-C| = 3\sqrt{2};\ -C = 0 + 3\sqrt{2}i.$
    $|-3C| = 9\sqrt{2};\ -3C = 0 + 9\sqrt{2}i.$
    $|-\tfrac{1}{3}C| = \sqrt{2};\ -\tfrac{1}{3}C = 0 + \sqrt{2}i.$

d $|C| = \sqrt{17};\ C = -1 + 4i.$
    $|-C| = \sqrt{17};\ -C = 1 - 4i.$
    $|-3c| = 3\sqrt{17};\ -3C = 3 - 12i.$
    $|-\tfrac{1}{3}C| = \tfrac{\sqrt{17}}{3};\ -\tfrac{1}{3}C = \tfrac{1}{3} - \tfrac{4}{3}i.$

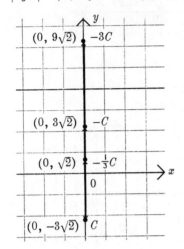

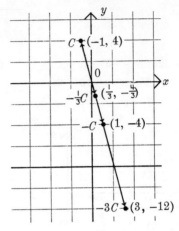

4   a $2\sqrt{3} - 2i = 4\left(\tfrac{\sqrt{3}}{2} - \tfrac{1}{2}i\right).$

b $-3 - 3\sqrt{3}i = 6\left(-\tfrac{1}{2} - \tfrac{\sqrt{3}}{2}i\right).$

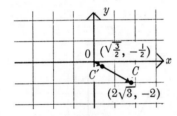

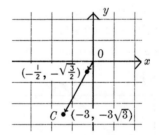

c $-4\sqrt{2} + 4\sqrt{2}i = 8\left(-\tfrac{\sqrt{2}}{2} + \tfrac{\sqrt{2}}{2}i\right).$

d $\tfrac{\sqrt{2}}{6} + \tfrac{\sqrt{2}}{6}i = \tfrac{1}{3}\left(\tfrac{\sqrt{2}}{2} + \tfrac{\sqrt{2}}{2}i\right).$

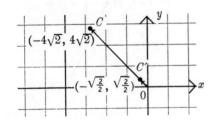

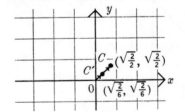

5 **a** $-3.5 + 0i.$ **b** $0 - 4i.$

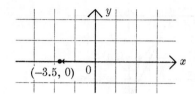

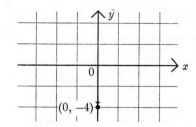

c $-8 - 8i.$ **d** $-6\sqrt{2} + 6\sqrt{2}i.$

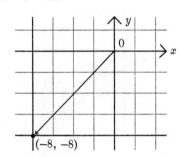

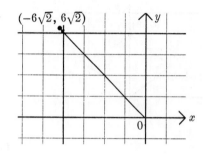

e $5 + 5\sqrt{3}i.$ **f** $6 - 2\sqrt{3}i.$

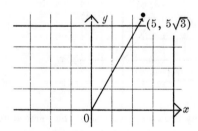

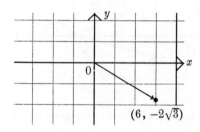

6 **a** Let $C = a + bi$. Then $|C| = \sqrt{a^2 + b^2}$. $-C = -a - bi$. Hence
$$|-C| = \sqrt{(-a)^2 + (-b)^2} = \sqrt{a^2 + b^2} = |C|.$$

b Let $C = c + di$, then $aC = ac + adi$ and $|aC| =$
$$\sqrt{(ac)^2 + (ad)^2} = \sqrt{a^2 c^2 + a^2 d^2} = \sqrt{a^2(c^2 + d^2)} = \sqrt{a^2}\sqrt{c^2 + d^2} = |a|\sqrt{c^2 + d^2} = |a| \cdot |C|.$$

7 **a** Let (a, b) be a point on the unit circle about the origin in the complex plane. Then the distance of (a, b) from the origin is 1; that is, $\sqrt{a^2 + b^2} = 1$. Hence, the magnitude of the corresponding complex number $a + bi$ is 1, so that the vector corresponding to $a + bi$ is its own normalization.

Let $a + bi$ be a given complex number such that the corresponding vector is its own normalization. This means that the vector, and hence the corresponding complex number, has magnitude 1, so that $\sqrt{a^2 + b^2} = 1$. But if $\sqrt{a^2 + b^2} = 1$, the point (a, b) in the complex plane is a distance of 1 unit from the origin, therefore (a, b) is on the unit circle about the origin in the complex plane.

1 a

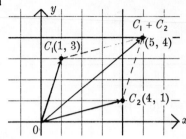

b

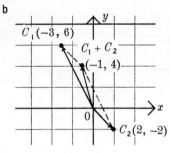

c

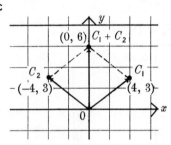

d

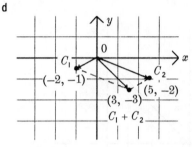

e

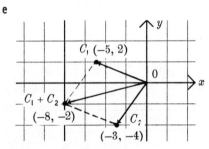

f

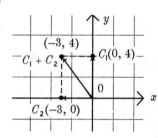

2 Construct the vector corresponding to $-C_2$ by drawing a vector of the same length as, but opposite direction from, the vector corresponding to C_2. Then use the parallelogram method with the vectors corresponding to C_1 and $-C_2$.

3 Construct the vector corresponding to C_1 and C_2 and let C_2 represent one side of the parallelogram and C_1 represent the diagonal of the parallelogram. Then the side of the parallelogram with its endpoint at the origin corresponds to the vector $C = C_1 - C_2$.

4 a $|a\vec{U}| = 5\sqrt{2} = |b\vec{V}|.$ b $|a\vec{U}| = 2 = |b\vec{V}|.$

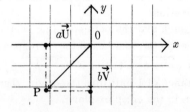

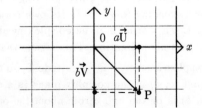

c $|a\vec{U}| = 3$; $|b\vec{V}| = 3\sqrt{3}$.

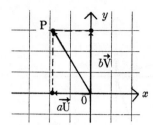

d $|a\vec{U}| = 0$; $|b\vec{V}| = 7.5$.

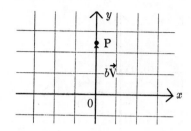

e $|a\vec{U}| = 4\sqrt{3}$; $|b\vec{V}| = 4$.

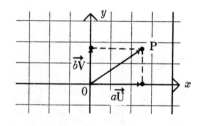

f $|a\vec{U}| = \frac{\sqrt{3}}{2}$; $|b\vec{V}| = 0$.

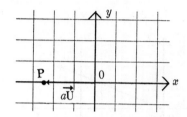

5 a

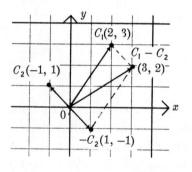

b

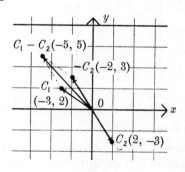

c

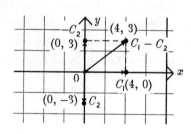

d

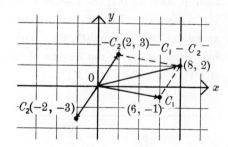

6 a $C_1C_2 = 1.$

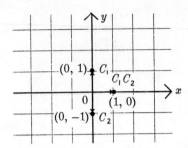

b $C_1C_2 = -1 - 3i.$

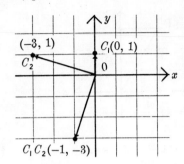

c $C_1C_2 = 5 + 2i.$

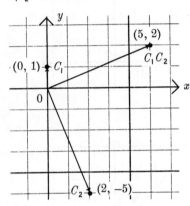

d $C_1C_2 = -2 + 4i.$

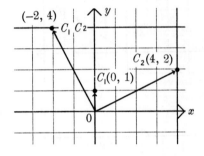

7 Let (a, b) be the coordinates of P_1 and (c, d) be the coordinates of P_2. Then (a, b) corresponds to C_1 and (c, d), corresponds to C_2. By definition of the distance between two points in the plane, $d(P_1, P_2) = \sqrt{(a - c)^2 + (b - d)^2}$. By the definition of the difference of two complex numbers, $C_1 - C_2 = C_1 + (-C_2) = (a - c, b - d)$. Hence, $|C_1 - C_2| = \sqrt{(a - c)^2 + (b - d)^2} = d(P_1, P_2)$.

8 Case I: Assume that the vectors corresponding to C_1, C_2, and C_3 are not contained in the same line. Let $\overrightarrow{OP_1}$ correspond to C_1, $\overrightarrow{OP_2}$ correspond to C_2 and $\overrightarrow{OP_3}$ correspond to $C_1 + C_2$. Then $d(P_1, P_3) = |\overrightarrow{OP_2}|$. In any triangle, the length of one side is less than the sum of the lengths of the other two sides. Hence, in $\triangle OP_1P_3$, $d(0, P_3) < d(0, P_1) + d(P_1, P_3)$.

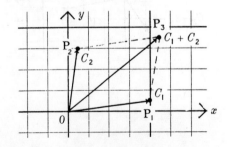

Since $d(0, P_3) = |C_1 + C_2|$, $d(0, P_1) = |C_1|$ and $d(P_1, P_3) = |C_2|$, it follows that $|C_1 + C_2| < |C_1| + |C_2|$.

Case II: If the vectors corresponding to C_1 and C_2 are contained in the same line, and if the vectors are oppositely directed, then P_3 is between P_1 and P_2. This means that $|C_1 + C_2| < |C_1| + |C_2|$. If the vectors have the same direction, then we can use similar triangles to show that $|C_1 + C_2| = |C_1| + |C_2|$.

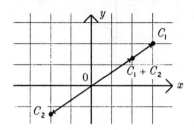
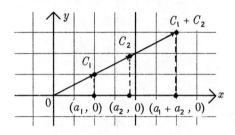

Hence, in all cases $|C_1 + C_2| \leqq |C_1| + |C_2|$.

Pages 420-421

1 a

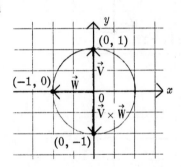

b

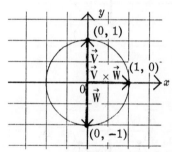

c

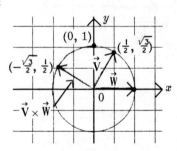

d

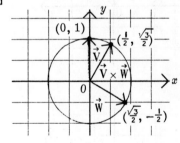

2 a

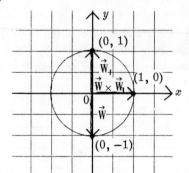

b

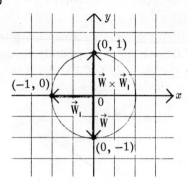

c

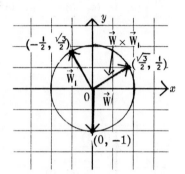

d

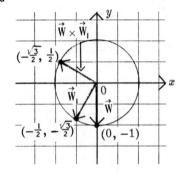

3 a

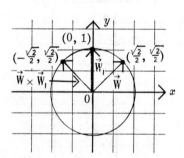

b

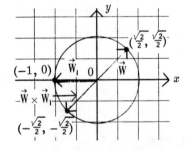

c

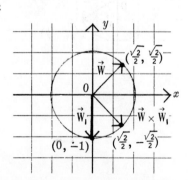

d

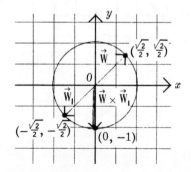

4 a

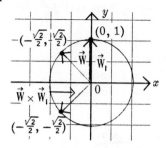

b

c

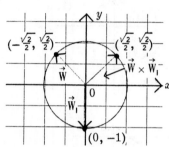

d

5 a False. For example, suppose that $\vec{W}_1$ corresponds to $(1, 0)$ and $\vec{W}_2$ corresponds to $(0, 1)$. Then $C_1 + C_2 = (1, 0) + (0, 1) = (1, 1)$ and $|C_1 + C_2| = \sqrt{1 + 1} = \sqrt{2}$. Hence $\vec{W}_1 + \vec{W}_2$, which corresponds to $(1, 1)$, is not a unit vector.

b True. Let $\vec{W}_1$ correspond to (a, b) and $\vec{W}_2$ to (c, d). Then $\vec{W}_1 \times \vec{W}_2$ corresponds to $(ac - bd, ad + bc)$ and $\vec{W}_2 \times \vec{W}_1$ corresponds to $(ca - db, cb + da)$. Since addition and multiplication of real numbers are commutative, $(ac - bd, ad + bc) = (ca - db, cb + da)$. Hence, $\vec{W}_1 \times \vec{W}_2 = \vec{W}_2 \times \vec{W}_1$.

c True. Let $\vec{W}_1$ correspond to (a, b), $\vec{W}_2$ to (c, d) and $\vec{W}_3$ to (e, f). Then $(\vec{W}_1 \times \vec{W}_2) \times \vec{W}_3$ corresponds to $((ac)e - (bd)e - (ad)f - (bc)f, (ac)f - (bd)f + (ad)e + (bc)e) = (a(ce) - a(df) - b(cf) - b(de), a(cf) + a(de) + b(ce) - b(df))$, which corresponds to $\vec{W}_1 \times (\vec{W}_2 \times \vec{W}_3)$.

d True. Let $\vec{W}_1$ correspond to (a, b). Then $(a, b) \cdot (1, 0) = (a - 0, 0 + b) = (a, b)$.

e True. Let $\vec{W}_1$ correspond to (a, b). Then $(a, b) \cdot (0, 0) = (0 - 0, 0 + 0) = (0, 0)$.

f True. Let $\vec{W}_1$ correspond to (a, b). Then $\vec{W}$ corresponds to $\left(\dfrac{a}{a^2 + b^2}, \dfrac{-b}{a^2 + b^2}\right)$.

The components of the complex number corresponding to $\vec{W}$ are determined as follows. Let (x, y) represent the complex number such that $(a, b) \cdot (x, y) = (1, 0)$. Then $(ax - by, ay + bx) = (1, 0)$. This is true if and only if $ax - by = 1$ and $ay + bx = 0$. Solving these equations for x and y, we obtain $x = \dfrac{a}{a^2 + b^2}$ and $y = \dfrac{-b}{a^2 + b^2}$. The vector $\vec{W}$ corresponding to $\left(\dfrac{a}{a^2 + b^2}, \dfrac{-b}{a^2 + b^2}\right)$ is a unit vector since

$$\sqrt{\left(\frac{a}{a^2+b^2}\right)^2 + \left(\frac{-b}{a^2+b^2}\right)^2} = \sqrt{\frac{a^2+b^2}{(a^2+b^2)^2}} = \sqrt{\frac{1}{a^2+b^2}} = 1. \text{ Note that } \sqrt{a^2+b^2} = 1$$

since (a, b) corresponds to the unit vector $\vec{W}_1$.

6 a $\vec{W}$ is rotated through an angle of 90° in a counterclockwise direction.

  b $\vec{W}$ is rotated through an angle of 90° in a clockwise direction.

Pages 425-426

1

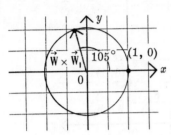

2

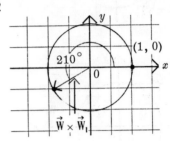

3

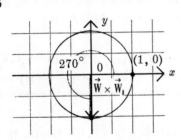

4

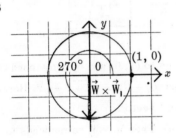

5

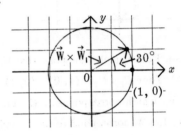

6

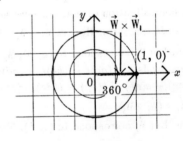

7

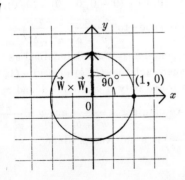

8

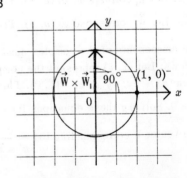

9   **10**

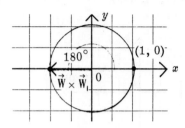

11 Let $\vec{W}_1 = |\vec{W}_1| \cdot \vec{W}_2$, where $\vec{W}_2$ is the unit vector that is the normalization of $\vec{W}_1$. Hence, $\vec{W} \times \vec{W}_1 = \vec{W} \times (|\vec{W}_1| \cdot \vec{W}_2) = |\vec{W}_1| \cdot (\vec{W} \times \vec{W}_2)$. Thus, $\vec{W} \times \vec{W}_2$ is the normalization of $\vec{W} \times \vec{W}_1$, and $|\vec{W}_1|$ is its length, so that $\vec{W} \times \vec{W}_1$ has the same length as $\vec{W}_1$. Further, $\vec{W} \times \vec{W}_2$ is the vector $\vec{W}_2$ rotated through an angle of θ in a counterclockwise direction. Since the direction of $\vec{W}_2$ is the same as that of $\vec{W}_1$, it follows that $\vec{W} \times \vec{W}_2$ is in the same direction as $\vec{W}_1$ when rotated through an angle of θ in a counterclockwise direction. Since $\vec{W} \times \vec{W}_1$ is in the same direction as $\vec{W} \times \vec{W}_2$, it follows that $\vec{W} \times \vec{W}_1$ is $\vec{W}_1$ rotated through an angle of θ in a counterclockwise direction.

12 Let $\vec{W} = |\vec{W}| \cdot \vec{W}_2$, where $\vec{W}_2$ is the unit vector that is the normalization of $\vec{W}$. Now $\vec{W} \times \vec{W}_1 = (|\vec{W}| \cdot \vec{W}_2) \times \vec{W}_1 = |\vec{W}| \cdot (\vec{W}_2 \times \vec{W}_1)$. Since $\vec{W}_2$ is a unit vector, by the theorem from exercise 11, $\vec{W}_2 \times \vec{W}_1$ is the vector $\vec{W}_1$ rotated through an angle of θ in a counter-clockwise direction. Hence, $\vec{W} \times \vec{W}_1 = |\vec{W}| \cdot (\vec{W}_2 \times \vec{W}_1)$ is the vector $\vec{W}_1$ rotated through an angle of θ in a counterclockwise direction and multiplied by the real number $|\vec{W}|$.

Pages 429-431

1

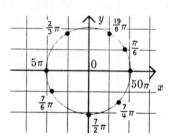

2 a $F\left(\frac{3\pi}{2}\right) = (0, -1)$;
$f\left(\frac{3\pi}{2}\right) = 0$; $g\left(\frac{3\pi}{2}\right) = -1$.

   b $F(3\pi) = (-1, 0)$; $f(3\pi) = -1$;
$g(3\pi) = 0$.

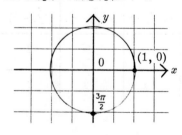

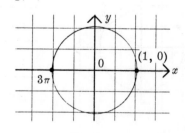

c $F(\frac{\pi}{2}) = (0, 1)$;
$f(\frac{\pi}{2}) = 0; g(\frac{\pi}{2}) = 1.$

d $F(4\pi) = (1, 0); f(4\pi) = 1;$
$g(4\pi) = 0.$

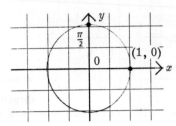

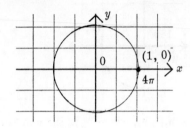

3 a

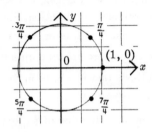

b

t	$\frac{\pi}{4}$	$\frac{3\pi}{4}$	$\frac{5\pi}{4}$	$\frac{7\pi}{4}$
$F(t)$	$(\frac{\sqrt{2}}{2}, \frac{\sqrt{2}}{2})$	$(-\frac{\sqrt{2}}{2}, \frac{\sqrt{2}}{2})$	$(-\frac{\sqrt{2}}{2}, -\frac{\sqrt{2}}{2})$	$(\frac{\sqrt{2}}{2}, -\frac{\sqrt{2}}{2})$
$f(t)$	$\frac{\sqrt{2}}{2}$	$-\frac{\sqrt{2}}{2}$	$-\frac{\sqrt{2}}{2}$	$\frac{\sqrt{2}}{2}$
$g(t)$	$\frac{\sqrt{2}}{2}$	$\frac{\sqrt{2}}{2}$	$-\frac{\sqrt{2}}{2}$	$-\frac{\sqrt{2}}{2}$

4 a Equilateral. The coordinates of P are $(\frac{1}{2}, \frac{\sqrt{3}}{2})$.

b See the graph for part a.

c

t	$\frac{\pi}{3}$	$\frac{2\pi}{3}$	$\frac{4\pi}{3}$	$\frac{5\pi}{3}$
$F(t)$	$(\frac{1}{2}, \frac{\sqrt{3}}{2})$	$(-\frac{1}{2}, \frac{\sqrt{3}}{2})$	$(-\frac{1}{2}, -\frac{\sqrt{3}}{2})$	$(\frac{1}{2}, -\frac{\sqrt{3}}{2})$
$f(t)$	$\frac{1}{2}$	$-\frac{1}{2}$	$-\frac{1}{2}$	$\frac{1}{2}$
$g(t)$	$\frac{\sqrt{3}}{2}$	$\frac{\sqrt{3}}{2}$	$-\frac{\sqrt{3}}{2}$	$-\frac{\sqrt{3}}{2}$

5 a Equilateral. The coordinates of P are $(\frac{\sqrt{3}}{2}, \frac{1}{2})$.

b See the graph for part a.

c

t	$\frac{\pi}{6}$	$\frac{5\pi}{6}$	$\frac{7\pi}{6}$	$\frac{11\pi}{6}$
$F(t)$	$(\frac{\sqrt{3}}{2}, \frac{1}{2})$	$(-\frac{\sqrt{3}}{2}, \frac{1}{2})$	$(-\frac{\sqrt{3}}{2}, -\frac{1}{2})$	$(\frac{\sqrt{3}}{2}, -\frac{1}{2})$
$f(t)$	$\frac{\sqrt{3}}{2}$	$-\frac{\sqrt{3}}{2}$	$-\frac{\sqrt{3}}{2}$	$\frac{\sqrt{3}}{2}$
$g(t)$	$\frac{1}{2}$	$\frac{1}{2}$	$-\frac{1}{2}$	$-\frac{1}{2}$

6 a The domain is the set of nonnegative real numbers. The range is $\{y \mid -1 \leq y \leq 1\}$.

b

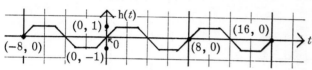
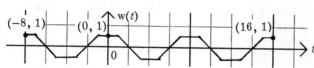

c See the graph for part b

d $(1, -1); (0, -1); (-1, -1)$

e

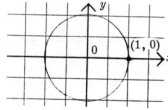

f

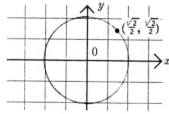

Pages 433-434

1 a $\sin t = 0;\ \cos t = 1.$

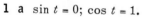

b $\sin t = -\frac{\sqrt{3}}{2};\ \cos t = \frac{1}{2}.$

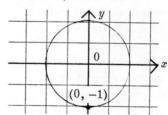

c $\sin t = \frac{\sqrt{2}}{2};\ \cos t = \frac{\sqrt{2}}{2}.$

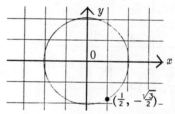

d $\sin t = -1;\ \cos t = 0.$

e $\sin t = \frac{\sqrt{2}}{2};\ \cos t = -\frac{\sqrt{2}}{2}.$

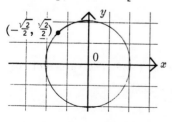

f $\sin t = \frac{\sqrt{3}}{2};\ \cos t = -\frac{1}{2}.$

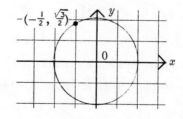

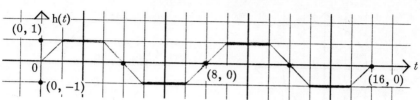

g $\sin t = -\frac{\sqrt{3}}{2}; \cos t = -\frac{1}{2}.$

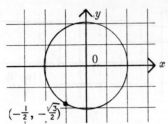

h $\sin t = 0; \cos t = -1.$

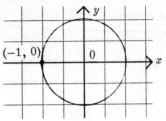

i $\sin t = 1; \cos t = 0.$

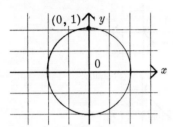

j $\sin t = -\frac{1}{2}; \cos t = \frac{\sqrt{3}}{2}.$

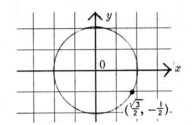

k $\sin t = -\frac{1}{2}; \cos t = -\frac{\sqrt{3}}{2}.$

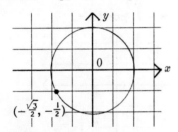

l $\sin t = \frac{1}{2}; \cos t = \frac{\sqrt{3}}{2}.$

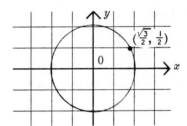

2 a $\frac{3}{5}$ **b** $\frac{12}{13}$ **c** $-\frac{8}{17}$ **d** $\frac{2\sqrt{2}}{3}$ **e** $-\frac{4}{5}$ **f** $\frac{\sqrt{7}}{4}$

3 a $\sin t$ decreases from 1 to 0.
  b $\sin t$ decreases from 0 to -1.
  c $\sin t$ increases from -1 to 0.

4 a $\sin t$ decreases from 1 to 0.
  b $\sin t$ increases from 0 to 1.
  c $\sin t$ decreases from 0 to -1.
  d $\sin t$ increases from -1 to 0.

5 a $\{\frac{7}{6}\pi, \frac{11}{6}\pi\}$ **d** $\{t \mid 0 \leqq t \leqq \frac{\pi}{4} \text{ or } \frac{5\pi}{4} \leqq t \leqq 2\pi\}$

  b $\{\frac{1}{3}\pi, \frac{5}{3}\pi\}$ **e** $\{\frac{\pi}{2}, \pi\}$

  c $\{t \mid \frac{\pi}{4} < t < \frac{5}{4}\pi\}$ **f** ϕ

6 a The values of $\sin\left(\frac{\pi}{2} + t\right)$ and $\sin\left(\frac{\pi}{2} - t\right)$ are the same. The values of $\cos\left(\frac{\pi}{2} + t\right)$ and $\cos\left(\frac{\pi}{2} - t\right)$ are additive inverses of each other.

b The values of sin $(\pi + t)$ and sin $(\pi - t)$ are additive inverses of each other. The values of cos $(\pi + t)$ and cos $(\pi - t)$ are the same.

7 a The values of sin t and sin $(\pi - t)$ are the same. The values of cos t and cos $(\pi - t)$ are additive inverses of each other.

b $\sin t = -\cos \left(\frac{\pi}{2} + t\right)$; $\cos t = \sin \left(\frac{\pi}{2} + t\right)$.

Pages 441-442

1 a and b

Function	Period	Greatest ordinate
sine	2π	1
g	2π	2
G	2π	$\frac{1}{2}$

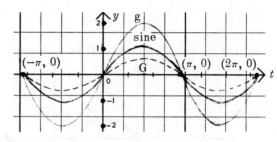

c and d

Function	Period	Greatest ordinate
sine	2π	1
h	2π	1
H	2π	$\frac{3}{2}$

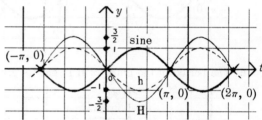

2 a and b

Function	Period	Greatest ordinate
sine	2π	1
ϕ	π	1
Φ	4π	1

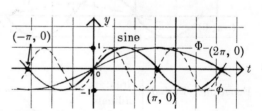

c and d

Function	Period	Greatest ordinate
sine	2π	1
h	2π	1
H	$\frac{2}{3}\pi$	1

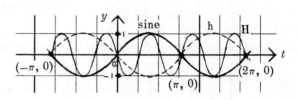

3 a

Function	Period	Greatest ordinate
sine	2π	1
g	π	$\frac{1}{2}$

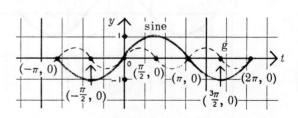

b The period of the graph of function h is 4π; the greatest ordinate is 2.

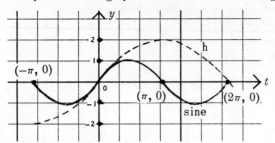

c The period of the graph of G is π; its greatest ordinate is 2.

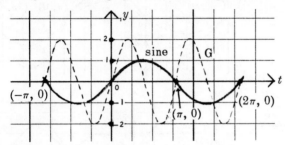

d The period of the graph of H is 4π; its greatest ordinate is $\frac{1}{2}$.

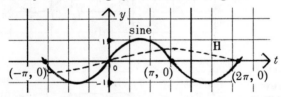

4 a

Function	Period	Greatest ordinate
sine	2π	1
h	2π	1

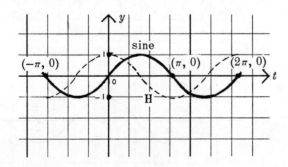

b The period of the graph of H is 2π; its greatest ordinate is 1.

5 a The period of the graph of g is 2π; its greatest ordinate is 2.

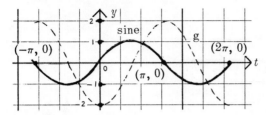

b The period of the graph of h is 2π; its greatest ordinate is $\frac{1}{2}$.

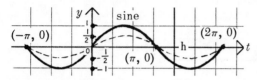

c The period of the graph of G is π; its greatest ordinate is 1.

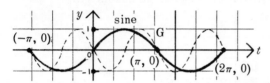

d The period of the graph of H is π; its greatest ordinate is $\frac{1}{2}$.

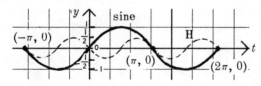

6 a The graph of the sine function is symmetric with respect to every line whose equation is of the form $t = (n + \frac{1}{2})\pi$, where n is an integer.

b The graph of the sine function is symmetric with respect to every point in the t-axis of the form $(n\pi, 0)$, where n is an integer.

Pages 445-446

1 a The fundamental period of g is 2π; its greatest ordinate is $\frac{3}{2}$.

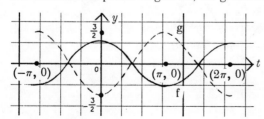

b The fundamental period of h is 4; its greatest ordinate is 1.

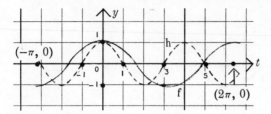

c The fundamental period of G is 2π; its greatest ordinate is 1.

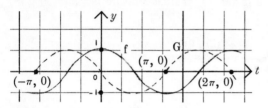

d The fundamental period of H is π; its greatest ordinate is $\frac{1}{2}$.

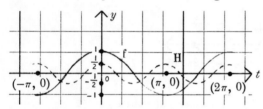

2 a

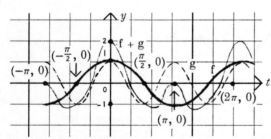

b

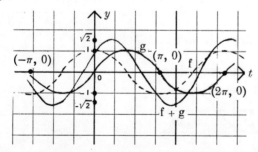

3 a $\cos t$ decreases from 0 to -1.

   b $\cos t$ increases from -1 to 0.

   c $\cos t$ increases from 0 to 1.

4 a $\{t \mid \frac{3}{2}\pi \leq t \leq 2\pi\}$ **c** $\{t \mid 0 \leq t \leq \frac{\pi}{2}\}$

   b $\{t \mid \frac{\pi}{2} \leq t \leq \pi\}$ **d** $\{t \mid \pi \leq t \leq \frac{3\pi}{2}\}$

5 a The fundamental period is 2π; the greatest ordinate is 5.

   b The fundamental period is 3π; the greatest ordinate is 1.

   c The fundamental period is 2π; the greatest ordinate is 1.5.

   d The fundamental period is $\frac{2\pi}{\alpha}$; the greatest ordinate is $|A|$.

6 a 1   **b** $\frac{1}{3}$ **c** π **d** α

7 a 1) $\triangle OQ'Q$ and $OP'P$ are right triangles

      2) $\sphericalangle Q'QO \cong \sphericalangle POP'$ because these two angles are both complements of $\sphericalangle Q'OQ$.

      3) $d(O, P) = d(O, Q) = 1$.

      4) $\therefore \triangle OQ'Q \cong \triangle OP'P$.

      5) $\therefore d(O, P') = d(Q', Q)$.

      6) $\therefore \cos t = \sin (t + \frac{\pi}{2})$

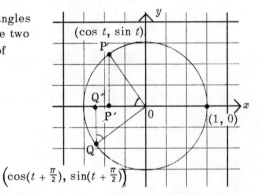

   b The steps of this proof are identical to those in part a.

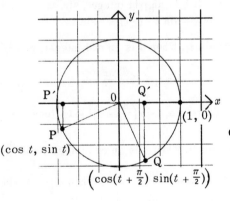

   c The steps of this proof are identical to those in part a.

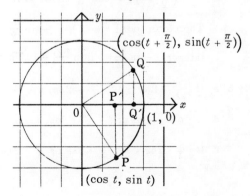

d If the point corresponding to t is $(1, 0)$, then the point corresponding to $t + \frac{\pi}{2}$ is $(0, 1)$. If the point corresponding to t is $(0, 1)$, then the point corresponding to $t + \frac{\pi}{2}$ is $(-1, 0)$. If the point corresponding to t is $(-1, 0)$, then the point corresponding to $t + \frac{\pi}{2}$ is $(0, -1)$. If the point corresponding to t is $(0, -1)$, then the point corresponding to $t + \frac{\pi}{2}$ is $(1, 0)$. In all four cases, $\cos t = \sin (t + \frac{\pi}{2})$.

Pages 448-449

1 a $\cos t$ **b** $-\sin t$ **c** $-\sin t$ **d** $-\cos t$ **e** $-\cos t$ **f** $\sin t$

2 a $\sin (t_1 + t_2) = \frac{63}{65}$; $\cos (t_1 + t_2) = -\frac{16}{65}$.

   b $\sin (t_1 + t_2) = \frac{77}{85}$; $\cos (t_1 + t_2) = -\frac{36}{85}$.

   c $\sin (t_1 + t_2) = \frac{\sqrt{6} + \sqrt{2}}{4}$; $\cos (t_1 + t_2) = \frac{\sqrt{6} - \sqrt{2}}{4}$.

   d $\sin (t_1 + t_2) = \frac{7 + 24\sqrt{3}}{50}$; $\cos (t_1 + t_2) = \frac{7\sqrt{3} - 24}{50}$;

3 $\sin \frac{5\pi}{12} = \sin (\frac{\pi}{4} + \frac{\pi}{6}) = \frac{\sqrt{6} + \sqrt{2}}{4}$; $\cos \frac{5\pi}{12} = \cos (\frac{\pi}{4} + \frac{\pi}{6}) = \frac{\sqrt{6} - \sqrt{2}}{4}$.

4 $\sin \frac{7\pi}{12} = \sin (\frac{\pi}{4} + \frac{\pi}{3}) = \frac{\sqrt{2} + \sqrt{6}}{4}$; $\cos \frac{7\pi}{12} = \cos (\frac{\pi}{4} + \frac{\pi}{3}) = \frac{\sqrt{2} - \sqrt{6}}{4}$.

5 a $\cos (n\pi + t) = \cos n\pi \cos t - \sin n\pi \sin t = \cos n\pi \cos t - 0 \cdot \sin t = \cos n\pi \cos t$. If n is an odd integer, then $\cos n\pi = -1$; hence, $\cos n\pi \cos t = -1 \cdot \cos t = -\cos t$.

   b $\sin (n\pi + t) = \sin n\pi \cos t + \sin t \cos n\pi$. If n is an odd integer, $\sin n\pi = 0$ and $\cos n\pi = -1$. Hence, $\sin (n\pi + t) = 0 \cdot \cos t + \sin t \cdot (-1) = -\sin t$.

   c $|\sin \left(\frac{n\pi}{2} + t\right)| = |\sin \frac{n\pi}{2} \cos t + \cos \frac{n\pi}{2} \sin t|$. When n is an odd integer, $\cos \frac{n\pi}{2} =$ 0. Hence, $|\sin \left(\frac{n\pi}{2} + t\right)| = |\sin \frac{n\pi}{2} \cos t + 0 \cdot \sin t| = |\sin \frac{n\pi}{2} \cos t| = |\sin \frac{n\pi}{2}| \, |\cos t|$. When n is an odd integer, $|\sin \frac{n\pi}{2}| = 1$. Therefore, $|\sin \left(\frac{n\pi}{2} + t\right)| = 1 \cdot |\cos t| = |\cos t|$.

   d $|\cos \left(\frac{n\pi}{2} + t\right)| = |\cos \frac{n\pi}{2} \cos t - \sin \frac{n\pi}{2} \sin t|$. When n is an odd integer, $\cos \frac{n\pi}{2} = 0$. Therefore, $|\cos \left(\frac{n\pi}{2} + t\right)| = |-\sin \frac{n\pi}{2} \sin t| = |-\sin \frac{n\pi}{2}| \, |\sin t|$. When n is an odd integer, $|-\sin \frac{n\pi}{2}| = |\sin \frac{n\pi}{2}| = 1$. Therefore, $|\cos \left(\frac{n\pi}{2} + t\right)| = 1 \cdot |\sin t| = |\sin t|$.

6 a $\{t \mid \frac{7\pi}{6} + 2n\pi \leqq t \leqq \frac{11\pi}{6} + 2n\pi, n \in \mathcal{I}\}$

   b $\{t \mid t = \frac{\pi}{4} + 2n\pi \text{ or } t = \frac{7\pi}{4} + 2n\pi, n \in \mathcal{I}\}$

   c $\{t \mid \frac{\pi}{3} + 2n\pi < t < \frac{2\pi}{3} + 2n\pi \text{ or } \frac{4\pi}{3} + 2n\pi < t < \frac{5\pi}{3} + 2n\pi, n \in \mathcal{I}\}$

d $\{t \mid t = \frac{\pi}{2} + 2n\pi$ or $t = \frac{3\pi}{2} + 2n\pi$ or $t = \frac{2\pi}{3} + 2n\pi$ or $t = \frac{4\pi}{3} + 2n\pi, \ n \in \mathcal{I}\}$

e $\{t \mid t = n\pi$ or $t = \frac{\pi}{3} + 2n\pi$ or $t = \frac{2\pi}{3} + 2n\pi, \ n \in \mathcal{I}\}$

f $\{t \mid t = (2n + 1)\frac{\pi}{2}$ or $t = \frac{\pi}{4} + 2n\pi$ or $t = \frac{7\pi}{4} + 2n\pi, \ n \in \mathcal{I}\}$

g $\{t \mid t = (2n + 1)\frac{\pi}{2}$ or $t = \frac{3\pi}{4} + 2n\pi$ or $t = \frac{7\pi}{4} + 2n\pi, \ n \in \mathcal{I}\}$

h $\emptyset$

Pages 452-454

1 a Quadrant II

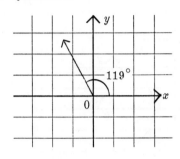

b Quadrant I

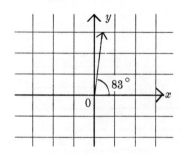

c Quadrant III

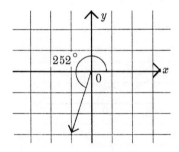

d Quadrant IV

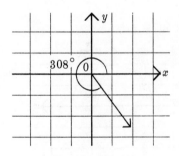

e Quadrant II

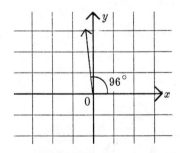

f Quadrant III

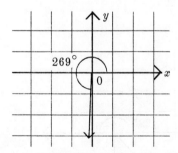

2 a Quadrant I
b Quadrant III

c Quadrant IV
d Quadrant II

3 **a** $\sin 30° = \frac{1}{2}$;

$\cos 30° = \frac{\sqrt{3}}{2}$.

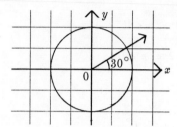

b $\sin 240° = -\frac{\sqrt{3}}{2}$;

$\cos 240° = -\frac{1}{2}$.

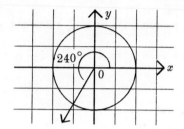

c $\sin 330° = -\frac{1}{2}$;

$\cos 330° = \frac{\sqrt{3}}{2}$.

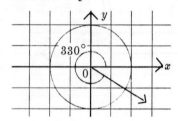

d $\sin 90° = 1$;

$\cos 90° = 0$.

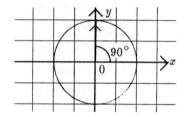

e $\sin 60° = \frac{\sqrt{3}}{2}$;

$\cos 60° = \frac{1}{2}$.

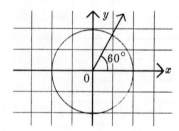

f $\sin 150° = \frac{1}{2}$;

$\cos 150° = -\frac{\sqrt{3}}{2}$.

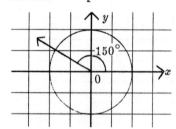

g $\sin 225° = -\frac{\sqrt{2}}{2}$;

$\cos 225° = -\frac{\sqrt{2}}{2}$.

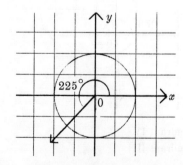

h $\sin 300° = -\frac{\sqrt{3}}{2}$;

$\cos 300° = \frac{1}{2}$.

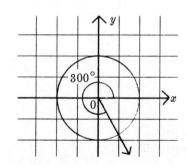

i $\sin 45° = \frac{\sqrt{2}}{2}$; $\cos 45° = \frac{\sqrt{2}}{2}$.

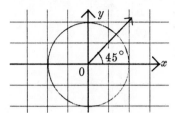

j $\sin 120° = \frac{\sqrt{3}}{2}$; $\cos 120° = -\frac{1}{2}$.

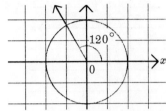

k $\sin 210° = -\frac{1}{2}$; $\cos 210° = -\frac{\sqrt{3}}{2}$.

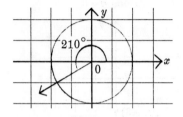

l $\sin 315° = -\frac{\sqrt{2}}{2}$; $\cos 315° = \frac{\sqrt{2}}{2}$.

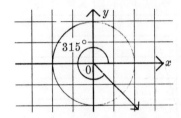

4 a 150° **c** 315° **e** 120° **g** 45°
b 330° **d** 225° **f** 120° **h** 225°

5 a $\sin \theta = \frac{4}{5}$; $\cos \theta = -\frac{3}{5}$.

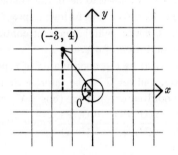

b $\sin \theta = -\frac{5}{13}$; $\cos \theta = \frac{12}{13}$.

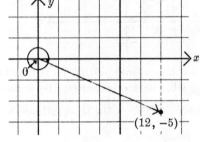

c $\sin \theta = \frac{15}{17}$; $\cos \theta = \frac{8}{17}$.

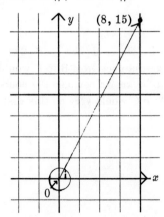

d $\sin \theta = -\frac{24}{25}$; $\cos \theta = -\frac{7}{25}$.

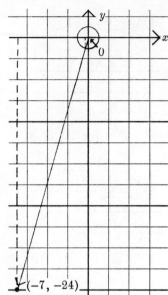

(-7, -24)

e $\sin \theta = 1$; $\cos \theta = 0$.

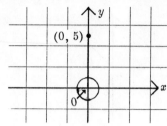

(0, 5)

f $\sin \theta = -1$; $\cos \theta = 0$.

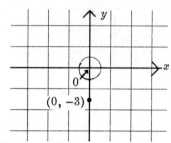

(0, -3)

6

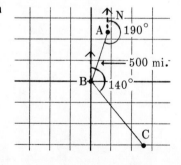

(a, b) P Q (cos $\frac{1}{3}$A, sin $\frac{1}{3}$A)

P' Q' 0

In the diagram at the left, the terminal side of $\frac{1}{3}$A is shown to be in the second quadrant. However, the following proof applies no matter which quadrant contains the terminal side of $\frac{1}{3}$A.

Let (a, b) be the coordinates of a point P in the terminal side of $\frac{1}{3}$A in standard position, and let Q be the intersection of ray OP with the unit circle. By definition, the coordinates of Q are (cos $\frac{1}{3}$A°, sin $\frac{1}{3}$A°). Since $\triangle OP'P \sim \triangle OQ'Q$, it follows that $\dfrac{d(P', P)}{d(Q', Q)} = \dfrac{d(O, P')}{d(O, Q')} = \dfrac{d(O, P)}{d(O, Q)}$. Since d(O, P) =

$\sqrt{a^2 + b^2}$, we have $\dfrac{a}{\cos \frac{1}{3}A°} = \dfrac{b}{\sin \frac{1}{3}A°} = \dfrac{\sqrt{a^2 + b^2}}{1}$. By solving this proportion we get

$\sin \frac{1}{3}A° = \dfrac{b}{\sqrt{a^2 + b^2}}$ and $\cos \frac{1}{3}A° = \dfrac{a}{\sqrt{a^2 + b^2}}$.

7 a $225°$ **b** $315°$ **c** $0°$ **d** $135°$ **e** $45°$ **f** $180°$ **g** $165°$ **h** $295°$

8 a

N
A 190°
500 mi.
B 140°
C

b No. The distance from B to C would have to be known because the course from A to C would vary as this distance varies.

Pages 457-458

1 Since a radian measure of 2π radians is equal to $360°$, we have $\frac{2\pi}{360} = \frac{y}{x}$, or $\frac{\pi}{180} = \frac{y}{x}$.

2 a $\frac{\pi}{6}$ c $\frac{10\pi}{9}$ e $\frac{4\pi}{15}$ g $\frac{5\pi}{4}$ i $\frac{5\pi}{12}$ k $\frac{3\pi}{2}$

   b $-\frac{2\pi}{3}$ d $-\frac{19\pi}{12}$ f $-\frac{3\pi}{4}$ h $-\frac{7\pi}{4}$ j $-\frac{7\pi}{9}$ l $-\frac{11\pi}{6}$

3 a $15°$ d $-450°$ g $225°$ j $-160°$

   b $-150°$ e $50°$ h $-306°$ k $240°$

   c $210°$ f $-115°$ i $84°$ l $-324°$

4 200π radians; $36,000°$

5

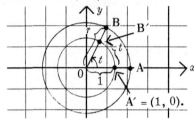

The length of the arc is rt units. In the diagram at the left, sector AOB is similar to sector A′OB′; hence, $\frac{\text{length of arc AB}}{t} = \frac{r}{1}$. Thus, the length of arc AB is rt units.

6 a 7.5 inches   b 6.0 inches

7 a 1.5 radians   b 2.25 radians

8 60 miles per hour is equivalent to 88 ft. per sec. Since the circumference of the wheel is 3π, the number of revolutions per second is $\frac{88}{3\pi}$, which, to the nearest integer, is 9 revolutions per second.

9 $\frac{\text{area of sector AOB}}{\text{area of circle O}} = \frac{t}{2\pi}$; hence, $\frac{\text{area of sector AOB}}{\pi r^2} = \frac{t}{2\pi}$. Therefore, the area of sector AOB is $\frac{\pi r^2 t}{2\pi}$, or $\frac{1}{2}r^2 t$.

Pages 460-461

1 a $c = 50$; $a = 16°$; $\beta = 74°$.   c $c \approx 52$; $b \approx 39$; $\beta \approx 48°$.

   b $a = 6$; $a \approx 67°$; $\beta \approx 23°$.   d $a \approx 18$; $b \approx 35$; $a = 62°$.

2 Approximately 372 ft.

3 Approximately $36°$

4 Approximately 14 inches

5 Approximately $96°$

6 In $\triangle ABC$, $\sin a = \frac{d(B, C)}{1} = d(B, C)$. Since $\overline{AB} \parallel \overline{CD}$, $\angle ABC \cong \angle BCD$, and since the measure of $\angle BCD$ is $90 - a$, that of $\angle CBD$ is a. In $\triangle BCD$, $\sin \angle CBD° = \frac{d(C, D)}{d(B, C)}$. That is, $\sin a = \frac{d(C, D)}{\sin a}$, which means that $d(C, D) = (\sin a)^2$.

7

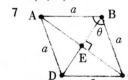

Let ABCD be a rhombus such that $d(A, B) = a$ and the measure of $\angle ABC$ is θ. Since diagonals $\overline{AC}$ and $\overline{BD}$ are perpendicular bisectors of each other and are also bisectors of the angles of the rhombus, $\triangle ABE$ is a right triangle, and the measure of $\angle ABE$ is $\frac{\theta}{2}$. In $\triangle ABE$, $\sin \frac{\theta}{2} = \frac{d(A, E)}{a}$. Therefore, $d(A, E) = a \sin \frac{\theta}{2}$, which means that the length of $\overline{AC}$ is $2a \sin \frac{\theta}{2}$.

Also, in $\triangle ABE$, $\cos \dfrac{\theta}{2} = \dfrac{d(E, B)}{a}$. Therefore, $d(E, B) = a \cos \dfrac{\theta}{2}$, which means that the length of $\overline{DB}$ is $2a \cos \dfrac{\theta}{2}$.

8 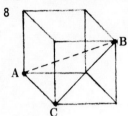 Let $\overline{AB}$ be a diagonal of the cube and $\overline{CB}$ be a diagonal of one of its faces. Let the length of $\overline{AC}$, an edge of the cube, be e. Then the length of $\overline{CB}$ is $e\sqrt{2}$ and that of $\overline{AB}$ is $e\sqrt{3}$. Let the measure of $\angle CAB$ be a. Then, in right triangle ABC,

$$\cos a = \frac{d(A, C)}{d(A, B)} = \frac{e}{e\sqrt{3}} = \frac{1}{\sqrt{3}} = \frac{\sqrt{3}}{3} = .577 \text{ (to three decimal}$$

places). Hence, $a = 55^\circ$ to the nearest degree.

Pages 463-464

1 a $c \approx 14$.   b $b \approx 20$.   c $a \approx 6.5$.

2 a $a \approx 83^\circ$.   b $\beta \approx 125^\circ$.   c $\gamma \approx 98^\circ$.

3 Approximately 588 ft.

4 102° and 78°

5 52 miles

6 23

7 In deriving the Law of Cosines we used the distance formula, and in deriving the distance formula, we used the Pythagorean theorem. Hence, to use the Law of Cosines to derive the Pythagorean theorem would involve circular reasoning.

Pages 466-468

1 a $b \approx 20$.   b $b \approx 22$.   c $\beta = 39^\circ$.

2 a None   b One

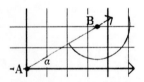 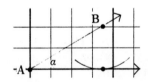

c Two   d Two

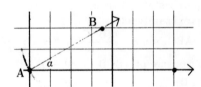

e One

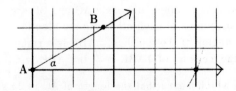

3 **a** None   **b** None   **c** None   **d** One   **e** One

All diagrams are combined in the figure below.

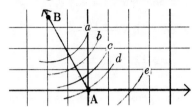

4 **a** $(0° < a < 90°$ and $a = c \sin \alpha)$ or $(0° < a < 90°$ and $a \geq c)$ or $(90° < a < 180°$ and $a > c).$

  b $0° < a < 90°$ and $c \sin \alpha < a < c.$

5 **a** One   **b** Two   **c** One   **d** Two

6 $025°$, or N $- 25° -$ E.

7 Approximately 36 miles

8 29,700 sq. ft.

9 The area of sector AOB is $\frac{1}{2}r^2 t$, as was shown in the answer to exercise 9, page 457. The area of $\triangle$AOB is $\frac{1}{2}r^2 \sin t$. Therefore, the area of the shaded portion is $\frac{1}{2}r^2 t - \frac{1}{2}r^2 \sin t = \frac{1}{2}r^2(t - \sin t)$.

10 Let β_1 denote the measure of $\sphericalangle$ADC and let β_2 denote the measure of $\sphericalangle$ADB. Then, in $\triangle$ABD, $\dfrac{\sin \alpha_2}{r} = \dfrac{\sin \beta_2}{c}$. Hence, $\sin \alpha_2 = \dfrac{r \sin \beta_2}{c}$. In $\triangle$ADC, $\dfrac{\sin \alpha_1}{s} = \dfrac{\sin \beta_1}{b}$. Therefore, $\sin \alpha_1 = \dfrac{s \sin \beta_1}{b}$. Hence, $\dfrac{\sin \alpha_2}{\sin \alpha_1} = \dfrac{\dfrac{r \sin \beta_2}{c}}{\dfrac{s \sin \beta_1}{b}} = \dfrac{br \sin \beta_2}{cs \sin \beta_1}$.

Since $\sphericalangle$ADC and $\sphericalangle$ADB are supplementary, $\beta_1 = \pi - \beta_2$ so that $\sin \beta_1 = \sin \beta_2$. Therefore, $\dfrac{\sin \alpha_2}{\sin \alpha_1} = \dfrac{br}{cs}$.

Pages 471-472

1 **a** $\sin(\pi - t) = \sin \pi \cos t - \sin t \cos \pi = 0 - (-1) \sin t = \sin t.$

  b $\cos(\pi - t) = \cos \pi \cos t + \sin \pi \sin t = (-1) \cos t + 0 = -\cos t.$

  c $\sin\left(\frac{3\pi}{2} - t\right) = \sin \frac{3\pi}{2} \cos t - \cos \frac{3\pi}{2} \sin t = (-1) \cos t - 0 = -\cos t.$

  d $\cos\left(\frac{3\pi}{2} - t\right) = \cos \frac{3\pi}{2} \cos t + \sin \frac{3\pi}{2} \sin t = 0 + (-1) \sin t = -\sin t.$

2 $\cos 2t = \cos^2 t - \sin^2 t$ [Identity IV]

$\qquad = \cos^2 t - (1 - \cos^2 t)$ [Identity III]

$\qquad = 2 \cos^2 t - 1.$

$\cos 2t = \cos^2 t - \sin^2 t$ [Identity IV]

$\qquad = 1 - \sin^2 t - \sin^2 t$ [Identity III]

$\qquad = 1 - 2 \sin^2 t.$

3 **a** $\cos 2(\frac{1}{2}\theta) = 1 - 2 \sin^2 \frac{1}{2}\theta.$

   $\therefore 2 \sin^2 \frac{1}{2}\theta = 1 - \cos \theta.$

   $\therefore \sin^2 \frac{1}{2}\theta = \dfrac{1 - \cos \theta}{2}.$

   $\therefore |\sin \frac{1}{2}\theta| = \sqrt{\dfrac{1 - \cos \theta}{2}}.$

b $\cos 2(\frac{1}{2}\theta) = 2 \cos^2 \frac{1}{2}\theta - 1.$

   $\therefore 2 \cos^2 \frac{1}{2}\theta = 1 + \cos \theta.$

   $\therefore \cos^2 \frac{1}{2}\theta = \dfrac{1 + \cos \theta}{2}.$

   $\therefore |\cos \frac{1}{2}\theta| = \sqrt{\dfrac{1 + \cos \theta}{2}}.$

4 **a** $\sin (t_1 + t_2) + \sin (t_1 - t_2) = \sin t_1 \cos t_2 + \sin t_2 \cos t_1 + \sin t_1 \cos t_2 - \sin t_2 \cos t_1$

[Identities II and VII]

$$= 2 \sin t_1 \cos t_2.$$

b $\sin (t_1 + t_2) - \sin (t_1 - t_2) = \sin t_1 \cos t_2 + \sin t_2 \cos t_1 - \sin t_1 \cos t_2 + \sin t_2 \cos t_1$

[Identities II and VII]

$$= 2 \sin t_2 \cos t_1$$
$$= 2 \cos t_1 \sin t_2.$$

5 **a** If $t_1 + t_2 = \alpha$ and $t_1 - t_2 = \beta$, then $t_1 = \dfrac{\alpha + \beta}{2}$ and $t_2 = \dfrac{\alpha - \beta}{2}$. Since $\sin (t_1 + t_2) + \sin (t_1 - t_2) = 2(\sin t_1) \cos t_2$, we have $\sin \alpha + \sin \beta = 2 \sin \dfrac{\alpha + \beta}{2} \cos \dfrac{\alpha - \beta}{2}$.

b In the identity $\sin (t_1 + t_2) - \sin (t_1 - t_2) = 2 \cos t_1 \sin t_2$, let $t_1 = \dfrac{\alpha + \beta}{2}$ and let $t_2 = \dfrac{\alpha - \beta}{2}$. Then $\sin \alpha - \beta = 2 \cos \dfrac{\alpha + \beta}{2} \sin \dfrac{\alpha - \beta}{2}$.

6 **a** $(\sin t + \cos t)^2 = \sin^2 t + 2 \sin t \cos t + \cos^2 t$

$$= 1 + 2 \sin t \cos t \quad \text{[Identity III]}$$
$$= 1 + \sin 2t. \quad \text{[Identity V]}$$

b $\dfrac{(1 + \sin t)^2}{\cos^2 t} = \dfrac{(1 + \sin t)^2}{(1 - \sin^2 t)} \quad \text{[Identity III]}$

$$= \dfrac{(1 + \sin t)^2}{(1 + \sin t)(1 - \sin t)}$$

$$= \dfrac{1 + \sin t}{1 - \sin t}.$$

c $\dfrac{\sin 2t + \sin t}{\cos 2t + \cos t + 1} = \dfrac{2 \sin t \cos t + \sin t}{2 \cos^2 t - 1 + \cos t + 1} \quad \text{[Identities V, IV, and III]}$

$$= \dfrac{\sin t (2 \cos t + 1)}{2 \cos^2 t + \cos t}$$

$$= \dfrac{\sin t (2 \cos t + 1)}{\cos t (2 \cos t + 1)}$$

$$= \dfrac{\sin t}{\cos t}.$$

d $\dfrac{\sin t}{1 + \cos t} + \dfrac{\cos t}{\sin t} = \dfrac{\sin^2 t + \cos t + \cos^2 t}{\sin t \,(1 + \cos t)}$

$$= \dfrac{1 + \cos t}{\sin t \,(1 + \cos t)} \quad \text{[Identity III]}$$

$$= \dfrac{1}{\sin t}$$

e $\cos\left(\tfrac{\pi}{6} - t\right) - \cos\left(\tfrac{\pi}{6} + t\right) = \cos\tfrac{\pi}{6}\cos t + \sin\tfrac{\pi}{6}\sin t - \cos\tfrac{\pi}{6}\cos t + \sin\tfrac{\pi}{6}\sin t$

$$\text{[Identities VI and I]}$$

$$= 2\,\sin\tfrac{\pi}{6}\,\sin t$$

$$= 2(\tfrac{1}{2})\,\sin t$$

$$= \sin t.$$

f $\dfrac{\sin 2t + 1}{\cos 2t} = \dfrac{2\,\sin t \cos t + 1}{\cos^2 t - \sin^2 t} \quad \text{[Identities V and IV]}$

$$= \dfrac{2\,\sin t \cos t + \sin^2 t + \cos^2 t}{\cos^2 t - \sin^2 t} \quad \text{[Identity III]}$$

$$= \dfrac{(\cos t + \sin t)^2}{(\cos t + \sin t)(\cos t - \sin t)}$$

$$= \dfrac{\cos t + \sin t}{\cos t - \sin t}$$

g $\dfrac{\cos (t_1 + t_2) + \cos (t_1 - t_2)}{2\,\cos t_2} = \dfrac{\cos t_1 \cos t_2 - \sin t_1 \sin t_2 + \cos t_1 \cos t_2 + \sin t_1 \sin t_2}{2\,\cos t_2}$

$$\text{[Identities I and VI]}$$

$$= \dfrac{2\,\cos t_1 \cos t_2}{2\,\cos t_2}$$

$$= \cos t_1.$$

h $\dfrac{\cos 2t}{\sin t} + \dfrac{\sin 2t}{\cos t} = \dfrac{\cos^2 t - \sin^2 t}{\sin t} + \dfrac{2\,\sin t \cos t}{\cos t} \quad \text{[Identities IV and V]}$

$$= \dfrac{\cos^2 t - \sin^2 t}{\sin t} + \dfrac{2\,\sin t}{1}$$

$$= \dfrac{\cos^2 t + \sin^2 t}{\sin t}$$

$$= \dfrac{1}{\sin t}. \quad \text{[Identity III]}$$

i $1 - 2\,\sin^2\dfrac{t}{2} = 1 - 2\left(1 - \cos^2\dfrac{t}{2}\right) \quad \text{[Identity III]}$

$$= 2\,\cos^2\dfrac{t}{2} - 1$$

$$= 2\left(\dfrac{1 + \cos t}{2}\right) - 1 \quad \text{[Half-angle formula]}$$

$$= 1 + \cos t - 1$$

$$= \cos t.$$

$$\text{j} \quad \frac{\cos^2 \frac{t}{2} - \cos t}{\sin^2 \frac{t}{2}} = \frac{\dfrac{1 + \cos t}{2} - \cos t}{\dfrac{1 - \cos t}{2}} \quad \text{[Half-angle formulas]}$$

$$= \frac{\dfrac{1 - \cos t}{2}}{\dfrac{1 - \cos t}{2}}$$

$$= 1.$$

7 a $\{t \mid t = \frac{\pi}{3} + 2n\pi \text{ or } t = \pi + 2n\pi \text{ or } t = \frac{5\pi}{3} + 2n\pi, \text{ where } n \in \mathcal{J}\}$

b $\{t \mid t = \frac{\pi}{6} + 2n\pi \text{ or } t = \frac{5\pi}{6} + 2n\pi, \text{ where } n \in \mathcal{J}\}$

c $\{t \mid t = \frac{n\pi}{2}, n \in \mathcal{J}\}$

d $\{t \mid t = \frac{2\pi}{3} + 2n\pi \text{ or } t = n\pi \text{ or } t = \frac{4\pi}{3} + 2n\pi, n \in \mathcal{J}\}$

e $\{t \mid t = n\pi, n \in \mathcal{J}\}$

f $\{t \mid t = \frac{\pi}{6} + 2n\pi \text{ or } t = \frac{5\pi}{6} + 2n\pi, \text{ or } t = n\pi, n \in \mathcal{J}\}$

Pages 479-481

1 a $y = -1.$ **b** $y = -x + \pi.$ **c** $y = \frac{\sqrt{2}}{2}x + \frac{\sqrt{2}}{2}(1 - \frac{\pi}{4}).$

2 a $y = -\frac{1}{2}x + \frac{\pi}{12} + \frac{\sqrt{3}}{2}.$ **b** $y = \frac{\sqrt{3}}{2}x - \frac{3 + 4\sqrt{3}\pi}{6}.$ **c** $y = -x - \frac{3\pi}{2}.$

3 a $(f + g)'(t) = 1 + \cos t.$ Assume that $(f + g)'(t) < 0$; that is, that $1 + \cos t < 0.$ This leads to $\cos t < -1$, which is impossible, since $-1 \leqq \cos t \leqq 1.$ Hence, it follows that $(f + g)'(t) \geqq 0$ for all t. This means that the graph of $f + g$ never decreases.

b (π, π)

c $(f + g)''(t) = -\sin t.$ Since $\sin t \geqq 0$ for $0 \leqq t \leqq \pi$, it follows that $-\sin t \leqq 0$ for $0 \leqq t \leqq \pi.$ This means that the graph of $f + g$ is concave downward for this interval. Since $\sin t \leqq 0$ for $\pi \leqq t \leqq 2\pi$, it follows that $-\sin t = (f + g)''(t) \geqq 0$ for this interval. Hence, the graph of $f + g$ is concave upward for this interval. The graph of $f + g$ is concave downward for the intervals $2n\pi \leqq t \leqq (2n + 1)\pi$, where $n \in \mathcal{J}.$ This graph is concave upward for the intervals $(2n + 1)\pi \leqq t \leqq 2(n + 1)\pi$, where $n \in \mathcal{J}.$

d $(f + g)(-t) = -t + \sin (-t) = -t - \sin t$ [since $-\sin t = \sin (-t)$]

$$= -(t + \sin t) = -(f + g)(t).$$

Therefore, $f + g$ is an odd function.

e

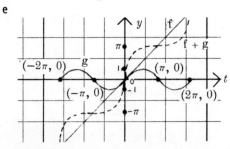

4 a

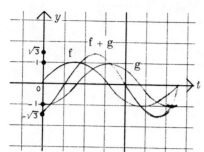

b $(f + g)'(t) = \cos t - (-\sin t) = \cos t + \sin t$. Hence, $(f + g)'(t) = 0$ if $\sin t + \cos t = 0$. This is true when $t = \frac{3\pi}{4}$ or $t = \frac{7\pi}{4}$.

c The graph of $f + g$ is increasing when $\cos t + \sin t \geq 0$, or $\sin t \geq -\cos t$. Hence, the graph is increasing for $0 \leq t \leq \frac{3}{4}\pi$ or $\frac{7}{4}\pi \leq t \leq 2\pi$. The graph of $f + g$ is decreasing when $\cos t + \sin t \leq 0$, or $\sin t \leq -\cos t$. Hence, the graph is decreasing for $\frac{3}{4}\pi \leq t \leq \frac{7}{4}\pi$.

d $(f + g)'' t = -\sin t + \cos t$. Hence, the graph of $f + g$ is concave upward when $-\sin t + \cos t \geq 0$; that is, when $\cos t \geq \sin t$. Therefore, the graph of $f + g$ is concave upward for the intervals $0 \leq t \leq \frac{\pi}{4}$ and $\frac{5\pi}{4} \leq t \leq 2\pi$. The graph is concave downward for the interval $\frac{\pi}{4} \leq t \leq \frac{5\pi}{4}$.

e See the graph for part a.

5 a $\dfrac{\sin \frac{1}{2}\epsilon}{\epsilon} = \dfrac{1}{2} \cdot \dfrac{\sin \frac{1}{2}\epsilon}{\frac{1}{2}\epsilon}$. As ϵ gets sufficiently close to 0, $\frac{1}{2}\epsilon$ gets close to 0.

Hence, $\dfrac{\sin \frac{1}{2}\epsilon}{\frac{1}{2}\epsilon}$ gets arbitrarily close to 1. Thus, $\dfrac{\sin \frac{1}{2}\epsilon}{\epsilon}$ gets arbitrarily close to $\frac{1}{2} \cdot 1 = \frac{1}{2}$.

b $\dfrac{\sin \epsilon}{3\epsilon} = \dfrac{\frac{1}{3} \cdot \sin \epsilon}{\epsilon}$. As ϵ gets sufficiently close to 0, $\dfrac{\sin \epsilon}{\epsilon}$ gets arbitrarily close to 1. Hence, $\dfrac{\sin \epsilon}{3\epsilon}$ gets arbitrarily close to $\frac{1}{3} \cdot 1 = \frac{1}{3}$.

c If $\epsilon = \pi - t$, then $\dfrac{\sin t}{\pi - t} = \dfrac{\sin (\pi - \epsilon)}{\epsilon}$. Since $\sin (\pi - \epsilon) = \sin \epsilon$, $\dfrac{\sin (\pi - \epsilon)}{\epsilon} = \dfrac{\sin \epsilon}{\epsilon}$. As t gets sufficiently close to π, $\epsilon = \pi - t$ also gets close to 0. Hence, $\dfrac{\sin t}{\pi - t} = \dfrac{\sin \epsilon}{\epsilon}$ gets arbitrarily close to 1.

6 a If t is close to t_0, but $t \neq t_0$, then $t = t_0 + \epsilon$, where $|\epsilon|$ is small. Then

$$\frac{\sin t - \sin t_0}{t - t_0} = \frac{\sin (t_0 + \epsilon) - \sin t_0}{(t_0 + \epsilon) - t_0} = \frac{\sin (t_0 + \epsilon) - \sin t_0}{\epsilon}.$$

b $\dfrac{\sin(t_0 + \epsilon) - \sin t_0}{\epsilon} = \dfrac{2\cos\left(\dfrac{t_0 + \epsilon + t_0}{2}\right)\sin\left(\dfrac{t_0 + \epsilon - t_0}{2}\right)}{\epsilon}$

$$= 2\cos\left(t_0 + \tfrac{\epsilon}{2}\right)\dfrac{\sin\frac{\epsilon}{2}}{\epsilon}$$

$$= \cos\left(t_0 + \tfrac{\epsilon}{2}\right) \cdot \dfrac{\sin\frac{\epsilon}{2}}{\frac{\epsilon}{2}}.$$

c It is close to $\cos t_0$. When ϵ is sufficiently close to 0, $\cos\left(t_0 + \tfrac{\epsilon}{2}\right)$ is close to

$\cos t_0$ and $\dfrac{\sin\frac{\epsilon}{2}}{\frac{\epsilon}{2}}$ is close to 1. Hence, $\cos\left(t_0 + \tfrac{\epsilon}{2}\right) \cdot \dfrac{\sin\frac{\epsilon}{2}}{\frac{\epsilon}{2}}$ is close to $\cos t_0 \cdot 1 =$

$\cos t_0$.

Chapter review
Pages 481-483

1 b	5 d	9 b	13 c	17 b
2 c	6 d	10 d	14 c	18 c
3 c	7 d	11 c	15 b	19 b
4 d	8 d	12 b	16 b	20 a

Cumulative review
Pages 483-484

1 a $\{x \mid x > 1\}$ **c** $\{x \mid x \leq -\tfrac{5}{4} \text{ or } x \geq 1\}$

  b $\{x \mid -2 \leq x \leq 6\}$ **d** $\{x \mid -\sqrt{3} < x < 0 \text{ or } x > \sqrt{3}\}$

2 a $P(0) = -9$ and $P(1) = 3$. Since $P(0)$ and $P(1)$ have
opposite signs, the graph of P must cross the x-axis
at least once between $x = 0$ and $x = 1$. Hence, P has
at least one zero between 0 and 1. $P(1) = 3$ and
$P(2) = -3$; hence, P has at least one zero between
1 and 2. $P(5) = -9$ and $P(6) = 33$; hence, P has at
least one zero between 5 and 6.

  b $\tfrac{1}{2}$

  c 1.7, 5.3

3 $y = 12x + 20$; $y = 12x - 7$. See graph 3.

4 $y = -2x + 9$; $y = 2x + 1$. See graph 4.

5 $f(x) = 3x^3 - 6x^2 + 5x - 8$.

3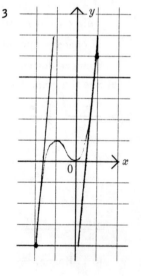

4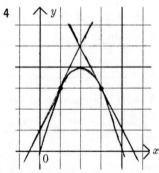

6 a $x^4 + 2x^2 - 8$

b Since $i^{4n} = 1$ for all $n \in \mathcal{I}^+$, $i^{4n} - 1 = 1 - 1 = 0$. Hence, $x - i$ is a factor of $x^{4n} - 1$. Similarly, $(-i)^{4n} = 1$ for all n in $\mathcal{I}^+$. Hence $(-i)^{4n} - 1 = 1 - 1 = 0$, which means that $x - (-i) = x + i$ is a factor of $x^{4n} - 1$.

7 a Fundamental period: 2π, greatest ordinate: 2

b Fundamental period: π; greatest ordinate: 1

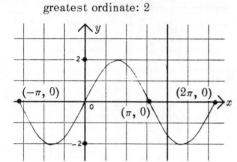

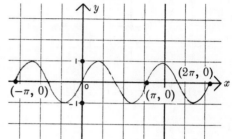

c, d The graphs for these two functions are the same. Fundamental period: 2π, greatest ordinate: 1

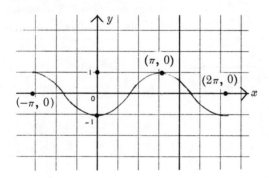

8 a

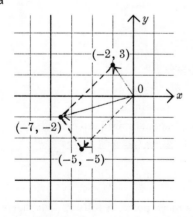

$(-2 + 3i) + (-5 - 5i) = -7 - 2i.$

b

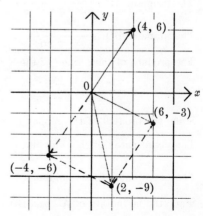

$(6 - 3i) - (4 + 6i) = 2 - 9i.$

c

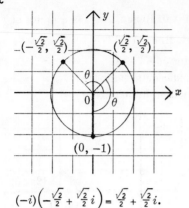

$$\left(-i\right)\left(-\frac{\sqrt{2}}{2}+\frac{\sqrt{2}}{2}\,i\right)=\frac{\sqrt{2}}{2}+\frac{\sqrt{2}}{2}\,i.$$

d

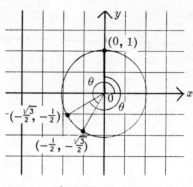

$$\left(-\frac{1}{2}-\frac{\sqrt{3}}{2}\,i\right)\left(-\frac{\sqrt{3}}{2}-\frac{1}{2}\,i\right)=i.$$

9 a

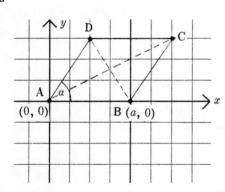

The coordinates of D are $(a\cos a,\ a\sin a)$. The coordinates of C are $(a + a\cos a,\ a\sin a)$

b The slope of $\overline{AC}$ is $\dfrac{a\sin a}{a + a\cos a} = \dfrac{\sin a}{1 + \cos a}.$

The slope of $\overline{BD}$ is $\dfrac{-a\sin a}{a - a\cos a} = \dfrac{-\sin a}{1 - \cos a}.$

The product of the slopes of these two diagonals is

$$\frac{\sin a}{1 + \cos a}\cdot\frac{-\sin a}{1 - \cos a} = \frac{-\sin^2 a}{1 - \cos^2 a} = \frac{-\sin^2 a}{\sin^2 a} = -1.$$

Since the product of the slopes is -1, the diagonals are perpendicular.

The coordinates of the midpoint of $\overline{AC}$ are $\dfrac{a + a\cos a}{2},\ \dfrac{a\sin a}{2}.$

The coordinates of the midpoint of $\overline{BD}$ are $\dfrac{a + a\cos a}{2},\ \dfrac{a\sin a}{2}.$

Since the midpoints of $\overline{AC}$ and $\overline{BD}$ are the same point, it follows that these two diagonals bisect each other.

10 $\frac{2}{\sqrt{3}}$ by $\frac{8}{3}$

Chapter 9
Other circular functions

1 a $\frac{\sqrt{3}}{3}$ or $\frac{1}{\sqrt{3}}$ **d** -1 **g** $-\frac{\sqrt{3}}{3}$ or $-\frac{1}{\sqrt{3}}$ **j** $\sqrt{3}$

  b $-\sqrt{3}$ **e** $-\sqrt{3}$ **h** $\sqrt{3}$ **k** -1

  c 1 **f** 1 **i** $-\frac{\sqrt{3}}{3}$ or $-\frac{1}{\sqrt{3}}$ **l** $\frac{\sqrt{3}}{3}$ or $\frac{1}{\sqrt{3}}$

2 From section 56/8, we have $\sin \alpha = \frac{a}{c}$

and $\cos \alpha = \frac{b}{c}$. Hence, $\tan \alpha = \frac{\sin \alpha}{\cos \alpha} = \frac{\frac{a}{c}}{\frac{b}{c}} = \frac{a}{b}$.

Similarly, $\sin \beta = \frac{b}{c}$ and $\cos \beta = \frac{a}{c}$, so that $\tan \beta = \frac{\frac{b}{c}}{\frac{a}{c}} = \frac{b}{a}$.

3 a $a \approx 25$.   **b** $\beta \approx 63°$.   **c** $a \approx 37°$.   **d** $a \approx 3.6$.

4 Approximately 1.3 miles   **5** $16°$ **6** Approximately 254 ft.

7 a $\tan (\pi - x) = \frac{\sin (\pi - x)}{\cos (\pi - x)} = \frac{\sin x}{-\cos x} = -\tan x$.

  b $\tan (\frac{\pi}{2} + x) = \dfrac{\sin (\frac{\pi}{2} + x)}{\cos (\frac{\pi}{2} + x)} = \dfrac{\sin \frac{\pi}{2} \cos x + \sin x \cos \frac{\pi}{2}}{\cos \frac{\pi}{2} \cos x - \sin \frac{\pi}{2} \sin x}$

$$= \frac{\cos x}{-\sin x}$$

$$= -\frac{1}{\tan x}.$$

  c $\tan (\frac{\pi}{2} - x) = \dfrac{\sin (\frac{\pi}{2} - x)}{\cos (\frac{\pi}{2} - x)} = \dfrac{\cos x}{\sin x} = \dfrac{1}{\tan x}$.

  d $\tan (\frac{3\pi}{2} + x) = \dfrac{\sin (\frac{3\pi}{2} + x)}{\cos (\frac{3\pi}{2} + x)} = \dfrac{\sin \frac{3\pi}{2} \cos x + \sin x \cos \frac{3\pi}{2}}{\cos \frac{3\pi}{2} \cos x - \sin \frac{3\pi}{2} \sin x}$

$$= \frac{-\cos x}{\sin x} = -\frac{1}{\tan x}.$$

8 a

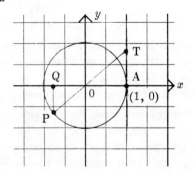

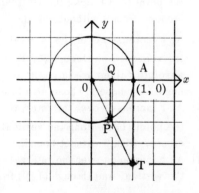

b Segments $\overline{PQ}$ and $\overline{AT}$ are perpendicular to the x-axis, so $\triangle OQP$ and $\triangle OAT$ are right triangles in all four cases. The vertical angles, $\sphericalangle QOP$ and $\sphericalangle AOT$, are congruent in all cases. Hence, in all four cases, $\triangle OQP \sim \triangle OAT$.

c Because $\triangle OQP \sim \triangle OAT$, $\dfrac{d(Q, P)}{d(A, T)} = \dfrac{d(O, Q)}{d(O, A)}$. By definition, $d(Q, P) = |\sin t|$,

$d(O, Q) = |\cos t|$, and $d(O, A) = 1$. Hence, $\dfrac{|\sin t|}{d(A, T)} = \dfrac{|\cos t|}{1}$ or $d(A, T) = \dfrac{|\sin t|}{|\cos t|} = |\tan t|$.

If P is in quadrant I or III, the ordinate of T is $d(A, T)$. In these quadrants $\dfrac{\sin t}{\cos t} > 0$, so that $\dfrac{|\sin t|}{|\cos t|} = \dfrac{\sin t}{\cos t} = \tan t$. Thus, in quadrant I and III, the ordinate of T is $\tan t$.

If P is in quadrant II or quadrant IV, the ordinate of T is $-d(A, T)$. In these quadrants, $\dfrac{\sin t}{\cos t} < 0$, so that $\dfrac{|\sin t|}{|\cos t|} = -\dfrac{\sin t}{\cos t} = -\tan t$. Therefore, in quadrants II and IV, the ordinate of T is $\tan t$.

d If $t = n\pi$, where $n \in \mathcal{I}$, then the point P is at $(-1, 0)$ or $(1, 0)$. In either case, the line through P and the origin intersects the vertical line through the point $A(1, 0)$ at the point $(1, 0)$. Hence, T has ordinate 0. However, $\tan n\pi = 0$ when $n \in \mathcal{I}$. Hence, the ordinate of T equals $\tan t$ when $t = n\pi$, with $n \in \mathcal{I}$.

e If $t = \dfrac{2n + 1}{2}\pi$, where $n \in \mathcal{I}$, the point P is at $(0, 1)$ or $(0, -1)$. In either case, the line through P and the origin is a vertical line that does not intersect the vertical line through $(1, 0)$. Hence, there is no intersection point T, so that the ordinate of T does not exist. Therefore, in these cases, $\tan t$ is not defined.

f [1] As t increases over the interval $0 \leq t < \dfrac{\pi}{2}$, the point T moves upward from $(1, 0)$ along the vertical line through this point. Hence $\tan t$ increases from 0 without bound in this interval.

[2] As t increases over the interval $\dfrac{\pi}{2} < t \leq \pi$, the point T moves upward along the vertical line through $(1, 0)$ from points that have negative ordinates whose absolute values are large up to the point $(1, 0)$. Hence, $\tan t$ increases from negative numbers whose absolute values are large to 0.

[3] As t increases over the interval $\pi \leq t < \dfrac{3\pi}{2}$, the point T moves upward from the point $(1, 0)$ along the vertical line through this point. Hence, $\tan t$ increases from 0 without bound.

[4] As t increases over the interval $\dfrac{3\pi}{2} < t \leq 2\pi$, the point T moves upward along the vertical line through $(1, 0)$ from points that have negative ordinates whose absolute values are large up to the point $(1, 0)$. Hence, $\tan t$ increases from negative numbers whose absolute values are large to 0.

[5] As t increases over the interval $-\pi \leq t < -\dfrac{\pi}{2}$, the point T moves upward from the point $(1, 0)$ along the vertical line through this point. Hence, $\tan t$ increases from 0 without bound.

[6] As t increases over the interval $-\dfrac{\pi}{2} < t \leq 0$, the point T moves upward along the vertical line through $(1, 0)$ from points that have negative ordinates whose

absolute values are large up to the point $(1, 0)$. Hence, tan t increases from negative numbers whose absolute values are large to 0.

Pages 492-493

1 a

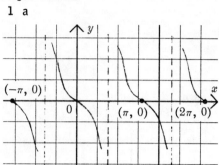

b

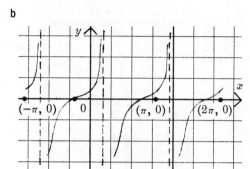

c

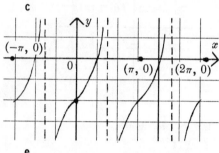

d

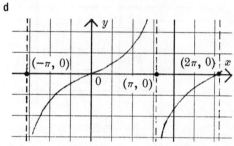

e

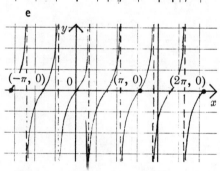

f

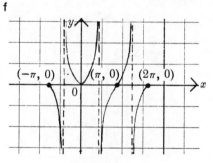

2 a $y = 2x + (1 - \frac{\pi}{2}).$

b $y = 4x + (\frac{4\pi}{3} - \sqrt{3}).$

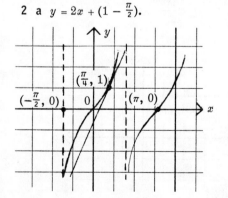

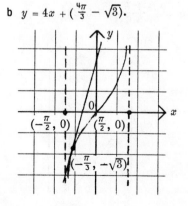

c $y = \frac{4}{3}x + (\frac{\sqrt{3}}{3} - \frac{2\pi}{9})$.

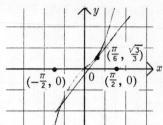

3 a $\tan \theta = \frac{12}{5} = 2.4000$.

$\theta \approx 67°$.

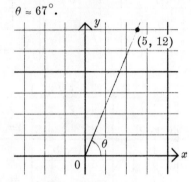

b $\tan \theta = -\frac{4}{6} \approx -.6667$.

$\theta \approx 326°$.

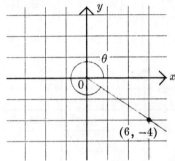

c $\tan \theta = \frac{7}{-5} = -1.4000$.

$\theta \approx 126°$.

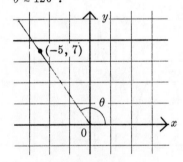

d $\tan \theta = \frac{2}{3} \approx .6667$.

$\theta \approx 214°$.

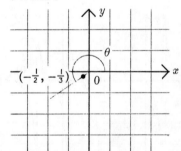

e $\tan \theta = \frac{-4.7}{3.6} \approx -1.3429$.

$\theta \approx 307°$.

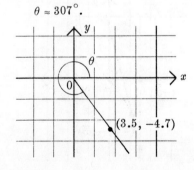

f $\tan \theta = \frac{6a^2}{-a^2} = -6$.

$\theta \approx 99°$.

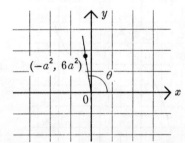

4 a $\tan 154° = -.4877$.

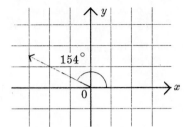

b $\tan 235° = 1.4281$.

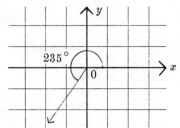

c $\tan 305° = -1.4281$.

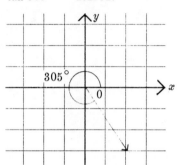

d $\tan (-20°) = -.3640$.

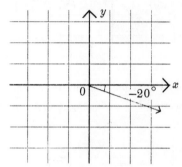

e $\tan (-190°) = -.1763$.

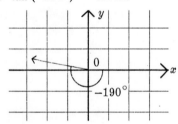

f $\tan 400° = .8391$.

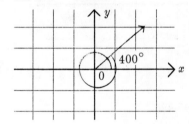

5 a $\tan x = \frac{5}{12}$.

c $\tan x = -\frac{15}{8}$.

b $\tan x = \frac{4}{3}$.

d $\tan x = -\frac{7}{24}$.

6 Let f be a strictly increasing function and let $f(x)$ be positive on the interval $a \leq x \leq b$. Then, if x_1 and x_2 are two numbers in this interval such that $x_1 < x_2$, it follows that $f(x_2) > f(x_1)$, or $f(x_2) - f(x_1) > 0$.

Now let us assume that $\frac{1}{f(x_2)} \geq \frac{1}{f(x_1)}$; that is, let us assume that $\frac{1}{f(x_2)} - \frac{1}{f(x_1)} \geq 0$. From this, it would follow that $\frac{f(x_1) - f(x_2)}{f(x_1) \cdot f(x_2)} \geq 0$. Since $f(x_1) > 0$ and $f(x_2) > 0$, the product $f(x_1) \cdot f(x_2) > 0$. Hence, multiplying both terms by $f(x_1) \cdot f(x_2)$, we get $f(x_1) - f(x_2) \geq 0$, or $f(x_1) \geq f(x_2)$. Since this contradicts the given condition that $f(x_2) > f(x_1)$, we reject the assumption that $\frac{1}{f(x_2)} \geq \frac{1}{f(x_1)}$. Hence, it must be the case that $\frac{1}{f(x_2)} < \frac{1}{f(x_1)}$.

Since x_1 and x_2 are arbitrary numbers in the interval $a \leq x \leq b$ such that $x_1 < x_2$, it follows that, on this interval, whenever $x_1 < x_2$, $\frac{1}{f(x_2)} < \frac{1}{f(x_1)}$. Since $\frac{1}{f(x)} = \frac{1}{f}(x)$, this means that $\frac{1}{f}$ is a strictly decreasing function over the interval $a \leq x \leq b$.

7 a

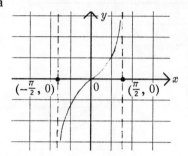

b Yes. Function f is one-to-one and, hence, has an inverse.

c Domain of f^{-1}: $\mathfrak{R}$; range: $\{y \mid -\frac{\pi}{2} < y < \frac{\pi}{2}\}$

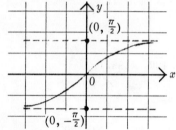

d $y = x$; $y = \frac{1}{2}x + (\frac{\pi}{4} - \frac{1}{2})$; $y = \frac{1}{4}x + (\frac{\sqrt{3}}{4} - \frac{\pi}{3})$.

Pages 495-496

1 a $\{\frac{\pi}{4}\}$

  b $\{x \mid -\frac{\pi}{2} < x \leq \frac{\pi}{6}\}$

  c $\{\frac{\pi}{3}\}$

  d $\{x \mid -\frac{\pi}{6} < x < \frac{\pi}{2}\}$

  e $\{-\frac{\pi}{4}\}$

  f $\{x \mid -\frac{\pi}{2} < x < 0 \text{ or } \frac{\pi}{4} < x < \frac{\pi}{2}\}$

  g $\{-\frac{\pi}{6}, \frac{\pi}{6}\}$

  h $\{x \mid -\frac{\pi}{2} < x < -\frac{\pi}{3} \text{ or } \frac{\pi}{3} < x < \frac{\pi}{2}\}$

  i $\{0, \frac{\pi}{6}\}$

  j $\{x \mid 0 \leq x \leq \frac{\pi}{4}\}$

2 In the following answers, decimal values are given to the nearest hundredth, and n represents any integer.

  a $\{\frac{\pi}{4} + n\pi, 1.25 + n\pi\}$

  b $\{x \mid -\frac{\pi}{2} + n\pi < x < -\frac{\pi}{4} + n\pi \text{ or } 1.25 + n\pi < x < \frac{\pi}{2} + n\pi\}$

  c $\{-1.11 + n\pi, 1.43 + n\pi\}$

  d $\{x \mid -.98 + n\pi < x < \frac{\pi}{4} + n\pi\}$

  e $\{.32 + n\pi, 1.37 + n\pi\}$

  f $\{x \mid -.64 + n\pi \leq x \leq \frac{\pi}{4}\}$

3 $y = 2x + (\frac{\pi}{2} - 1)$ and $y = 2x + (1 - \frac{\pi}{2})$.

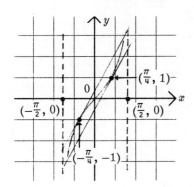

4 If $0 < x < \frac{\pi}{2}$, the point P is a point on the unit circle and in quadrant I. In this case, the area of $\triangle$ OAP is less than the area of sector OAP, which is less than the area of $\triangle$ OAT. Since the coordinates of P are $(\cos x, \sin x)$, the altitude from P to segment $\overline{OA}$ is of length $\sin x$. Since $d(O, A) = 1$, the area of $\triangle$ OAP is $\frac{1}{2}(1)(\sin x) = \frac{1}{2} \sin x$. The area of sector OAP is $\frac{1}{2}(1^2)(x) = \frac{1}{2}x$. Since $d(A, T) = \tan x$, the area of $\triangle$ OAT is $\frac{1}{2}(1)(\tan x) = \frac{1}{2} \tan x$. Hence, $\frac{1}{2} \sin x < \frac{1}{2}x < \frac{1}{2} \tan x$, or $\sin x < x < \tan x$.

5 $\tan x = \dfrac{\sin x}{\cos x}$, so $|\tan x| = \left|\dfrac{\sin x}{\cos x}\right| = \dfrac{|\sin x|}{|\cos x|}$, where $\cos x \neq 0$. If $\cos x \neq 0$, then $0 < |\cos x| \leq 1$; hence, $\dfrac{1}{|\cos x|} \geq 1$. Multiplying by $|\sin x|$, we have $\dfrac{|\sin x|}{|\cos x|} \geq |\sin x|$. Hence, $|\tan x| \geq |\sin x|$.

Pages 498-499

1 a $\frac{\sqrt{3}}{3}$ d 0   g 1   j 1

   b $-\frac{\sqrt{3}}{3}$ e $-\frac{\sqrt{3}}{3}$ h -1 k $\sqrt{3}$

   c $-\sqrt{3}$ f $-\sqrt{3}$ i $-\frac{\sqrt{3}}{3}$ l -1

2 a   b

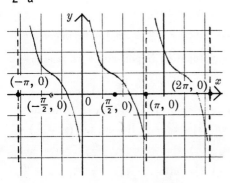

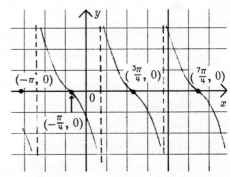

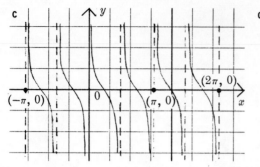 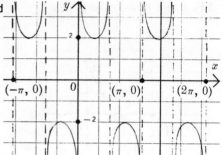

c (graph)   **d** (graph)

3 a $\cot\left(\frac{\pi}{2} + x\right) = \dfrac{\cos\left(\frac{\pi}{2} + x\right)}{\sin\left(\frac{\pi}{2} + x\right)} = \dfrac{\cos\frac{\pi}{2}\cos x - \sin\frac{\pi}{2}\sin x}{\sin\frac{\pi}{2}\cos x + \sin x\cos\frac{\pi}{2}}$

$$= \dfrac{0 \cdot \cos x - 1 \cdot \sin x}{1 \cdot \cos x + 0 \cdot \sin x} = \dfrac{-\sin x}{\cos x} = -\tan x.$$

b $\cot\left(\frac{3\pi}{2} - x\right) = \dfrac{\cos\left(\frac{3\pi}{2} - x\right)}{\sin\left(\frac{3\pi}{2} - x\right)} = \dfrac{\cos\frac{3\pi}{2}\cos x + \sin\frac{3\pi}{2}\sin x}{\sin\frac{3\pi}{2}\cos x - \sin x\cos\frac{3\pi}{2}}$

$$= \dfrac{0 \cdot \cos x + (-1)\sin x}{(-1)\cos x - 0 \cdot \sin x} = \dfrac{-\sin x}{-\cos x} = \tan x.$$

c $\cot\left(\frac{3\pi}{2} + x\right) = \dfrac{\cos\left(\frac{3\pi}{2} + x\right)}{\sin\left(\frac{3\pi}{2} + x\right)} = \dfrac{\cos\frac{3\pi}{2}\cos x - \sin\frac{3\pi}{2}\sin x}{\sin\frac{3\pi}{2}\cos x + \sin x\cos\frac{3\pi}{2}}$

$$= \dfrac{0 \cdot \cos x - (-1)\sin x}{(-1)\cos x + 0 \cdot \sin x} = \dfrac{\sin x}{-\cos x} = -\tan x.$$

d $\cot x + \tan x = \dfrac{\cos x}{\sin x} + \dfrac{\sin x}{\cos x} = \dfrac{\cos^2 x + \sin^2 x}{\sin x \cdot \cos x} = \dfrac{1}{\sin x\cos x}.$

4 a $\left\{\frac{\pi}{4}\right\}$ **b** $\left\{\frac{\pi}{3}\right\}$ **c** $\left\{\frac{5\pi}{6}\right\}$ **d** $\left\{\frac{2\pi}{3}\right\}$ **e** $\left\{\frac{\pi}{4}, \frac{\pi}{2}\right\}$ **f** $\left\{\frac{\pi}{4}\right\}$

5 Let $d(D, C) = t$. In $\triangle ABC$, $\cot \alpha = \dfrac{d + t}{d(B, C)}$; hence, $t = d(B, C) \cdot \cot \alpha - d$. In $\triangle DBC$, $\cot \theta = \dfrac{t}{d(B, C)}$; hence, $t = d(B, C) \cdot \cot \theta$. Thus, $d(B, C) \cdot \cot \alpha - d = d(B, C) \cdot \cot \theta$ or $d(B, C)\,(\cot \alpha - \cot \theta) = d$. Therefore, $d(B, C) = \dfrac{d}{\cot \alpha - \cot \theta}$.

6 a $\cot(-x) = \dfrac{\cos(-x)}{\sin(-x)} = \dfrac{\cos x}{-\sin x} = -\cot x$. Since $\cot(-x) = -\cot(x)$, $\cot(x) = -\cot(-x)$. Hence the cotangent function is an odd function.

b $\cot(x + \pi) = \dfrac{\cos(x + \pi)}{\sin(x + \pi)} = \dfrac{-\cos x}{-\sin x} = \cot x$. Since π is the smallest number a such that $\cot(x + a) = \cot x$, the cotangent function is periodic with fundamental period π.

c Let x_1 and x_2 be two real numbers in the interval $-\frac{\pi}{2} < x < \frac{\pi}{2}$ such that $x_1 < x_2$. Since the tangent function is strictly increasing over this interval, it follows that $\tan x_1 < \tan x_2$. Now let $x_1 = x_3 - \frac{\pi}{2}$ and $x_2 = x_4 - \frac{\pi}{2}$. Hence, $\tan\left(x_3 - \frac{\pi}{2}\right) < \tan\left(x_4 - \frac{\pi}{2}\right)$ and $-\tan\left(x_3 - \frac{\pi}{2}\right) > -\tan\left(x_4 - \frac{\pi}{2}\right)$. But $-\tan\left(x_3 - \frac{\pi}{2}\right) = \cot x_3$ and $-\tan\left(x_4 - \frac{\pi}{2}\right) = \cot x_4$. Hence, $\cot x_3 > \cot x_4$. Further, since $-\frac{\pi}{2} < x_1 < x_2 < \frac{\pi}{2}$, it follows that $0 < x_1 + \frac{\pi}{2} < x_2 + \frac{\pi}{2} < \pi$, or $0 < x_3 < x_4 < \pi$. Thus, when $0 < x_3 < x_4 < \pi$, $\cot x_3 > \cot x_4$, and, since x_3 and x_4 are arbitrary numbers in this interval, it follows that the cotangent function is strictly decreasing over the interval $0 < x < \pi$.

7 a No, the slope remains the same.

b Yes. If m is the slope of the given line, then $-m$ is the slope of the line's reflection.

c The slope of the tangent line to the graph of the tangent function at an arbitrary point $(x_0, \tan x_0)$ is $\dfrac{1}{\cos^2 x_0}$. If this tangent line is translated $\frac{\pi}{2}$ units to the right and then reflected in the x-axis, the line obtained is the tangent line to the graph of the cotangent function at the point $(x_1, \cot x_1)$ where $x_1 = x_0 + \frac{\pi}{2}$.

   By parts a and b of this exercise, the slope of this tangent line to the graph of the cotangent function is $-\dfrac{1}{\cos^2 x_0}$. Hence, $\cot' x_1 = -\dfrac{1}{\cos^2 x_0}$. Since $x_0 = x_1 - \frac{\pi}{2}$, this is equivalent to $\cot' x_1 = -\dfrac{1}{\cos^2(x_1 - \frac{\pi}{2})}$. Because $\cos(-x) = \cos x$, $\cos(x_1 - \frac{\pi}{2}) = \cos(\frac{\pi}{2} - x_1) = \sin x_1$. Therefore, $\cot' x_1 = -\dfrac{1}{\sin^2 x_1}$. Finally, since x_0 is an arbitrary number and, hence, x_1 is arbitrary, $\cot' x = -\dfrac{1}{\sin^2 x}$.

8 Let $(x_0, \cot x_0)$ be an arbitrary point on the graph of the cotangent function. Then a line with slope m through this point has the equation $\ell(x) = m(x - x_0) + \cot x_0$. Therefore, the vertical distance from an arbitrary point, $(x, \cot x)$, where $x_1 \ne x_0$, on the graph of the cotangent function to the line ℓ is given by $|\cot x - \quad m(x - x_0) + \cot x_0| = \left|\dfrac{\cot x - \cot x_0}{x - x_0} - m\right| |x - x_0|$.

   Now consider the expression $\dfrac{\cot x - \cot x_0}{x - x_0}$. From the definition $\cot x = \dfrac{\cos x}{\sin x}$, we see that this expression can be written as

$$\frac{\dfrac{\cos x}{\sin x} - \dfrac{\cos x_0}{\sin x_0}}{x - x_0} = \frac{\sin x_0 \cos x - \cos x_0 \sin x}{x - x_0} \cdot \frac{1}{\sin x \sin x_0}$$

$$= \frac{\sin(x_0 - x)}{x - x_0} \cdot \frac{1}{\sin x \sin x_0}$$

$$= -\frac{\sin(x - x_0)}{x - x_0} \cdot \frac{1}{\sin x \sin x_0}$$

As x gets close to x_0, $x - x_0$ approaches 0 and, therefore, $\dfrac{\sin(x - x_0)}{x - x_0}$ approaches 1.

Also, as x gets close to x_0, $\sin x$ approaches $\sin x_0$; therefore $\dfrac{1}{\sin x \sin x_0}$ approaches $\dfrac{1}{\sin^2 x_0}$. Thus, $\dfrac{\cot x - \cot x_0}{x - x_0}$ gets arbitrarily close to $-\dfrac{1}{\sin^2 x_0}$ as x gets sufficiently close to x_0.

From the above results, we see that, if the slope m of the line ℓ through the point $(x_0, \cot x_0)$ on the graph of the cotangent function is $\dfrac{-1}{\sin^2 x_0}$, then the graph of the cotangent function will be closer to ℓ for x sufficiently near x_0 than to any other line. That is, the slope of the tangent line to the graph of the cotangent function at the point $(x_0, \cot x_0)$ is $-\dfrac{1}{\sin^2 x_0}$. Since x_0 is any value such that $\cot x$ is defined, we have

$$\cot' x = -\frac{1}{\sin^2 x}, \text{ where } \sin x \neq 0.$$

Pages 501-502

1 a $\frac{2\sqrt{3}}{3}$ b $-\sqrt{2}$ c -2 d -1 e $\sqrt{2}$ f $-\frac{2\sqrt{3}}{3}$

2 a 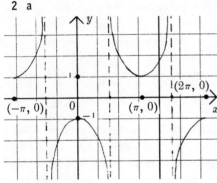 b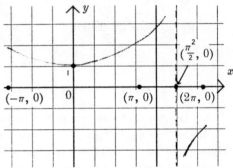

c 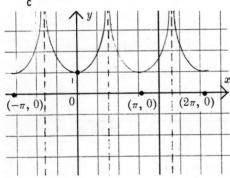 d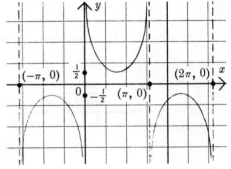

3 a $\sec(\pi - x) = \dfrac{1}{\cos(\pi - x)} = \dfrac{1}{\cos \pi \cos x + \sin \pi \sin x}$

$$= \frac{1}{(-1)\cos x + 0} = -\frac{1}{\cos x} = -\sec x.$$

b $\sec(\pi + x) = \dfrac{1}{\cos(\pi + x)} = \dfrac{1}{\cos \pi \cos x - \sin \pi \sin x}$

$$= \frac{1}{(-1)\cos x - 0} = -\frac{1}{\cos x} = -\sec x.$$

c $\sec(2\pi - x) = \dfrac{1}{\cos(2\pi - x)} = \dfrac{1}{\cos 2\pi \cos x + \sin 2\pi \sin x}$

$$= \dfrac{1}{(1)\cos x + 0} = \dfrac{1}{\cos x} = \sec x.$$

d $\sin x \sec x = \sin x \cdot \dfrac{1}{\cos x} = \dfrac{\sin x}{\cos x} = \tan x.$

4 a $\{x \mid 0 \leqq x < \frac{\pi}{3} \text{ or } \frac{\pi}{2} < x < \frac{3\pi}{2} \text{ or } \frac{5\pi}{3} < x \leqq 2\pi\}$

b $\{\frac{\pi}{4}, \frac{3\pi}{4}, \frac{5\pi}{4}, \frac{7\pi}{4}\}$

c $\{x \mid \frac{\pi}{6} \leqq x < \frac{\pi}{2} \text{ or } \frac{\pi}{2} < x \leqq \frac{5\pi}{6} \text{ or } \frac{7\pi}{6} \leqq x < \frac{3\pi}{2} \text{ or } \frac{3\pi}{2} < x \leqq \frac{11\pi}{6}\}$

d $\emptyset$

e $\{\frac{\pi}{3}, \frac{5\pi}{3}\}$

f $\{x \mid \frac{\pi}{4} < x < \frac{\pi}{2} \text{ or } \frac{\pi}{2} < x < \frac{3\pi}{2} \text{ or } \frac{3\pi}{2} < x < \frac{7\pi}{4}\}$

5 a $\dfrac{\tan x}{\sec x} = \dfrac{\dfrac{\sin x}{\cos x}}{\dfrac{1}{\cos x}} = \sin x.$

b $\dfrac{\sec x}{\cot x} = \dfrac{\dfrac{1}{\cos x}}{\dfrac{\cos x}{\sin x}} = \dfrac{\sin x}{\cos^2 x}.$

c $\sec^2 x - 1 = \dfrac{1}{\cos^2 x} - 1 = \dfrac{\sin^2 x}{\cos^2 x}.$

d $(\cot x)(\sin x - \sec x) = \dfrac{\cos x}{\sin x}\left(\sin x - \dfrac{1}{\cos x}\right)$

$$= \dfrac{\cos x}{\sin x}\left(\dfrac{\sin x \cos x - 1}{\cos x}\right) = \cos x - \dfrac{1}{\sin x}.$$

6 Since $\cos x > 0$ and the cosine function is strictly decreasing on the interval $0 \leqq x < \frac{\pi}{2}$, it follows that the function $\dfrac{1}{\cos}$ is strictly increasing on this interval. Since $\dfrac{1}{\cos}(x) = \dfrac{1}{\cos x} = \sec x$, the secant function is strictly increasing on this interval.

7 From the definition of the sine function, it follows that $|\sin x| \leqq 1$. When $\cos x \neq 0$, it follows that $|\cos x|$ is positive. If we now divide both sides of $|\sin x| \leqq 1$ by $|\cos x|$, we have $\dfrac{|\sin x|}{|\cos x|} \leqq \dfrac{1}{|\cos x|}$. But $\dfrac{|\sin x|}{|\cos x|} = \left|\dfrac{\sin x}{\cos x}\right| = \tan x$, $\dfrac{1}{|\cos x|} = \left|\dfrac{1}{\cos x}\right| = |\sec x|$. Hence, $|\tan x| \leqq |\sec x|$ when $\cos x \neq 0$.

Page 504

1 a $\frac{2\sqrt{3}}{3}$ b $\sqrt{2}$ c -2 d -1 e 1 f $-\frac{2\sqrt{3}}{3}$

2 a

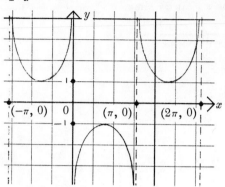

b

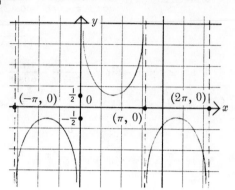

c

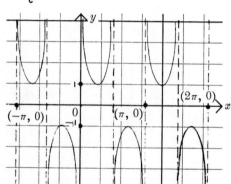

d

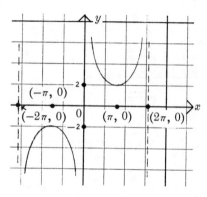

3 a $\csc(\pi - x) = \dfrac{1}{\sin(\pi - x)} = \dfrac{1}{\sin \pi \cos x - \sin x \cos \pi}$

$= \dfrac{1}{0 - (-1)\sin x} = \dfrac{1}{\sin x} = \csc x.$

b $\csc(\pi + x) = \dfrac{1}{\sin(\pi + x)} = \dfrac{1}{\sin \pi \cos x + \sin x \cos \pi}$

$= \dfrac{1}{0 + (-1)\sin x} = -\dfrac{1}{\sin x} = -\csc x.$

c $\csc\left(\dfrac{\pi}{2} + x\right) = \dfrac{1}{\sin\left(\dfrac{\pi}{2} + x\right)} = \dfrac{1}{\sin \dfrac{\pi}{2} \cos x + \sin x \cos \dfrac{\pi}{2}}$

$= \dfrac{1}{(1)\cos x + 0} = \dfrac{1}{\cos x} = \sec x.$

d $\csc\left(\dfrac{3\pi}{2} - x\right) = \dfrac{1}{\sin\left(\dfrac{3\pi}{2} - x\right)} = \dfrac{1}{\sin \dfrac{3\pi}{2} \cos x - \sin x \cos \dfrac{3\pi}{2}}$

$= \dfrac{1}{(-1)\cos x - 0} = -\dfrac{1}{\cos x} = -\sec x.$

e $\csc\left(\dfrac{3\pi}{2} + x\right) = \dfrac{1}{\sin\left(\dfrac{3\pi}{2} + x\right)} = \dfrac{1}{\sin \dfrac{3\pi}{2} \cos x + \sin x \cos \dfrac{3\pi}{2}}$

$= \dfrac{1}{(-1)\cos x + 0} = -\dfrac{1}{\cos x} = -\sec x.$

4 a $\{\frac{\pi}{4}, \frac{3\pi}{4}\}$

   b $\{x \mid \frac{\pi}{6} < x < \frac{5\pi}{6} \text{ or } \frac{7\pi}{6} < x < \frac{11\pi}{6}\}$

   c $\{\frac{\pi}{3}, \frac{2\pi}{3}, \frac{4\pi}{3}, \frac{5\pi}{3}\}$

   d $\{0 < x < \pi \text{ or } \pi < x < 2\pi\}$

   e $\{\frac{5\pi}{4}, \frac{7\pi}{4}\}$

   f $\{\frac{7\pi}{6}, \frac{11\pi}{6}\}$

5 a $\csc(-x) = \dfrac{1}{\sin(-x)} = -\dfrac{1}{\sin x} = -\csc x.$ Hence, $\csc(x) = -\csc(-x)$, which establishes that the cosecant function is an odd function.

   b $\csc(x + 2\pi) = \dfrac{1}{\sin(x + 2\pi)} = \dfrac{1}{\sin x \cos 2\pi + \sin 2\pi \cos x}$

   $$= \dfrac{1}{(1)\sin x + 0} = \dfrac{1}{\sin x} = \csc x.$$

   Since 2π is the smallest number a such that $\csc(x + a) = \csc x$, it follows that cosecant function is periodic with fundamental period 2π.

6 a $\dfrac{\sec x}{\csc x} = \dfrac{\dfrac{1}{\cos x}}{\dfrac{1}{\sin x}} = \dfrac{\sin x}{\cos x}.$

   b $\dfrac{\cot^2 x}{\csc^2 x} = \dfrac{\dfrac{\cos^2 x}{\sin^2 x}}{\dfrac{1}{\sin^2 x}} = \cos^2 x.$

   c $\tan x (\cos x + \csc x) = \dfrac{\sin x}{\cos x}\left(\cos x + \dfrac{1}{\sin x}\right)$

   $$= \dfrac{\sin x}{\cos x}\left(\dfrac{\sin x \cos x + 1}{\sin x}\right)$$

   $$= \sin x + \dfrac{1}{\cos x}.$$

   d $\sec x + \csc x = \dfrac{1}{\cos x} + \dfrac{1}{\sin x}.$

7 1) The cosecant function is periodic with a fundamental period of 2π.

   2) The cosecant function is an increasing function over the intervals $(2n + \frac{1}{2})\pi \leqq x < (2n + 1)\pi$ and $(2n + 1)\pi < x \leqq (2n + \frac{3}{2})\pi$, where $n \in \mathcal{I}$.

   3) The cosecant function is a decreasing function over the intervals $2n\pi < x \leqq (2n + \frac{1}{2})\pi$ and $(2n + \frac{3}{2})\pi \leqq x < (2n + 2)\pi$, where $n \in \mathcal{I}$.

   4) For the intervals $2n\pi < x < (2n + 1)\pi$, where $n \in \mathcal{I}$, $\csc x$ has a minimum value of 1 when $x = (2n + \frac{1}{2})\pi$.

   5) For the intervals $(2n + 1)\pi < x < (2n + 2)\pi$, where $n \in \mathcal{I}$, $\csc x$ has a maximum value of -1 when $x = (2n + \frac{3}{2})\pi$.

6) The cosecant function is an odd function.

7) The graph of the cosecant function is concave upward for $2n\pi < x < (2n + 1)\pi$ and concave downward for $(2n + 1)\pi < x < (2n + 2)\pi$

8) The graph of the cosecant function has the vertical lines $x = n\pi$, where $n \in \mathcal{I}$, as asymptotes.

8 Since $-1 \leqq \cos x \leqq 1$, it follows that $|\cos x| \leqq 1$. If $\sin x \neq 0$, then $|\sin x|$ is positive. Thus, we can divide both sides of $|\cos x| \leqq 1$ by $|\sin x|$ to obtain $\dfrac{|\cos x|}{|\sin x|} \leqq$ $\dfrac{1}{|\sin x|}$. Now $\dfrac{|\cos x|}{|\sin x|} = \left|\dfrac{\cos x}{\sin x}\right| = |\cot x|$ and $\dfrac{1}{|\sin x|} = \left|\dfrac{1}{\sin x}\right| = |\csc x|$. Hence, $|\cot x| \leqq |\csc x|$ for all values of x for which the two expressions are defined.

9 a $\ell(x) = \dfrac{\csc x_2 - \csc x_1}{x_2 - x_1}(x - x_1) + \csc x_1$. Therefore $\ell(x) - \csc x = \dfrac{\csc x_2 - \csc x_1}{x_2 - x_1}(x - x_1)$ $(\csc x_1 - \csc x)$. To prove that $\ell(x) - \csc x > 0$, we need to show that $\dfrac{\csc x_2 - \csc x_1}{x_2 - x_1} > \dfrac{\csc x_1 - \csc x}{x - x_1}$. Using the definition $\csc x = \dfrac{1}{\sin x}$, we can show that this inequality is equivalent to $\dfrac{\sin x_1 - \sin x_2}{x_2 - x_1} \cdot \dfrac{1}{\sin x_1 \sin x_2} >$ $\dfrac{\sin x_1 - \sin x}{x - x_1} \cdot \dfrac{1}{\sin x_1 \sin x_2}$. Since $\sin x_1 > 0$ and $\sin x_2 > 0$, it follows that $\sin x_1 \sin x_2 > 0$. Thus, if we multiply both sides of the inequality by $\sin x_1 \sin x_2$, we obtain $\dfrac{\sin x_1 - \sin x_2}{x_2 - x_1} > \dfrac{\sin x_1 - \sin x}{x - x_1}$. Next multiplying both sides by -1, we have $\dfrac{\sin x_2 - \sin x_1}{x_2 - x_1} < \dfrac{\sin x - \sin x_1}{x - x_1}$. In Chapter 8 (see pages 438-439) we proved that this inequality holds for all values of x in the interval $0 < x < \frac{\pi}{2}$, where $x_1 < x < x_2$. Therefore, if we reverse the steps given above, we will have shown that $\ell(x) - \csc x > 0$ for $0 < x < \frac{\pi}{2}$.

b The results of part a establish that the graph of the cosecant function is concave upward for the interval $0 < x < \frac{\pi}{2}$. Because any point on the graph between $(x_1, \csc x_1)$ and $(x_2, \csc x_2)$ lies below the line segment determined by these two points and because x_1 and x_2 are arbitrary, it follows that the graph is concave upward for this entire interval.

Pages 506-508

1 a $\tan(x_1 + x_2) = \dfrac{\tan x_1 + \tan x_2}{1 - (\tan x_1) \tan x_2}$. Therefore

$\tan(x_1 - x_2) = \tan\left(x_1 + (-x_2)\right) = \dfrac{\tan x_1 + \tan(-x_2)}{1 - (\tan x_1) \tan(-x_2)}$.

Since $\tan(-x_2) = -\tan x_2$, we have

$\tan(x_1 - x_2) = \dfrac{\tan x_1 + (-\tan x_2)}{1 - \tan x_1 (-\tan x_2)} = \dfrac{\tan x_1 - \tan x_2}{1 + (\tan x_1) \tan x_2}$.

b $\sin(x_1 - x_2) = \sin x_1 \cos x_2 - \sin x_2 \cos x_1$ and $\cos(x_1 - x_2) = \cos x_1 \cos x_2 +$

$\sin x_1 \sin x_2$. Therefore, $\tan(x_1 - x_2) = \dfrac{\sin(x_1 - x_2)}{\cos(x_1 - x_2)} = \dfrac{\sin x_1 \cos x_2 - \sin x_2 \cos x_1}{\cos x_1 \cos x_2 + \sin x_1 \sin x_2}$.

If we divide both numerator and denominator by $\cos x_1 \cos x_2$, we get

$$\tan(x_1 - x_2) = \frac{\dfrac{\sin x_1 \cos x_2 - \sin x_2 \cos x_1}{\cos x_1 \cos x_2}}{\dfrac{\cos x_1 \cos x_2 + \sin x_1 \sin x_2}{\cos x_1 \cos x_2}}$$

$$= \frac{\dfrac{\sin x_1}{\cos x_1} - \dfrac{\sin x_2}{\cos x_2}}{1 + \dfrac{\sin x_1 \sin x_2}{\cos x_1 \cos x_2}}$$

$$= \frac{\tan x_1 - \tan x_2}{1 + \tan x_1 \tan x_2}.$$

2 a $\cot(x_1 + x_2) = \dfrac{\cos(x_1 + x_2)}{\sin(x_1 + x_2)} = \dfrac{\cos x_1 \cos x_2 - \sin x_1 \sin x_2}{\sin x_1 \cos x_2 + \sin x_2 \cos x_1}$

$$= \frac{\dfrac{\cos x_1 \cos x_2 - \sin x_1 \sin x_2}{\sin x_1 \sin x_2}}{\dfrac{\sin x_1 \cos x_2 + \sin x_2 \cos x_1}{\sin x_1 \sin x_2}}$$

$$= \frac{\dfrac{\cos x_1 \cos x_2}{\sin x_1 \sin x_2} - 1}{\dfrac{\cos x_2}{\sin x_2} + \dfrac{\cos x_1}{\sin x_1}}$$

$$= \frac{\cot x_1 \cot x_2 - 1}{\cot x_2 + \cot x_1}.$$

b $\cot(2x) = \cot(x + x) = \dfrac{\cot x \cot x - 1}{\cot x + \cot x} = \dfrac{\cot^2 x - 1}{2 \cot x}$.

c $\cot(x_1 - x_2) = \dfrac{\cot x_1 \cot(-x_2) - 1}{\cot x_1 + \cot(-x_2)}$. Since $\cot(-x_2) = -\cot x_2$, we have

$$\cot(x_1 - x_2) = \frac{\cot x_1 (-\cot x_2) - 1}{\cot x_1 + (-\cot x_2)}$$

$$= \frac{-\cot x_1 \cot x_2 - 1}{\cot x_1 - \cot x_2} = -\frac{\cot x_1 \cot x_2 + 1}{\cot x_1 - \cot x_2}.$$

3 $\left|\sin \tfrac{1}{2}x\right| = \sqrt{\dfrac{1 - \cos x}{2}}$ and $\left|\cos \tfrac{1}{2}x\right| = \sqrt{\dfrac{1 + \cos x}{2}}$. Hence, $\left|\tan \tfrac{1}{2}x\right| = \dfrac{\left|\sin \tfrac{1}{2}x\right|}{\left|\cos \tfrac{1}{2}x\right|}$

$$= \frac{\sqrt{\dfrac{1 - \cos x}{2}}}{\sqrt{\dfrac{1 + \cos x}{2}}} = \sqrt{\frac{1 - \cos x}{1 + \cos x}} \text{ and } \left|\cot \tfrac{1}{2}x\right| = \frac{\left|\cos \tfrac{1}{2}x\right|}{\left|\sin \tfrac{1}{2}x\right|} = \frac{\sqrt{\dfrac{1 + \cos x}{2}}}{\sqrt{\dfrac{1 - \cos x}{2}}} = \sqrt{\frac{1 + \cos x}{1 - \cos x}}.$$

4 a $\sin^2 x + (\sin^2 x)\tan^2 x = \sin^2 x\,(1 + \tan^2 x)$

$$= \sin^2 x \sec^2 x$$

$$= \sin^2 x \cdot \frac{1}{\cos^2 x}$$

$$= \frac{\sin^2 x}{\cos^2 x}$$

$$= \tan^2 x.$$

b $(1 - \sin^2 x)(\sec^2 x - 1) = \cos^2 x \tan^2 x$

$$= \cos^2 x \cdot \frac{\sin^2 x}{\cos^2 x}$$

$$= \sin^2 x.$$

c $\dfrac{1 + \sec x}{\tan x} = \dfrac{1 + \dfrac{1}{\cos x}}{\dfrac{\sin x}{\cos x}} = \dfrac{\dfrac{\cos x + 1}{\cos x}}{\dfrac{\sin x}{\cos x}} = \dfrac{\cos x + 1}{\sin x}$

$$= \frac{\cos x}{\sin x} + \frac{1}{\sin x} = \cot x + \csc x.$$

d $\dfrac{(\sec x - 1)^2}{\tan^2 x} = \dfrac{(\sec x - 1)^2}{\sec^2 x - 1} = \dfrac{(\sec x - 1)^2}{(\sec x + 1)(\sec x - 1)} = \dfrac{\sec x - 1}{\sec x + 1}.$

e $\dfrac{\sec x + \csc x}{\tan x + \cot x} = \dfrac{\dfrac{1}{\cos x} + \dfrac{1}{\sin x}}{\dfrac{\sin x}{\cos x} + \dfrac{\cos x}{\sin x}} = \dfrac{\dfrac{\sin x + \cos x}{\cos x \sin x}}{\dfrac{\sin^2 x + \cos^2 x}{\cos x \sin x}}$

$$= \frac{\sin x + \cos x}{1} = \sin x + \cos x.$$

f $\dfrac{2 \tan x}{\sec^2 x - 2\tan^2 x} = \dfrac{2 \tan x}{1 + \tan^2 x - 2\tan^2 x} = \dfrac{2 \tan x}{1 - \tan^2 x} = \tan 2x.$

g $\dfrac{1 - \tan^2 x}{\sec^2 x} = \dfrac{1 - \dfrac{\sin^2 x}{\cos^2 x}}{\dfrac{1}{\cos^2 x}} = \dfrac{\dfrac{\cos^2 x - \sin^2 x}{\cos^2 x}}{\dfrac{1}{\cos^2 x}}$

$$= \cos^2 x - \sin^2 x = \cos 2x.$$

h $\dfrac{\tan x_1 + \tan x_2}{\tan x_1 - \tan x_2} = \dfrac{\dfrac{\sin x_1}{\cos x_1} + \dfrac{\sin x_2}{\cos x_2}}{\dfrac{\sin x_1}{\cos x_1} - \dfrac{\sin x_2}{\cos x_2}} = \dfrac{\dfrac{\sin x_1 \cos x_2 + \sin x_2 \cos x_1}{\cos x_1 \cos x_2}}{\dfrac{\sin x_1 \cos x_2 - \sin x_2 \cos x_1}{\cos x_1 \cos x_2}}$

$$= \frac{\sin x_1 \cos x_2 + \sin x_2 \cos x_1}{\sin x_1 \cos x_2 - \sin x_2 \cos x_1}$$

$$= \frac{\sin (x_1 + x_2)}{\sin (x_1 - x_2)}.$$

i $\dfrac{1 + \sec^2 x}{\tan x} = \dfrac{1 + \dfrac{1}{\cos^2 x}}{\dfrac{\sin x}{\cos x}} = \dfrac{\dfrac{\cos^2 x + 1}{\cos^2 x}}{\dfrac{\sin x}{\cos x}} = \dfrac{\cos^2 x + 1}{\sin x \cos x}.$

5 a Let A be the point of intersection of ℓ_1 with the x-axis; B, the point of intersection of ℓ_2 with the x-axis; and C, the point of intersection of ℓ_1 and ℓ_2. In $\triangle ABC$, the measure of $\angle BCA$ is θ. Since a_1 is the measure of an exterior angle of $\triangle ABC$, it follows that $a_1 = a_2 + \theta$. Hence, $\theta = a_1 - a_2$.

b $\tan \theta = \tan(a_1 - a_2) = \dfrac{\tan a_1 - \tan a_2}{1 + (\tan a_1) \tan a_2}.$ But $\tan a_1 = m_1$ and $\tan a_2 = m_2$, where

m_1 and m_2 are the slopes of ℓ_1 and ℓ_2, respectively. Hence, $\tan \theta = \dfrac{m_1 - m_2}{1 + m_1 m_2}.$

6 a

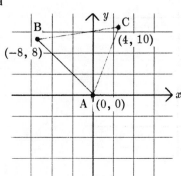

$\angle CAB° \approx 67.$
$\angle ABC° \approx 54.$
$\angle BCA° \approx 59.$

b

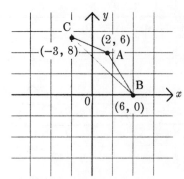

$\angle CAB° \approx 145.$
$\angle ABC° \approx 15.$
$\angle BCA° \approx 20.$

c

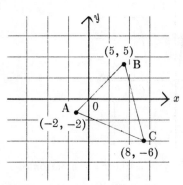

$\angle CAB° \approx 67.$
$\angle ABC° \approx 60.$
$\angle BCA° \approx 53.$

d

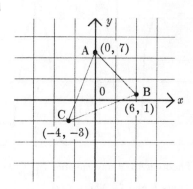

$\angle CAB° \approx 67.$
$\angle ABC° \approx 67.$
$\angle BCA° \approx 46.$

1 a $f(t) = \sin t - \cos t$.

   b $f(t) = 2 \sin t + 2\sqrt{3} \cos t$.

   c $f(t) = \frac{\sqrt{3}}{4} \sin 2t - \frac{1}{4} \cos 2t$.

   d $f(t) = \sqrt{2} \sin 3t - \sqrt{2} \cos 3t$.

2 a $f(t) = 2 \sin (t + \frac{\pi}{3})$.

   b $f(t) = 2\sqrt{2} \sin (t - \frac{\pi}{4})$.

   c $f(t) = (\sqrt{3} - 1) \sin 2t$.

   d $f(t) = 4 \sin (\frac{t}{2} - \frac{\pi}{3})$.

3 a $\{t \mid t = \frac{\pi}{6} + 2n\pi, n \in \mathfrak{I}\}$

   b $\{t \mid t = \frac{\pi}{4} + 2n\pi, n \in \mathfrak{I}\}$

   c $\{t \mid t = \frac{\pi}{3} + 2n\pi \text{ or } t = (2n + 1)\pi, n \in \mathfrak{I}\}$.

   d $\{t \mid t = \frac{\pi}{3} + 2n\pi \text{ or } t = \frac{4\pi}{3} + 2n\pi, n \in \mathfrak{I}\}$

4 a

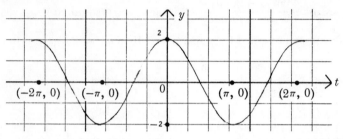

   b

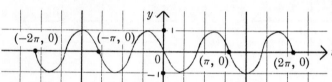

   c

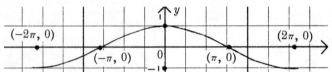

   d

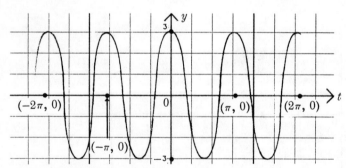

5 By Theorem 43/9 any member $f_{A, \beta}$ of this family is a linear combination of functions f_1 and f_2, where $f_1(t) = \sin (at)$ and $f_2(t) = \cos (at)$. Hence, the sum of any two members of the family is a linear combination of f_1 and f_2. By the converse stated in Theorem 43/9, this linear combination of f_1 and f_2 is a sinusoidal function defined by an equation of the form $f(t) = A \sin (at + \beta)$. Thus, the family is closed under addition.

Page 519

Rate of rotation	Period	Frequency
1 $\frac{1}{2}$ radian per second	4π seconds	$\frac{1}{4}\pi$ cycles per second
2 2π radians per second	1 second	1 cycle per second
3 $\frac{\pi}{2}$ radians per second	4 seconds	$\frac{1}{4}$ cycle per second
4 10 radians per second	$\frac{\pi}{5}$ seconds	$\frac{5}{\pi}$ cycles per second

5 $F = \{(t, (\frac{1}{2}\cos 10t, \frac{1}{2}\sin 10t)) \mid t \in \Re\}.$

6 $F = \{(t, (\frac{1}{4}\cos 200\pi t, \frac{1}{4}\sin 200\pi t)) \mid t \in \Re\}.$

7 $F = \{(t, (2\cos 8\pi t, 2\sin 8\pi t)) \mid t \in \Re\}.$

Pages 521-522

1 a 1 radian per second
  b $f(t) = 10 \sin t.$
  c Period: 2π sec.; amplitude: 10; frequency: $\frac{1}{2\pi}$ cycles per second
2 a π radians per second
  b $f(t) = 4 \sin \pi t.$
  c Period: 2 sec.; amplitude: 4; frequency: $\frac{1}{2}$ cycle per second
3 a 8π radians per second
  b $f(t) = 2 \sin 8\pi t.$
  c Period: $\frac{1}{4}$ sec.; amplitude: 2; frequency: 4 cycles per second
4 a $0; 5\sqrt{2}; -10$
  b $t = \frac{1}{3}; \frac{4}{3}$ sec.
  c 10 units; 10 units
  d 4 sec.
  e 15 units per second; 7.5 units per second
5 $f(t) = 0.001 \sin 1760\pi t.$
6 a $f(t) = 3 \sin t.$

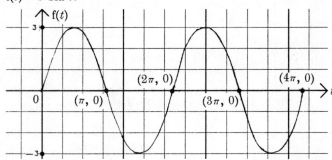

b $f(t) = \frac{1}{2} \sin 2t.$

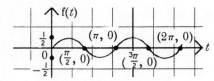

c $f(t) = 2 \sin \pi t$.

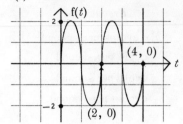

d $f(t) = 1.5 \sin \frac{2}{3}t$.

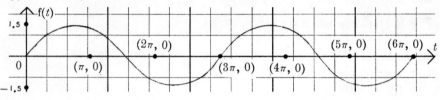

Pages 523-524

1 a $\frac{\pi}{4}$ **b** $f(t) = 2 \sin (\pi t + \frac{\pi}{4})$.

c

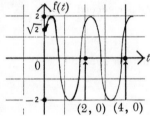

2 (a) $-\frac{\pi}{3}$ **(b)** $f(t) = 2 \sin (\pi t - \frac{\pi}{3})$.

(c)

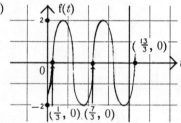

3 (a) π or $-\pi$ **(b)** $f(t) = 2 \sin (\pi t - \pi)$ or $f(t) = 2 \sin (\pi t + \pi)$.

(c)

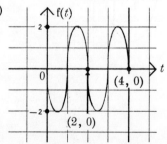

4 $f(t) = 3 \sin (4\pi t - \frac{\pi}{2})$.

5 a $f(t) = 3 \sin (4t + \frac{\pi}{4})$.

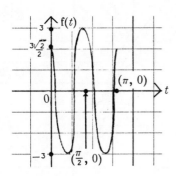

b $f(t) = 4 \sin (\frac{1}{2}t - \pi)$.

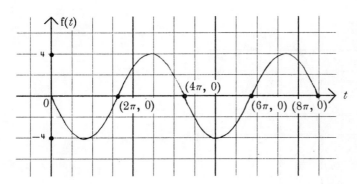

c $f(t) = \frac{1}{2} \sin (\frac{\pi}{2}t + \frac{3\pi}{2})$.

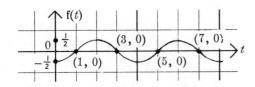

d $f(t) = 2.5 \sin (\frac{\pi}{4}t - \frac{\pi}{2})$.

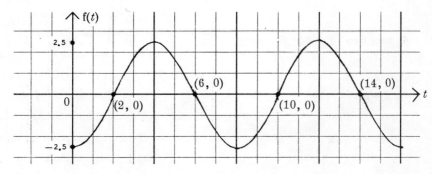

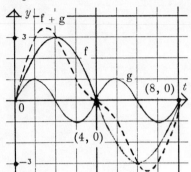

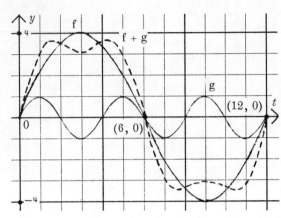

1

Function	Period	Frequency
f	8	$\frac{1}{8}$
g	4	$\frac{1}{4}$
f + g	8	$\frac{1}{8}$

2

Function	Period	Frequency
f	12	$\frac{1}{12}$
g	4	$\frac{1}{4}$
f + g	12	$\frac{1}{12}$

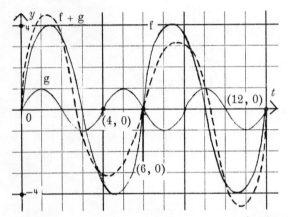

3

Function	Period	Frequency
f	6	$\frac{1}{6}$
g	4	$\frac{1}{4}$
f + g	12	$\frac{1}{12}$

4

Function	Period	Frequency
f	10	$\frac{1}{10}$
g	2	$\frac{1}{2}$
f + g	10	$\frac{1}{10}$

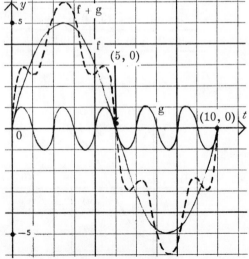

5 The period of f + g is the least common multiple of the periods of f and g.

Chapter review
Pages 525-527

1 d	5 c	9 b	13 b	17 b	21 a
2 d	6 c	10 c	14 a	18 b	22 b
3 b	7 b	11 a	15 d	19 c	23 a
4 d	8 b	12 d	16 b	20 d	24 d

Cumulative review
Pages 527-528

1 $\{x \mid |x| < 3\}$

2 $f\big(f(x)\big) = f\left(\dfrac{ax + b}{cx - a}\right) = \dfrac{a\left(\dfrac{ax + b}{cx - a}\right) + b}{c\left(\dfrac{ax + b}{cx - a}\right) - a} = \dfrac{\dfrac{a^2x + ab + bcx - .ab}{cx - a}}{\dfrac{acx + bc - acx + a^2}{cx - a}} = \dfrac{a^2x + bcx}{bc + a^2} = \dfrac{x(a^2 + bc)}{a^2 + bc}$

$= x$, when $a^2 + bc \neq 0$.

3 Let ℓ be defined by $\ell(x) = mx + b$. If ℓ contains $(0, 0)$, then $0 = m \cdot 0 + b$, or $b = 0$. Thus, ℓ is defined by $\ell(x) = mx$. Now $\ell(-x) = m(-x) = -mx$ and $-\ell(x) = -mx$. Hence, if ℓ contains $(0, 0)$, $\ell(-x) = -\ell(x)$.

Now suppose that $\ell(-x) = -\ell(x)$. Since $-\ell(x) = -(mx + b) = -mx - b$ and $\ell(-x) = m(-x) + b = -mx + b$, we have $-mx - b = -mx + b$ or $-b = b$. But $-b = b$ only if $b = 0$. Hence, ℓ is defined by $\ell(x) = mx$ and the graph of ℓ contains the point $(0, 0)$.

4 56 ft. per sec.

5 a $\{-2, 2, 1 + i, 1 - i\}$

b The equation of the tangent at $(2, 0)$ is $y = 8x - 16$. The equation of the tangent at $(-2, 0)$ is $y = -40x - 80$.

6 a Since $b = r$ and $a = h$, $V = \frac{\pi}{3}b^2a$. But in the right triangle, $b^2 = (2\sqrt{3})^2 - a^2 = 12 - a^2$. Hence, $V = \frac{\pi}{3}(12 - a^2)a = 4\pi a - \frac{\pi}{3}a^3$.

b $a = 2$; $b = 2\sqrt{2}$.

7 $a = -\frac{3}{2}$; $b = -6$; hence, $P(x) = x^3 - \frac{3}{2}x^2 - 6x$.

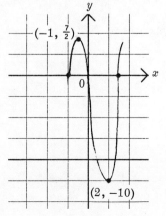

8 a $\sin(x_1 + x_2) < \sin x_1 + \sin x_2$.

b $\cos(x_1 + x_2) < \cos x_1 + \cos x_2$.

c $\sin 2x_1 > \cos 2x_2$.

d $\tan(x_1 + x_2) > \tan 2x_1$.

9 a

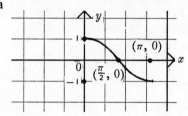

b Yes; f is a one-to-one function and every one-to-one function has an inverse.

c Domain of f^{-1}: $\{x \mid -1 \leqq x \leqq 1\}$

Range of f^{-1}: $\{y \mid 0 \leqq y \leqq \pi\}$

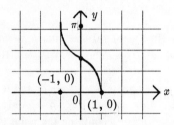

d $f^{-1}(\tfrac{1}{2}) = \tfrac{\pi}{3}$; $f^{-1}(-\tfrac{\sqrt{3}}{2}) = \tfrac{5\pi}{6}$; $f^{-1}(\tfrac{\sqrt{2}}{2}) = \tfrac{\pi}{4}$.

10 a $\{x \mid \tfrac{\pi}{3} + 2n\pi < x < \tfrac{2\pi}{3} + 2n\pi$ or $\tfrac{4\pi}{3} + 2n\pi < x < \tfrac{5\pi}{3} + 2n\pi,\ n \in \mathcal{I}\}$

b $\{x \mid x = \tfrac{7\pi}{6} + 2n\pi$ or $x = \tfrac{11\pi}{6} + 2n\pi,\ n \in \mathcal{I}\}$

c $\{x \mid \tfrac{\pi}{3} + 2n\pi < x < \tfrac{\pi}{2} + 2n\pi$ or $\tfrac{3\pi}{2} + 2n\pi < x < \tfrac{5\pi}{3} + 2n\pi,\ n \in \mathcal{I}\}$

d $\{x \mid x = \tfrac{\pi}{4} + n\pi,\ \tfrac{\pi}{3} + n\pi,\ \tfrac{3\pi}{4} + n\pi,$ or $\tfrac{2\pi}{3} + n\pi,\ n \in \mathcal{I}\}$

e $\{x \mid x = n\pi,\ \tfrac{\pi}{3} + 2n\pi,$ or $\tfrac{5\pi}{3} + 2n\pi,\ n \in \mathcal{I}\}$

f $\{x \mid x \in \mathcal{R}\}$

11 a

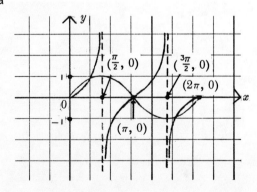

b $\sin' x = \cos x$ and $\tan' x = \dfrac{1}{\cos^2 x}$. The slope of the tangent to the graph of the sine function at $x = \pi$ is $\cos \pi = -1$.

The slope of the tangent to the graph of the tangent function at $x = \pi$ is $\dfrac{1}{\cos^2 \pi} = \dfrac{1}{(-1)^2} = 1$. Since the product of the two slopes is -1, the tangent lines are perpendicular.

12 8.4 mi.

Chapter 10
Exponential functions

Pages 535-536

1 a 100 milligrams; 25 milligrams; 6.25 milligrams
   b 1 to 16
   c 6400 milligrams
   d 7 days

2 a $\frac{1}{4}W_0$; $\frac{1}{16}W_0$; $\frac{1}{64}W_0$

   b $W(t) = W_0(\frac{1}{2})^{t/2}$

   c 8 times as great

   d 8 days

3 a $\frac{1}{2}$ hour

   b 0.4 milligrams; 6.4 milligrams; 102.4 milligrams

   c 1 hour

4 a $4N_0$; $8N_0$; $64N_0$

   b $N(t) = N_0(2)^{t/12}$

   c 64 to 1

5 a $n = 10$.   **b** 6,400,000; 12,800,000; 25,600,000

6 a $1040   **b** $1040.40   **c** $1040.60

7 The culture in which the number of bacteria doubles every $4\frac{4}{5}$ hours

Pages 539-540

1	**a** 1	**d** 125	**g** 4	**j** 6.43
	b $\frac{1}{4}$	**e** 64	**h** 1	**k** 71,900
	c $\frac{16}{9}$	**f** 1	**i** 0.00000001	**l** 0.00349

2 a $\dfrac{5}{x^3}$ **c** $\dfrac{1}{125x^3}$ **e** $5x^2$ **g** $\dfrac{y^4}{x^5}$

   b $\dfrac{y^3}{x^2}$ **d** $\dfrac{5y^2}{x}$ **f** $\dfrac{y^3}{x^2}$ **h** $\dfrac{3}{5x^4y^3}$

3 a $\{\frac{1}{3}, -\frac{1}{3}\}$ **c** $\{x \mid x > \frac{1}{5}$ or $x < 0\}$

   b $\{3\}$ **d** $\{x \mid |x| \leq 2$ and $x \neq 0\}$

4 **a** 7.53×10^1 **e** 7.12×10^5

    b 4.56×10^0 **f** 6.17×10^3

    c 1.46×10^{-1} **g** 2.45×10^{-2}

    d 5.5×10^{-4} **h** 4.3×10^{-5}

5 **a** $2 \times 10^3 = 2000.$ **c** $1.2 \times 10^{-4} = 0.00012$

    b $2 \times 10^5 = 200,000.$ **d** $1.5 \times 10^2 = 150.$

6 **a** $\dfrac{(13 \times 10^4)(6.3 \times 10^{-1})}{(2.8 \times 10^1)(3.9 \times 10^{-2})} = 7.5 \times 10^4 = 75,000.$

    b $\dfrac{(3.4 \times 10^2)(5.1 \times 10^0)}{(8.5 \times 10^{-1})(8.5 \times 10^{-1})} = 2.4 \times 10^3 = 2400.$

    c $\dfrac{(3.8 \times 10^{-2})(4.2 \times 10^1)}{(2.4 \times 10^0)(1.9 \times 10^3)} = 3.5 \times 10^{-4} = 0.00035.$

    d $\dfrac{(1.21 \times 10^{-1})(9.0 \times 10^2)}{(1.8 \times 10^1)(5.5 \times 10^1)} = 1.1 \times 10^{-1} = 0.11.$

7 **a** Because $m > n$, $m - n$ is a positive integer. Hence, $a^n \cdot a^{m-n} = a^m$. Therefore,

    $a^{m-n} = \dfrac{a^m}{a^n}.$

    b Since $m < n$, $n - m$ is a positive integer. Hence, $a^m \cdot a^{n-m} = a^n$, so $a^m = \dfrac{a^n}{a^{n-m}}$.

    Multiplying both sides by $\dfrac{1}{a^n}$, we have $\dfrac{1}{a^n} \cdot a^m = \dfrac{1}{a^n} \cdot \dfrac{a^n}{a^{n-m}}$, or $\dfrac{a^m}{a^n} = \dfrac{1}{a^{n-m}}$. By

    definition, $\dfrac{1}{a^{n-m}} = a^{-(n-m)} = a^{m-n}$. Hence, $\dfrac{a^m}{a^n} = a^{m-n}$.

8 **a** Suppose that one of the integers m and n is positive and the other is negative,

    say $m > 0$ and $n < 0$. Then $a^m \cdot a^n = a^m \cdot \dfrac{1}{a^{-n}} = \dfrac{a^m}{a^{-n}}$, where $-n$ is positive. By

    the theorem in exercise 7a, $\dfrac{a^m}{a^{-n}} = a^{m-(-n)} = a^{m+n}.$

    Now suppose that $m < 0$ and $n < 0$. Then $a^m \cdot a^n = \dfrac{1}{a^{-m}} \cdot \dfrac{1}{a^{-n}}$, where $-m$ and

    $-n$ are positive. Hence, $\dfrac{1}{a^{-m}} \cdot \dfrac{1}{a^{-n}} = \dfrac{1}{a^{-m+(-n)}} = \dfrac{1}{a^{-(m+n)}}$, where $-(m+n)$ is

    positive. By definition $\dfrac{1}{a^{-(m+n)}} = a^{m+n}.$

    Therefore, when only one of the numbers is negative or when both are negative, $a^m \cdot a^n = a^{m+n}$.

    b Suppose that $m < 0$ and $n > 0$. Then $-m > 0$ so that $(a^m)^n = \left(\dfrac{1}{a^{-m}}\right)^n = \dfrac{1}{(a^{-m})^n} = \dfrac{1}{a^{-mn}} = a^{mn}.$

Next suppose that $m > 0$ and $n < 0$. Then $-n > 0$ so that $(a^m)^n = \dfrac{1}{(a^m)^{-n}} = \dfrac{1}{a^{-mn}} = a^{mn}$.

Finally, suppose that $m < 0$ and $n < 0$. Then $-m > 0$ and $-n > 0$. Hence,

$$(a^m)^n = \frac{1}{(a^m)^{-n}} = \frac{1}{(1/a^{-m})^{-n}} = \frac{1}{1/(a^{-m})^{-n}} = \frac{1}{1/a^{mn}} = a^{mn}.$$

c If n is negative, then $-n > 0$. Hence, $(ab)^n = \dfrac{1}{(ab)^{-n}} = \dfrac{1}{a^{-n}b^{-n}} = \dfrac{1}{a^{-n}} \cdot \dfrac{1}{b^{-n}} = a^n b^n$.

9 a Suppose that one of the integers m and n is zero and that the other is different from 0, say $m = 0$ and $n \neq 0$. Then $a^m \cdot a^n = a^0 \cdot a^n = 1 \cdot a^n = a^n = a^{0+n} = a^{m+n}$.

Now suppose that $m = n = 0$. Then $a^m \cdot a^n = a^0 \cdot a^0 = 1 \cdot 1 = 1 = a^{0+0} = a^{m+n}$.

b Suppose that $m = 0$ and $n \neq 0$. Then $(a^m)^n = (a^0)^n = 1^n = 1 = a^{0 \cdot n} = a^{mn}$.

Next suppose that $m \neq 0$ and $n = 0$. Then $(a^m)^n = (a^m)^0 = 1 = a^{m \cdot 0} = a^{mn}$.

Finally, suppose that $m = n = 0$. Then $(a^m)^n = (a^0)^0 = 1^0 = 1 = 1^{0 \cdot 0} = a^{mn}$.

c $(ab)^0 = 1 = 1 \cdot 1 = a^0 b^0$.

Pages 542-543

1 a 5   c 2   e $\frac{1}{2}$ g $\frac{1}{5}$ i $\frac{2}{3}$ k 1.8

   b 4   d 3   f $\frac{1}{8}$ h $\frac{1}{3}$ j $\frac{8}{9}$ l 2.5

2 a $(9 \cdot 16)^{\frac{1}{2}} = 144^{\frac{1}{2}} = 12.$ $9^{\frac{1}{2}} \cdot 16^{\frac{1}{2}} = 3 \cdot 4 = 12.$

   b $(8 \cdot 27)^{\frac{1}{3}} = (216)^{\frac{1}{3}} = 6.$ $8^{\frac{1}{3}} \cdot 27^{\frac{1}{3}} = 2 \cdot 3 = 6.$

   c $(\frac{1}{4} \cdot \frac{1}{36})^{-\frac{1}{2}} = (\frac{1}{144})^{-\frac{1}{2}} = 12.$ $\frac{1}{4}^{-\frac{1}{2}} \cdot \frac{1}{36}^{-\frac{1}{2}} = 2 \cdot 6 = 12.$

   d $(5\frac{4}{9} \cdot 1\frac{11}{25})^{\frac{1}{2}} = (\frac{196}{25})^{\frac{1}{2}} = \frac{14}{5}.$ $(5\frac{4}{9})^{\frac{1}{2}} \cdot (1\frac{11}{25})^{\frac{1}{2}} = \frac{7}{3} \cdot \frac{6}{5} = \frac{14}{5}.$

   e $(0.125 \cdot 216)^{-\frac{1}{3}} = 27^{-\frac{1}{3}} = \frac{1}{3}.$ $0.125^{-\frac{1}{3}} \cdot 216^{-\frac{1}{3}} = 2 \cdot \frac{1}{6} = \frac{1}{3}.$

3 a $\{0.16\}$ c $\{x \mid x \geq 27\}$

   b $\{\frac{1}{4}\}$ d $\{x \mid x < 0 \text{ or } x > \frac{1}{32}\}$

4 Consider the polynomial $x^q - a^q$, where $a > 0$ and q is a positive integer. By definition $(a^q)^{1/q}$ represents the real positive zero of this polynomial. But since $a^q - a^q = 0$, it follows that a is the real positive zero of this polynomial. Hence, $(a^q)^{1/q} = a$.

5 a $3 \times 10^0 = 3.$ b $3 \times 10^{-2} = 0.03.$

Pages 545-546

1 a $\cos \frac{3\pi}{2} + i \sin \frac{3\pi}{2} = -i.$ c $\cos \frac{4\pi}{3} + i \sin \frac{4\pi}{3} = -\frac{1}{2} - \frac{\sqrt{3}}{2}i.$

   b $\cos \frac{\pi}{2} + i \sin \frac{\pi}{2} = i.$ d $\cos \frac{7\pi}{2} + i \sin \frac{7\pi}{2} = -i.$

2 a $\left(\cos \frac{3\pi}{2} + i \sin \frac{3\pi}{2}\right)^5 = \cos \frac{15\pi}{2} + i \sin \frac{15\pi}{2} = -i.$

b $\left(\cos \frac{3\pi}{4} + i \sin \frac{3\pi}{4}\right)^3 = \cos \frac{9\pi}{4} + i \sin \frac{9\pi}{4} = \frac{\sqrt{2}}{2} + \frac{\sqrt{2}}{2}i.$

c $\left(\cos \frac{2\pi}{3} + i \sin \frac{2\pi}{3}\right)^4 = \cos \frac{8\pi}{3} + i \sin \frac{8\pi}{3} = -\frac{1}{2} + \frac{\sqrt{3}}{2}i.$

d $\left(\cos \frac{7\pi}{6} + i \sin \frac{7\pi}{6}\right)^2 = \cos \frac{7\pi}{3} + i \sin \frac{7\pi}{3} = \frac{1}{2} + \frac{\sqrt{3}}{2}i.$

3 a $\frac{\sqrt{2}}{2} + \frac{\sqrt{2}}{2}i = \cos \frac{\pi}{4} + i \sin \frac{\pi}{4}.$ $\left(\cos \frac{\pi}{4} + i \sin \frac{\pi}{4}\right)^2 = \cos \frac{\pi}{2} + i \sin \frac{\pi}{2} = i.$ Hence,

$\frac{\sqrt{2}}{2} + \frac{\sqrt{2}}{2}i$ is a square root of i.

b $\frac{1}{2} + \frac{\sqrt{3}}{2}i = \left(\cos \frac{\pi}{3} + i \sin \frac{\pi}{3}\right).$ $\left(\cos \frac{\pi}{3} + i \sin \frac{\pi}{3}\right)^3 = \cos \pi + i \sin \pi = -1.$ Hence,

$\frac{1}{2} + \frac{\sqrt{3}}{2}i$ is a cube root of -1.

c $-\frac{\sqrt{3}}{2} - \frac{1}{2}i = \cos \frac{7\pi}{6} + i \sin \frac{7\pi}{6}.$ $\left(\cos \frac{7\pi}{6} + i \sin \frac{7\pi}{6}\right)^3 = \cos \frac{7\pi}{2} + i \sin \frac{7\pi}{2} = -i.$ Hence,

$-\frac{\sqrt{3}}{2} - \frac{1}{2}i$ is a cube root of $-i$.

d $-\frac{\sqrt{3}}{2} + \frac{1}{2}i = \cos \frac{5\pi}{6} + i \sin \frac{5\pi}{6}.$ $\left(\cos \frac{5\pi}{6} + i \sin \frac{5\pi}{6}\right)^4 = \cos \frac{10\pi}{3} + i \sin \frac{10\pi}{3} = -\frac{1}{2} - \frac{\sqrt{3}}{2}i.$

Hence, $-\frac{\sqrt{3}}{2} + \frac{1}{2}i$ is a fourth root of $-\frac{1}{2} - \frac{\sqrt{3}}{2}i.$

4 a $(2 - 2\sqrt{3}i)^3 = 4^3\left(\frac{1}{2} - \frac{\sqrt{3}}{2}i\right)^3 = 4^3\left(\cos \frac{5\pi}{3} + i \sin \frac{5\pi}{3}\right)^3 = 64(\cos 5\pi + i \sin 5\pi) = -64.$

b $(-2 + 2i)^4 = \left(2\sqrt{2}\left(-\frac{\sqrt{2}}{2} + \frac{\sqrt{2}}{2}i\right)\right)^4 = (2\sqrt{2})^4\left(\cos \frac{3\pi}{4} + i \sin \frac{3\pi}{4}\right)^4 = 64(\cos 3\pi + i \sin 3\pi) = -64.$

c $(1 - i)^6 = \left(\sqrt{2}\left(\frac{\sqrt{2}}{2} - \frac{\sqrt{2}}{2}i\right)\right)^6 = (\sqrt{2})^6\left(\cos \frac{7\pi}{4} + i \sin \frac{7\pi}{4}\right)^6 = 8\left(\cos \frac{21\pi}{2} + i \sin \frac{21\pi}{2}\right) = 8.$

d $(\sqrt{3} - i)^2 = \left(2\left(\frac{\sqrt{3}}{2} - \frac{1}{2}i\right)\right)^2 = 2^2\left(\cos \frac{11\pi}{6} + i \sin \frac{11\pi}{6}\right)^2 = 4\left(\cos \frac{11\pi}{3} + i \sin \frac{11\pi}{3}\right) = 2 - 2\sqrt{3}i.$

5 a $\frac{1}{\cos \theta + i \sin \theta} = \frac{1}{\cos \theta + i \sin \theta} \cdot \frac{\cos \theta - i \sin \theta}{\cos \theta - i \sin \theta} = \frac{\cos \theta - i \sin \theta}{\cos^2 \theta + \sin^2 \theta} = \cos \theta - i \sin \theta.$

Since $\cos \theta = \cos (-\theta)$ and $\sin \theta = -\sin (-\theta)$, $\cos \theta - i \sin \theta = \cos (-\theta) + i \sin (-\theta).$

b Suppose that n is a positive integer; then $-n$ is negative. $(\cos \theta + i \sin \theta)^{-n} =$

$\frac{1}{(\cos \theta + i \sin \theta)^n} = \frac{1}{\cos n\theta + i \sin n\theta}.$ By the result in part a, $\frac{1}{\cos n\theta + i \sin n\theta} =$

$\cos (-n\theta) + i \sin (-n\theta).$ Hence, De Moivre's Theorem holds for negative integral

exponents.

Pages 549-550

1 a $\cos \frac{2\pi}{3} + i \sin \frac{2\pi}{3} = -\frac{1}{2} + \frac{\sqrt{3}}{2}i;$

$\cos \frac{4\pi}{3} + i \sin \frac{4\pi}{3} = -\frac{1}{2} - \frac{\sqrt{3}}{2}i;$

$\cos 2\pi + i \sin 2\pi = 1 + 0i.$

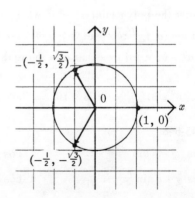

b $\cos \frac{\pi}{2} + i \sin \frac{\pi}{2} = 0 + i;$

$\cos \pi + i \sin \pi = -1 + 0i;$

$\cos \frac{3\pi}{2} + i \sin \frac{3\pi}{2} = 0 - i;$

$\cos 2\pi + i \sin 2\pi = 1 + 0i.$

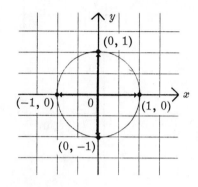

c $\cos \frac{\pi}{3} + i \sin \frac{\pi}{3} = \frac{1}{2} + \frac{\sqrt{3}}{2}i;$

$\cos \frac{2\pi}{3} + i \sin \frac{2\pi}{3} = -\frac{1}{2} + \frac{\sqrt{3}}{2}i;$

$\cos \pi + i \sin \pi = -1 + 0i;$

$\cos \frac{4\pi}{3} + i \sin \frac{4\pi}{3} = -\frac{1}{2} - \frac{\sqrt{3}}{2}i;$

$\cos \frac{5\pi}{3} + i \sin \frac{5\pi}{3} = \frac{1}{2} - \frac{\sqrt{3}}{2}i;$

$\cos 2\pi + i \sin 2\pi = 1 + 0i.$

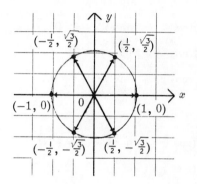

d $\cos \frac{\pi}{6} + i \sin \frac{\pi}{6} = \frac{\sqrt{3}}{2} + \frac{1}{2}i;$ $\quad \cos \frac{7\pi}{6} + i \sin \frac{7\pi}{6} = -\frac{\sqrt{3}}{2} - \frac{1}{2}i;$

$\cos \frac{\pi}{3} + i \sin \frac{\pi}{3} = \frac{1}{2} + \frac{\sqrt{3}}{2}i;$ $\quad \cos \frac{4\pi}{3} + i \sin \frac{4\pi}{3} = -\frac{1}{2} - \frac{\sqrt{3}}{2}i;$

$\cos \frac{\pi}{2} + i \sin \frac{\pi}{2} = 0 + 1i;$ $\quad \cos \frac{3\pi}{2} + i \sin \frac{3\pi}{2} = 0 - 1i;$

$\cos \frac{2\pi}{3} + i \sin \frac{2\pi}{3} = -\frac{1}{2} + \frac{\sqrt{3}}{2}i;$ $\quad \cos \frac{5\pi}{3} + i \sin \frac{5\pi}{3} = \frac{1}{2} - \frac{\sqrt{3}}{2}i;$

$\cos \frac{5\pi}{6} + i \sin \frac{5\pi}{6} = -\frac{\sqrt{3}}{2} + \frac{1}{2}i;$ $\quad \cos \frac{11\pi}{6} + i \sin \frac{11\pi}{6} = \frac{\sqrt{3}}{2} - \frac{1}{2}i;$

$\cos \pi + i \sin \pi = -1 + 0i;$ $\quad \cos 2\pi + i \sin 2\pi = 1 + 0i.$

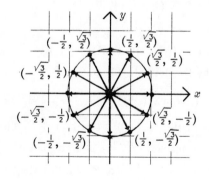

2 a $5(\cos \frac{2\pi}{3} + i \sin \frac{2\pi}{3}) = -\frac{5}{2} + \frac{5\sqrt{3}}{2}i;$

$5(\cos \frac{4\pi}{3} + i \sin \frac{4\pi}{3}) = -\frac{5}{2} - \frac{5\sqrt{3}}{2}i;$

$5(\cos 2\pi + i \sin 2\pi) = 5 + 0i.$

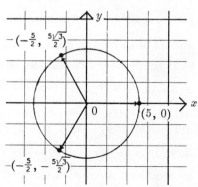

b $2(\cos \frac{2\pi}{5} + i \sin \frac{2\pi}{5}) \approx 0.61 + 1.90i;$

$2(\cos \frac{4\pi}{5} + i \sin \frac{4\pi}{5}) \approx -1.61 + 1.18i;$

$2(\cos \frac{6\pi}{5} + i \sin \frac{6\pi}{5}) \approx -1.61 - 1.18i;$

$2(\cos \frac{8\pi}{5} + i \sin \frac{8\pi}{5}) \approx 0.61 - 1.90i;$

$2(\cos 2\pi + i \sin 2\pi) = 2 + 0i.$

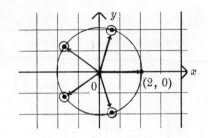

c $\frac{3}{2}(\cos \frac{\pi}{2} + i \sin \frac{\pi}{2}) = 0 + \frac{3}{2}i;$

$\frac{3}{2}(\cos \pi + i \sin \pi) = -\frac{3}{2} + 0i;$

$\frac{3}{2}(\cos \frac{3\pi}{2} + i \sin \frac{3\pi}{2}) = 0 - \frac{3}{2}i;$

$\frac{3}{2}(\cos 2\pi + i \sin 2\pi) = \frac{3}{2} + 0i.$

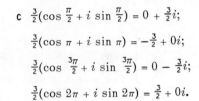

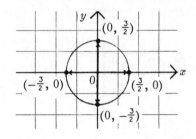

d $2(\cos \frac{\pi}{4} + i \sin \frac{\pi}{4}) = \sqrt{2} + \sqrt{2}i;$

$2(\cos \frac{\pi}{2} + i \sin \frac{\pi}{2}) = 0 + 2i;$

$2(\cos \frac{3\pi}{4} + i \sin \frac{3\pi}{4}) = -\sqrt{2} + \sqrt{2}i;$

$2(\cos \pi + i \sin \pi) = -2 + 0i;$

$2(\cos \frac{5\pi}{4} + i \sin \frac{5\pi}{4}) = -\sqrt{2} - \sqrt{2}i;$

$2(\cos \frac{3\pi}{2} + i \sin \frac{3\pi}{2}) = 0 - 2i;$

$2(\cos \frac{7\pi}{4} + i \sin \frac{7\pi}{4}) = \sqrt{2} - \sqrt{2}i;$

$2(\cos 2\pi + i \sin 2\pi) = 2 + 0i.$

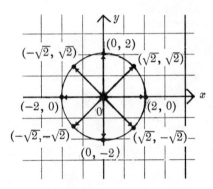

3 a By De Moivre's Theorem $(\cos \frac{\theta}{q} + i \sin \frac{\theta}{q})^q = \cos \theta + i \sin \theta.$ Hence, $\cos \frac{\theta}{q} + i \sin \frac{\theta}{q}$ is a qth root of $C = \cos \theta + i \sin \theta.$

b By Formula III for exponents, $(\omega^k C^{1/q})^q = (\omega^k)^q (C^{1/q})^q = (\omega^k)^q \cdot C.$ By Theorem 46/10, $\omega = \cos \frac{2\pi}{q} + i \sin \frac{2\pi}{q}$ and by De Moivre's Theorem, $\omega^k = \cos \frac{2k\pi}{q} + i \sin \frac{2k\pi}{q}.$ Again by De Moivre's Theorem, $(\omega^k)^q = \cos 2k\pi + i \sin 2k\pi.$ Since k is an integer, $\cos 2k\pi + i \sin 2k\pi = 1.$ Hence, $(\omega^k)^q \cdot C = 1 \cdot C = C.$ Thus, by the definition of the qth root of a complex number, $\omega^k C^{1/q}$ is a qth root of $C.$

c By De Moivre's Theorem $\left(\cos \frac{\theta + 2k\pi}{q} + i \sin \frac{\theta + 2k\pi}{q}\right)^q = \cos(\theta + 2k\pi) + i \sin(\theta + 2k\pi).$ But because the cosine and sine functions have period $2\pi,$ $\cos(\theta + 2k\pi) = \cos \theta$ and $\sin(\theta + 2k\pi) = \sin \theta.$ Hence, $\cos(\theta + 2k\pi) + i \sin(\theta + 2k\pi) = \cos \theta + i \sin \theta.$ Hence, the numbers $\cos \frac{\theta + 2k\pi}{q} + i \sin \frac{\theta + 2k\pi}{q}$ for $k = 1, 2, ..., q$ are the distinct qth roots of $C = \cos \theta + i \sin \theta.$

4 a $-1 = \cos \pi + i \sin \pi$; hence $\theta = \pi$. By the theorem from exercise 3c, the 3 distinct roots of -1 are

$$\cos \frac{\pi + 2\pi}{3} + i \sin \frac{\pi + 2\pi}{3} = \cos \pi + i \sin \pi = -1 + 0i,$$

$$\cos \frac{\pi + 4\pi}{3} + i \sin \frac{\pi + 4\pi}{3} = \cos \frac{5\pi}{3} + i \sin \frac{5\pi}{3} = \frac{1}{2} - \frac{\sqrt{3}}{2}i,$$

$$\cos \frac{\pi + 6\pi}{3} + i \sin \frac{\pi + 6\pi}{3} = \cos \frac{7\pi}{3} + i \sin \frac{7\pi}{3} = \frac{1}{2} + \frac{\sqrt{3}}{2}i.$$

See graph at left below.

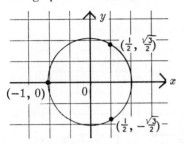 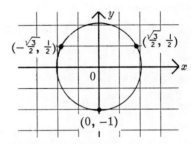

b $i = \cos \frac{\pi}{2} + i \sin \frac{\pi}{2}$, so $\theta = \frac{\pi}{2}$. Hence, the cube roots of i are

$$\cos \frac{\frac{\pi}{2} + 2\pi}{3} + i \sin \frac{\frac{\pi}{2} + 2\pi}{3} = \cos \frac{5\pi}{6} + i \sin \frac{5\pi}{6} = -\frac{\sqrt{3}}{2} + \frac{1}{2}i,$$

$$\cos \frac{\frac{\pi}{2} + 4\pi}{3} + i \sin \frac{\frac{\pi}{2} + 4\pi}{3} = \cos \frac{3\pi}{2} + i \sin \frac{3\pi}{2} = 0 - i,$$

$$\cos \frac{\frac{\pi}{2} + 6\pi}{3} + i \sin \frac{\frac{\pi}{2} + 6\pi}{3} = \cos \frac{13\pi}{6} + i \sin \frac{13\pi}{6} = \frac{\sqrt{3}}{2} + \frac{1}{2}i.$$

See graph at right above.

c $-i = \cos \frac{3\pi}{2} + i \sin \frac{3\pi}{2}$. Hence, the sixth roots of $-i$ are

$$\cos \frac{7\pi}{12} + i \sin \frac{7\pi}{12}, \quad \cos \frac{11\pi}{12} + i \sin \frac{11\pi}{12},$$

$$\cos \frac{5\pi}{4} + i \sin \frac{5\pi}{4} = -\frac{\sqrt{2}}{2} - \frac{\sqrt{2}}{2}i,$$

$$\cos \frac{19\pi}{12} + i \sin \frac{19\pi}{12},$$

$$\cos \frac{23\pi}{12} + i \sin \frac{23\pi}{12},$$

$$\cos \frac{9\pi}{4} + i \sin \frac{9\pi}{4} = \frac{\sqrt{2}}{2} + \frac{\sqrt{2}}{2}i.$$

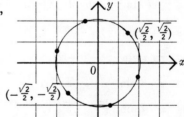

d Since $-\frac{1}{2} + \frac{\sqrt{3}}{2}i = \cos \frac{2\pi}{3} + i \sin \frac{2\pi}{3}$, the fourth roots of $-\frac{1}{2} + \frac{\sqrt{3}}{2}i$ are

$$\cos \frac{2\pi}{3} + i \sin \frac{2\pi}{3} = -\frac{1}{2} + \frac{\sqrt{3}}{2}i,$$

$$\cos \frac{7\pi}{6} + i \sin \frac{7\pi}{6} = -\frac{\sqrt{3}}{2} - \frac{1}{2}i,$$

$$\cos \frac{5\pi}{3} + i \sin \frac{5\pi}{3} = \frac{1}{2} - \frac{\sqrt{3}}{2}i,$$

$$\cos \frac{13\pi}{6} + i \sin \frac{13\pi}{6} = \frac{\sqrt{3}}{2} + \frac{1}{2}i.$$

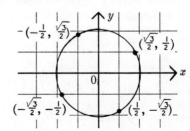

5 $\left(|C|^{1/q}(\cos \dfrac{\theta + 2k\pi}{q} + i \sin \dfrac{\theta + 2k\pi}{q}\right)^q$

$= (|C|^{1/q})^q \cdot \left(\cos \dfrac{\theta + 2k\pi}{q} + i \sin \dfrac{\theta + 2k\pi}{q}\right)^q = |C| \left(\cos (\theta + 2k\pi) + i \sin (\theta + 2k\pi)\right)$

$= |C| (\cos \theta + i \sin \theta) = C$.

Since, for each value of k, where $k = 1, 2, \ldots, q$, the value of $\cos \dfrac{\theta + 2k\pi}{q} +$

$i \sin \dfrac{\theta + 2k\pi}{q}$ is distinct, the numbers $|C|^{1/q} \left(\cos \dfrac{\theta + 2k\pi}{q} + i \sin \dfrac{\theta + 2k\pi}{q}\right)$ are the

distinct qth roots of C.

6 a $-8i = 2^3(\cos \dfrac{3\pi}{2} + i \sin \dfrac{3\pi}{2})$. Hence, the cube roots of $-8i$ are

$2(\cos \dfrac{7\pi}{6} + i \sin \dfrac{7\pi}{6}) = -\sqrt{3} - i$,

$2(\cos \dfrac{11\pi}{6} + i \sin \dfrac{11\pi}{6}) = \sqrt{3} - i$,

$2(\cos \dfrac{5\pi}{2} + i \sin \dfrac{5\pi}{2}) = 0 + 2i$.

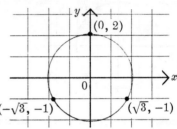

b $4i = 2^2(\cos \dfrac{\pi}{2} + i \sin \dfrac{\pi}{2})$. Hence, the square roots of $4i$ are

$2(\cos \dfrac{5\pi}{4} + i \sin \dfrac{5\pi}{4}) = -\sqrt{2} - \sqrt{2}i$,

$2(\cos \dfrac{9\pi}{4} + i \sin \dfrac{9\pi}{4}) = \sqrt{2} + \sqrt{2}i$.

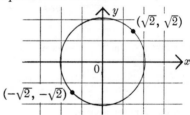

c $-64 = 2^6(\cos \pi + i \sin \pi)$. Hence, the sixth roots of -64 are

$2(\cos \dfrac{\pi}{2} + i \sin \dfrac{\pi}{2}) = 0 + 2i$, $2(\cos \dfrac{5\pi}{6} + i \sin \dfrac{5\pi}{6}) = -\sqrt{3} + i$,

$2(\cos \dfrac{7\pi}{6} + i \sin \dfrac{7\pi}{6}) = -\sqrt{3} - i$,

$2(\cos \dfrac{3\pi}{2} + i \sin \dfrac{3\pi}{2}) = 0 - 2i$,

$2(\cos \dfrac{11\pi}{6} + i \sin \dfrac{11\pi}{6}) = \sqrt{3} - i$,

$2(\cos \dfrac{13\pi}{6} + i \sin \dfrac{13\pi}{6}) = \sqrt{3} + i$.

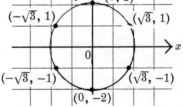

d $-8 - 8\sqrt{3}i = 16(-\dfrac{1}{2} - \dfrac{\sqrt{3}}{2}i) = 2^4(\cos \dfrac{4\pi}{3} + i \sin \dfrac{4\pi}{3})$. Hence, the fourth roots of

$-8 - 8\sqrt{3}i$ are

$2(\cos \dfrac{5\pi}{6} + i \sin \dfrac{5\pi}{6}) = -\sqrt{3} + i$,

$2(\cos \dfrac{4\pi}{3} + i \sin \dfrac{4\pi}{3}) = -1 - 3\sqrt{3}i$,

$2(\cos \dfrac{11\pi}{6} + i \sin \dfrac{11\pi}{6}) = \sqrt{3} - i$,

$2(\cos \dfrac{7\pi}{3} + i \sin \dfrac{7\pi}{3}) = 1 + \sqrt{3}i$.

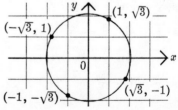

1 a 125   c 512   e 0.01024   g 0.001   i 32   k 625

   b 8   d 125   f 0.09   h $\frac{1}{9}$ j $\frac{1}{343}$ l 0.00001

2 a The solid dots in the graph at the left below represent the points in the graph of
    $\exp_2$. (Graph near x-axis is not to scale.)

   b The small circles in the graph at the left below represent the points in the graph
    of $\exp_4$. (Graph near x-axis is not to scale.)

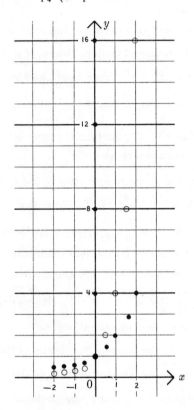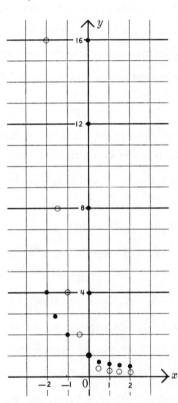

3 The solid dots in the graph at the right above represent the points in the graph of
   $\exp_{\frac{1}{2}}$. The circles represent the points in the graph of $\exp_{\frac{1}{4}}$.

4 We know that $\exp_{1/a}(x)$, where $a > 1$, is $\left(\frac{1}{a}\right)^x$ But $\left(\frac{1}{a}\right)^x = \frac{1}{a^x} = a^{-x} = \exp_a(-x)$.

   Since the graph of f: $f(x) = \exp_a(-x)$ is the reflection in the y-axis of the graph
   of $\exp_a$, it follows that the graph of $\exp_{1/a}$ is the reflection in the y-axis of the
   graph of $\exp_a$.

5 a $(a^{r_1})^{r_2} = (a^{p_1/q_1})^{p_2/q_2}$, where q_1 and q_2 are positive integers and p_1 and p_2 are
    integers. By Definition 49/10, we have
$$(a^{p_1/q_1})^{p_2/q_2} = (a^{1/q_1}{}^{p_1})^{p_2/q_2} = (a^{p_1p_2})^{1/q_1q_2} = a^{p_1p_2/q_1q_2} = a^{(p_1/q_1)(p_2/q_2)} = a^{r_1r_2}.$$

b $(ab)^{r_1} = (ab)^{p/q}$, where p is an integer and q is a positive integer. By Definition 49/10, we have $(ab)^{p/q} = [(ab)^{1/q}]^p = [(ab)^p]^{1/q} = (a^p b^p)^{1/q} = a^{p/q} b^{p/q} = a^{r_1} b^{r_1}$.

6 a Since $a > 1$, it follows that if n is a positive integer, $a^n > 1$. If m and n are integers such that $m > n$, then $m - n$ is a positive integer. Therefore $a^{m-n} > 1$. If both sides of $a^{m-n} > 1$ are multiplied by a^n, we have $a^n \cdot a^{m-n} > a^n$. Since $a^n \cdot a^{m-n} = a^{n+m-n} = a^m$, this is equivalent to $a^m > a^n$. Hence, $\exp_a$ defined on the integers is a strictly increasing function.

b If $0 < a < 1$, then $a = \dfrac{1}{b}$, where $b > 1$. By part a of this exercise, the function $\exp_b$ defined on the integers is a strictly increasing function. Hence, if m and n are integers such that $m > n$, it follows that $b^m > b^n$. Since $b = \dfrac{1}{a}$, we have $\left(\dfrac{1}{a}\right)^m > \left(\dfrac{1}{a}\right)^n$, or $\dfrac{1}{a^m} > \dfrac{1}{a^n}$. From this last inequality, it follows immediately that $a^n > a^m$. Therefore, since $m > n$ implies that $a^n > a^m$, the function $\exp_a$ defined on the integers is a strictly decreasing function whenever $0 < a < 1$.

7 a Assume that $a > 1$ and that $\dfrac{p_1}{q_1} > \dfrac{p_2}{q_2}$ where p_1 and p_2 are integers and q_1 and q_2 are positive integers. If we further assume that $a^{p_1/q_1} \leq a^{p_2/q_2}$, it follows that $(a^{p_1/q_1})^{q_1 q_2} \leq (a^{p_2/q_2})^{q_1 q_2}$, or $a^{p_1 q_2} \leq a^{p_2 q_1}$. But since $\dfrac{p_1}{q_1} > \dfrac{p_2}{q_2}$, $p_1 q_2 > p_2 q_1$. Hence, by the theorem of exercise 6a, $a^{p_1 q_2} > a^{p_2 q_1}$. Since this contradicts the result arrived at by assuming that $a^{p_1/q_1} \leq a^{p_2/q_2}$, we must reject this assumption. Therefore, it follows that if $a > 1$ and $\dfrac{p_1}{q_1} > \dfrac{p_2}{q_2}$, then $a^{p_1/q_1} > a^{p_2/q_2}$. Hence, $\exp_a$, when $a > 1$, is a strictly increasing function defined on the rationals.

b If $0 < a < 1$, then $a = \dfrac{1}{b}$, where $b > 1$. Hence, by the theorem from part a of this exercise, the function $\exp_b$ is a strictly increasing function defined on the rationals. If $\dfrac{p_1}{q_1} > \dfrac{p_2}{q_2}$, where p_1 and p_2 are integers and q_1 and q_2 are positive integers, then it follows that $b^{p_1/q_1} > b^{p_2/q_2}$ or, since $b = \dfrac{1}{a}$, $\left(\dfrac{1}{a}\right)^{p_1/q_1} > \left(\dfrac{1}{a}\right)^{p_2/q_2}$ Because $\left(\dfrac{1}{a}\right)^{p_1/q_1} = \dfrac{1}{a^{p_1/q_1}}$ and $\left(\dfrac{1}{a}\right)^{p_2/q_2} = \dfrac{1}{a^{p_2/q_2}}$, it follows that $\dfrac{1}{a^{p_1/q_1}} > \dfrac{1}{a^{p_2/q_2}}$, which implies that $a^{p_1/q_1} < a^{p_2/q_2}$. Thus, if $0 < a < 1$ and $\dfrac{p_1}{q_1} > \dfrac{p_2}{q_2}$, then $a^{p_1/q_1} < a^{p_2/q_2}$, which implies that $\exp_a$ defined on the rationals is strictly decreasing when $0 < a < 1$.

8 a $\{5\}$ **c** $\{-4\}$ **e** $\{6\}$ **g** $\{\frac{1}{2}\}$ **i** $\{-1\}$

   b $\{4\}$ **d** $\{-3\}$ **f** $\{-\frac{3}{5}\}$ **h** $\{3\}$ **j** $\{-\frac{3}{11}\}$

1 **a** 81   **b** 16   **c** 1,000,000   **d** 3

2 **a** True. The function $\exp_3$ is strictly increasing and $3\sqrt{2} = \sqrt{18}$ is greater than $\sqrt{3}$.

   b True. The function $\exp_2$ is strictly increasing and $\pi\sqrt{3} > 1 + \sqrt{3}$.

   c False. The function $\exp_{\frac{3}{4}}$ is strictly decreasing and $2\sqrt{5} = \sqrt{20}$ is greater than $\sqrt{19}$.

   d True. The function $\exp_{0.5}$ is strictly decreasing and $\pi < \frac{22}{7}$.

3 **a** $\{x \mid x > \frac{4}{3}\}$ **b** $\{x \mid x < \frac{1}{2}\}$ **c** $\{x \mid x < 5\}$ **d** $\{x \mid x > 1\}$ **e** $\{x \mid x < \frac{1}{4}\}$ **f** $\{x \mid x > \frac{2}{5}\}$

4 If $\frac{p}{q} < \frac{m}{n}$, then $pn < qm$. Hence, $qm - pn > 0$ and $pn - qm < 0$, which imply that

$pn - qm < qm - pn$. If we add $pm - qn$ to both sides of this inequality, we obtain
$$pn - qm + pm - qn < qm - pn + pm - qn,$$
which is equivalent to
$$p(m + n) - q(m + n) < p(m - n) + q(m - n),$$
which is equivalent to
$$(p - q)(m + n) < (p + q)(m - n).$$
Hence, $\dfrac{p - q}{p + q} < \dfrac{m - n}{m + n}$.

5 **a** By Theorem 7/2, there exists a rational number r such that $x_1 < r < x_2$. By Definition 50/10, $\exp_a x_1 = $ l.u.b. $\{\exp_a r_1 \mid r_1 \leq x_1 \text{ and } r_1 \text{ is rational}\}$. Since $r_1 \leq x_1$, it follows that $r_1 < r$. Further, since $\exp_a$ defined on the rationals is strictly increasing, it follows that $\exp_a r_1 < \exp_a r$. Since this is true for all $r_i < x_1$, it follows that $\exp_a r$ is an upper bound for $\{\exp_a r_1 \mid r_1 \leq x_1 \text{ and } r_1 \text{ is rational}\}$. Hence, $\exp_a x_1 \leq \exp_a r$, or $\exp_a r > \exp_a x_1$.

   b Since $r < x_2$, there is a rational number r_2 such that $r < r_2 < x_2$, and, since $\exp_a$ is strictly increasing, $\exp_a r < \exp_a r_2$. Since $\exp_a x_2 = $ l.u.b. $\{\exp_a r_2 \mid r_2 \leq x_2 \text{ and } r_2 \text{ is rational}\}$, it follows that $\exp_a r_2 \leq \exp_a x_2$ and, hence, that $\exp_a r < \exp_a x_2$.

   c Since, by part a, $\exp_a x_1 < \exp_a r$ and, by part b, $\exp_a r < \exp_a x_2$, we have $\exp_a x_1 < \exp_a x_2$. If $a > 1$ and x_1 and x_2 are real numbers such that $x_1 < x_2$, then $\exp_a x_1 < \exp_a x_2$. Hence, the function $\exp_a$ defined on the real numbers is strictly increasing when $a > 1$.

6 If $0 < a < 1$, then $a = \dfrac{1}{b}$, where $b > 1$. By exercise 5, the function $\exp_b$ defined on the real numbers is strictly increasing. Hence, if $x_1 < x_2$, $\exp_b x_1 < \exp_b x_2$. Since $b = \dfrac{1}{a}$, this implies that $\exp_{1/a} x_1 < \exp_{1/a} x_2$ or $\dfrac{1}{a^{x_1}} < \dfrac{1}{a^{x_2}}$. Hence, $a^{x_2} < a^{x_1}$, or $\exp_a x_2 < \exp_a x_1$. Thus, the function $\exp_a$ defined on the real numbers is strictly decreasing when $0 < a < 1$.

7 **a** If $a > 0$, then $\exp_{1/a}(-x) = \left(\dfrac{1}{a}\right)^{-x} = \dfrac{1}{a^{-x}} = a^x = \exp_a x$.

   b If $0 < a < 1$, then $\dfrac{1}{a} > 1$ so that $\exp_{1/a}$ is not bounded above and has 0 as its greatest lower bound. Since, by part a, $\exp_{1/a}(-x) = \exp_a x$, the functions $\exp_{1/a}$

and $\exp_a$ have the same domain and range. Therefore, $\exp_a$, where $0 < a < 1$, defined on the real numbers is not bounded above and has 0 as its greatest lower bound.

8 Since $a \neq b$, $a - b \neq 0$, so that $(a - b)^2 > 0$. Hence, $a^2 - 2ab + b^2 > 0$ or $a^2 + b^2 > 2ab$. From this last inequality, it follows that $a^2 + b^2 + 2ab > 2ab + 2ab$, or $(a + b)^2 > 4ab$. Because a and b are positive, $a + b > 0$ and $4ab > 0$. Therefore, we can take the square root of both sides of $(a + b)^2 > 4ab$ to obtain $a + b > 2\sqrt{ab}$,

or $\dfrac{a + b}{2} > \sqrt{ab}$.

9 a $\left(\dfrac{x_1 + x_2}{2}, \dfrac{y_1 + y_2}{2} \right)$

b $\left(\dfrac{x_1 + x_2}{2}, 2^{(x_1 + x_2)/2} \right) = \left(\dfrac{x_1 + x_2}{2}, (2^{x_1} \cdot 2^{x_2})^{\frac{1}{2}} \right) = \left(\dfrac{x_1 + x_2}{2}, \sqrt{y_1 y_2} \right)$.

c By the lemma from exercise 8, $\dfrac{y_1 + y_2}{2} > \sqrt{y_1 y_2}$; so the ordinate of point M is greater than the ordinate of point Q. Since they both have the same abscissa, this means that point Q is directly below point M.

d The slope of $\overline{P_1 P_2}$ is the same as the slope of $\overline{P_1 M}$, which is $\dfrac{\dfrac{y_1 + y_2}{2} - y_1}{\dfrac{x_1 + x_2}{2} - x_1}$. The slope of $\overline{P_1 Q}$ is $\dfrac{\sqrt{y_1 y_2} - y_1}{\dfrac{x_1 + x_2}{2} - x_1}$. Since $\sqrt{y_1 y_2} < \dfrac{y_1 + y_2}{2}$, the slope of $\overline{P_1 Q}$ is less than the slope of $\overline{P_1 P_2}$. Let the coordinates of M be (x_3, y_3) and consider the point (x_3, y_4) on $\overline{P_1 P_2}$. Because the slope of $\overline{P_1 P_2}$ is greater than the slope of $P_1 Q$, it follows that $\dfrac{y_4 - y_1}{x_3 - x_1} > \dfrac{y_3 - y_1}{x_3 - x_1}$, which implies that $y_4 > y_3$. Therefore, M_1 is below the point on $\overline{P_1 P_2}$ that has the same abscissa. By an argument similar to the one given in part c, Q_1 is below M_1. Hence, Q_1 is below the point on $\overline{P_1 P_2}$ with the same abscissa.

e Because Q is below M, the slope of $\overline{Q P_2}$, or $\overline{M_2 P_2}$, is greater than the slope of $\overline{M P_2}$, or $\overline{P_1 P_2}$. If the coordinates of M_2 are (x_5, y_5), then the coordinates of the point on $\overline{P_1 P_2}$ with the same abscissa are (x_5, y_6). Thus, we have $\dfrac{y_5 - y_2}{x_5 - x_2} > \dfrac{y_6 - y_2}{x_5 - x_2}$. Since M_2 is to the left of P_2, $x_5 < x_2$; hence, $x_5 - x_2 < 0$. Thus, if we multiply both sides of $\dfrac{y_5 - y_2}{x_5 - x_2} > \dfrac{y_6 - y_2}{x_5 - x_2}$ by $x_5 - x_2$, we obtain $y_5 - y_2 < y_6 - y_2$. This implies that $y_5 < y_6$ and, hence, that M_2 is below the point on $\overline{P_1 P_2}$ with the same abscissa. By an argument similar to the one given for part c, Q_2 is below M_2. Therefore, Q_2 is below the point on $\overline{P_1 P_2}$ with the same abscissa.

f They suggest that the graph of $\exp_2$ is always concave upward.

g It seems reasonable that the graph of $\exp_{1/2}$ is also concave upward.

1 a $\frac{1}{4}k \approx 0.173.$ d $k \approx 0.693.$ g $2\sqrt{2}k \approx 1.960.$

   b $\frac{1}{2}k \approx 0.347.$ e $\sqrt{2}k \approx 0.980.$ h $4k \approx 2.773.$

   c $\frac{\sqrt{2}}{2}k \approx 0.490.$ f $2k \approx 1.386.$ i $4\sqrt{2}k \approx 3.920.$

2

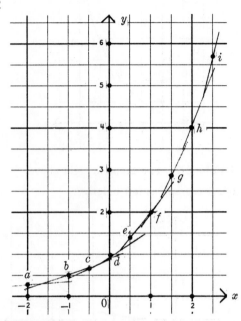

3 If $\exp_2$ had a horizontal tangent at some point on its graph, it would be the case that its slope function would equal 0 at this point; that is, it would be the case that $2^x \cdot k = 0$. But because $k \neq 0$ and $2^x \neq 0$ for all x in $\Re$, it follows that $\exp_2{}' = 2^x \cdot k$ is different from 0 for all x in $\Re$. Hence, $\exp_2$ does not have a horizontal tangent at any point on its graph.

4 a $f'(x) = 5k \cdot 2^x.$ c $F'(x) = \frac{k}{3} \cdot 2^x.$

   b $g'(x) = -3k \cdot 2^x.$ d $G'(x) = \frac{-3k}{4} \cdot 2^x.$

5 $(0, \frac{1}{k})$, which is approximately $(0, 1.440)$

6 a Let $f(x) = 2^x$; then $f'(x) = k \cdot 2^x = k \cdot f(x)$. Hence, $f''(x) = \left(k \cdot f(x)\right)' = k \cdot f'(x) = k \cdot \left(k \cdot f(x)\right) = k^2 \cdot f(x)$, or $k^2 \exp_2 x$.

   b Since $k > 0$, $k^2 > 0$ and $\exp_2 x > 0$ for all x in $\Re$. Therefore, $k^2 \exp_2 x > 0$ for all x in $\Re$. Hence, the graph of $\exp_2$ is always concave upward.

7 If a is a real number, $\exp_2(x + a) = 2^{x+a} = 2^a \cdot 2^x = 2^a \exp_2 x$, where 2^a is a real number. Hence, $\exp'_2(x + a) = 2^a \cdot \exp'_2 x = 2^a \cdot k \cdot 2^x$. Also, $2^a \cdot k \cdot 2^x = k \cdot 2^x \cdot 2^a = k \cdot 2^{x+a} = k \cdot \exp_2(x + a)$. Therefore, $\exp'_2(x + a) = k \cdot \exp_2(x + a)$.

8 a $f'(x) = k \cdot 2^{x+2}$. $f'(-1) = k \cdot 2^{(-1+2)} = k \cdot 2^1 \approx 1.39$. See graph at left below.

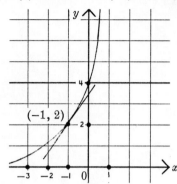 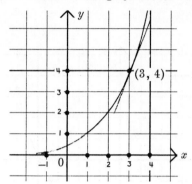

b $g'(x) = k \cdot 2^{x-1}$. $g'(3) = k \cdot 2^{3-1} = k \cdot 2^2 \approx 2.77$. See graph at right above.

c $F'(x) = k \cdot 2^{x+4}$. $F'(0) = k \cdot 2^4 \approx 11.09$. See graph at left below.

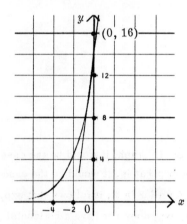 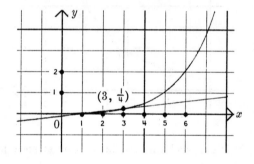

d $G'(x) = k \cdot 2^{x-5}$. $G'(3) = k \cdot 2^{-2} = \dfrac{k}{4} \approx 0.173$. See graph at right above.

9 a $\exp_2'(x_0) = -\exp_{\frac{1}{2}}'(x_0)$; the fact that the graphs are reflections of each other in the y-axis means that the tangents are reflections of each other in the y-axis. Hence, the slopes of the tangents to the graphs at the points (x_0, y) and $(-x_0, y)$ are the negatives of each other.

b Since $\exp_2(-x) = \exp_{\frac{1}{2}}(x)$, the value of $\exp_2'(-x_0)$ is the slope of the tangent line to $\exp_{\frac{1}{2}}$ at the point $\left(x_0, (\tfrac{1}{2})^{x_0}\right)$. This, in turn, is the negative of the slope of the tangent line to the graph of $\exp_2$ at the point $(-x_0, 2^{-x_0})$. That is, $\exp_2'(-x_0) = \exp_{\frac{1}{2}}'(x_0) = -k \cdot \exp_2(-x_0)$. Hence, $\exp_2'(-x) = -k \cdot \exp_2(-x)$.

c $\exp_{\frac{1}{2}}'(x) = \exp_2'(-x) = -k \exp_2(-x) = -k \exp_{\frac{1}{2}} x.$

10 a $f'(x) = -k \cdot \frac{1}{2}^{x+2}.$ $f'(-2) = k \cdot \frac{1}{2}^0 = -k \approx 0.69.$ See graph at left below.

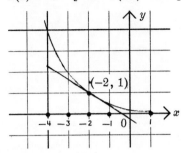
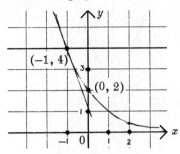

b $g'(x) = -k \cdot \frac{1}{2}^{x-1}.$ $g'(-1) = -k \cdot 4 \approx -2.77.$ See graph at right above.

c $F'(x) = -3k\frac{1}{2}^{x-3}.$ $F'(2) = -6k \approx -4.16.$ See graph at left below.

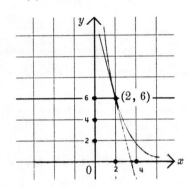
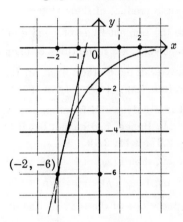

d $G'(x) = -3(-k)\frac{1}{2}^{x+1}.$ $G'(-2) = 6k \approx 4.16.$ See graph at right above.

Pages 572-573

1 a $f(x) = 4^x = 2^{2x};$ therefore, $f'(x) = 2k \cdot 2^{2x} = 2k \cdot 4^x.$

  b $g(x) = (\frac{1}{2})^x = 2^{-x};$ therefore, $g'(x) = -k \cdot 2^{-x} = -k(\frac{1}{2})^x.$

  c $F(x) = 8^x = 2^{3x};$ therefore, $F'(x) = 3k \cdot 2^{3x} = 3k \cdot 8^x.$

  d $G(x) = 0.25^x = 2^{-2x};$ therefore, $G'(x) = -2k \cdot 2^{-2x} = -2k \cdot (\frac{1}{4})^x.$

2 $\ell(x) = x + 1.$

3 a The graphs are reflections of each other in the y-axis. Since $f(x) = e^x$, $f(-x) = e^{-x}$, which is $g(x)$. Since $f(x)$ and $f(-x)$ are reflections of each other in the y-axis, $f(x)$ and $g(x) = f(-x)$ are reflections of each other in the y-axis. See graph at the top of the next page.

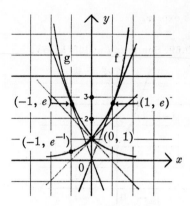

b See the graph for part a. The tangent lines are reflections of each other in the y-axis, so that their slopes are the negatives of each other.

c See the graph for part a. The tangent lines are perpendicular to each other since the product of their slopes is -1.

d Since the tangent lines of f and g at the points (x_0, e^{x_0}) and $(-x_0, e^{x_0})$, respectively, are reflections of each other in the y-axis, their slopes are the negatives of each other. That is, the slopes of the tangents are e^{x_0} and $-e^{x_0}$. Therefore, $\exp_e'(-x) = -\exp_e(-x)$.

4 No. If f is a polynomial function of positive degree, then f$'$ is of degree $n-1$, when $(n-1) \geqq 0$. Hence, $f(x)$ cannot equal $f'(x)$ for all x in $\Re$.

5 $2,\ 2.25,\ 2.37,\ 2.44,\ 2.49$

6 If $f(x) = a^x$, then $f'(x) = ak \cdot \exp_a x$, where $2^a = a$. Hence, $f'(x_0) = ak \cdot \exp_a x_0 = ak \cdot a^{x_0}$ and $f'(x_0 + h) = ak \cdot \exp_a (x_0 + h) = ak \cdot a^{x_0+h} = ak \cdot a^{x_0} \cdot a^h$.

Hence, the slope of the tangent line at $(x_0 + h,\ a^{x_0+h})$ is a^h times the slope of the tangent at $(x_0,\ a^{x_0})$.

7 $\exp_e'(x) = \exp_e(x)$. Hence, $\exp_e'(x_0) = e^{x_0}$. Thus an equation for the tangent line at $(x_0,\ e^{x_0})$ is $y - e^{x_0} = e^{x_0}(x - x_0)$. If $y = 0$, then we have $0 - e^{x_0} = e^{x_0}(x - x_0)$ or $-1 = x - x_0$. Hence, $x = x_0 - 1$ and the x-intercept is $(x_0 - 1, 0)$.

8 Let $f(x) = 2^x$ and $g(x) = ax$, where $a \in \Re$. Then $(f \circ g)(x) = f\big(g(x)\big) = f(ax) = 2^{ax}$. Hence, $(f \circ g)'(x) = ak \cdot 2^{ax}$. Now $f'(x) = k \cdot 2^x$ so that $f'\big(g(x)\big) = k \cdot 2^{ax}$. Also, $g'(x) = a$. Hence, $f'\big(g(x)\big) \cdot g'(x) = k \cdot 2^{ax} \cdot a = (f \circ g)'(x)$.

Pages 575-576

1 a $f'(x) = 20 \cdot e^{2x}$.

   c $F'(x) = -40 \cdot e^{10x}$.

  b $g'(x) = -0.15 \cdot e^{-3x}$.

   d $G'(x) = 10 \cdot e^{0.1x}$.

2 a $c(-x) = \frac{1}{2}e^{-x} + \frac{1}{2}e^{-(-x)} = \frac{1}{2}e^x + \frac{1}{2}e^{-x} = c(x)$. Therefore, c is an even function.

  b $c'(x) = \frac{1}{2}e^x - \frac{1}{2}e^{-x} = \frac{1}{2}e^{-x}(e^{2x} - 1)$. Now $\frac{1}{2}e^{-x} > 0$ for all $x \in \Re$. If $x > 0$,

    $e^{2x} > 1$, so $e^{2x} - 1 > 0$ and, hence, $c'(x) > 0$. Thus, the graph of c is strictly increasing if $x > 0$. On the other hand, $e^{2x} < 1$ if $x < 0$, so $e^{2x} - 1 < 0$ for $x < 0$. Therefore, $c'(x) < 0$ if $x < 0$, and thus the graph of c is strictly decreasing if $x < 0$. Finally, $e^{2x} - 1 = 0$ if $2x = 0$, or $x = 0$, so that the tangent to the graph of c at $(0, 1)$ is horizontal. Since $c''(x) = \frac{1}{2}e^x + \frac{1}{2}e^{-x}$, $c''(x) > 0$ for all $x \in \Re$. Hence, the graph of c is concave upward at $x = 0$. Thus $(0, 1)$ is a minimum point.

c As we have seen in part b, $c''(x) = \frac{1}{2}e^x + \frac{1}{2}e^{-x}$. For all $x \in \Re$, e^x and e^{-x} are positive and, hence, $c''(x) > 0$ for all $x \in \Re$. Thus, the graph of c is concave upward for all $x \in \Re$.

d

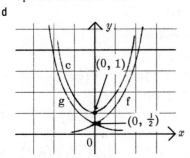

3 a $s(-x) = \frac{1}{2}e^{-x} - \frac{1}{2}e^{-(-x)} = \frac{1}{2}e^{-x} - \frac{1}{2}e^{(x)} = g(x) - f(x) = -s(x)$.
  Hence, s is an odd function.

b $s'(x) = \frac{1}{2}e^x - (-\frac{1}{2}e^{-x}) = \frac{1}{2}e^x + \frac{1}{2}e^{-x}$. Since $\frac{1}{2}e^x > 0$ for all x in $\Re$ and $\frac{1}{2}e^{-x} > 0$ for all x in $\Re$, $s'(x) > 0$ for all x in $\Re$. Therefore, s is a strictly increasing function.

c $s''(x) = \frac{1}{2}e^x + (-1)\frac{1}{2}e^{-x} = \frac{1}{2}e^x - \frac{1}{2}e^{-x}$. As was shown in the answer for exercise 2b, this function is greater than 0 for $x > 0$ and less than 0 for $x < 0$. Therefore, s is concave upward when $x > 0$ and concave downward when $x < 0$. $s''(0) = \frac{1}{2}e^0 - \frac{1}{2}e^0 = 0$; also, $s(0) = 0$. Since $s''(x) = 0$ at $(0, 0)$ and since the concavity of the graph changes at this point, $(0, 0)$ is an inflection point.

d

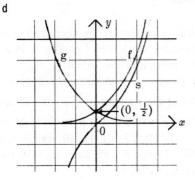

4 a $\cos h^2 x - \sin h^2 x = (\frac{1}{2}e^x + \frac{1}{2}e^{-x})^2 - (\frac{1}{2}e^x - \frac{1}{2}e^{-x})^2$

$= \frac{1}{4}e^{2x} + \frac{1}{2} + \frac{1}{4}e^{-2x} - \frac{1}{4}e^{2x} + \frac{1}{2} - \frac{1}{4}e^{-2x}$

$= 1$.

b $\sinh (2x) = \frac{1}{2}e^{2x} - \frac{1}{2}e^{-2x}$.

$$2 \sinh x \cdot \cosh x = 2(\frac{1}{2}e^x - \frac{1}{2}e^{-x})(\frac{1}{2}e^x + \frac{1}{2}e^{-x}) = 2(\frac{1}{4}e^{2x} - \frac{1}{4}e^{-2x})$$
$$= \frac{1}{2}e^{2x} - \frac{1}{2}e^{-2x} = \sinh (2x).$$

c $\cosh (2x) = \frac{1}{2}e^{2x} + \frac{1}{2}e^{-2x}$.

$$\cosh^2 x + \sinh^2 x = (\frac{1}{2}e^x + \frac{1}{2}e^{-x})^2 + (\frac{1}{2}e^x - \frac{1}{2}e^{-x})^2$$
$$= \frac{1}{4}e^{2x} + \frac{1}{2} + \frac{1}{4}e^{-2x} + \frac{1}{4}e^{2x} - \frac{1}{2} + \frac{1}{4}e^{-2x}$$
$$= \frac{1}{2}e^{2x} + \frac{1}{2}e^{-2x} = \cosh (2x).$$

d $\cosh' x = \frac{1}{2}e^x + (-1)\frac{1}{2}e^{-x} = \frac{1}{2}e^x - \frac{1}{2}e^{-x} = \sinh x$.

e $\sinh' x = \frac{1}{2}e^x - (-1)\frac{1}{2}e^{-x} = \frac{1}{2}e^x + \frac{1}{2}e^{-x} = \cosh x$.

5 a $(f \circ g)(x) = f(x + a) = e^{x+a}$. $(f \circ g)'(x) = e^{x+a}$. $f'(x) = e^x$; $f'\left(g(x)\right) = e^{x+a}$; and $g'(x) = 1$. Therefore, $f'\left(g(x)\right) \cdot g'(x) = e^{x+a} \cdot 1 = (f \circ g)'(x)$.

b $(f \circ g)(x) = f(cx) = e^{cx}$. $(f \circ g)'(x) = c \cdot e^{cx}$. $f'(x) = e^x$; $f'\left(g(x)\right) = e^{cx}$; and $g'(x) = c$. Therefore, $f'\left(g(x)\right) \cdot g'(x) = e^{cx} \cdot c = (f \circ g)'(x)$.

c $(f \circ g)(x) = f(cx + a) = e^{cx+a}$. $(f \circ g)'(x) = c \cdot e^{cx+a}$. $f'(x) = e^x$; $f'\left(g(x)\right) = e^{cx+a}$; and $g'(x) = c$. Therefore, $f'\left(g(x)\right) \cdot g'(x) = e^{cx+a} \cdot c = (f \circ g)'(x)$.

6 Let $G(x) = A \cdot a^{cx}$, where $x \in \Re$ and let $e^\beta = a$. Then $G(x) = A(e^\beta)^{cx} = Ae^{\beta cx}$. By Theorem 51/10, $G'(x) = \beta cA \cdot e^{\beta cx}$. Since $e^\beta = a$, this is equivalent to $G'(x) = \beta cA \cdot a^{cx}$.

Pages 580-581

1 a Since $d(t) = \frac{g}{2}t^2$, $d'(t) = gt$. $d'(1) = g$; $d'(2.5) = 2.5g$; and $d'(4\frac{1}{4}) = 4\frac{1}{4}g$.

b Since $d'(t) = gt$, $d''(t) = g$, which is a constant.

2 a 80 ft. per second; 48 ft. per second; −32 ft. per second. The velocity is negative, because the ball is falling back to the ground.

b 144 ft. **c** −96 ft. per second.

d $h''(t) = -32$ and, since $h''(t)$ is the acceleration at time t, the acceleration is constant. The acceleration is negative, because the force of gravity is in a direction exactly opposite to the original direction of the object.

3 a Since $f(t) = 10 \sin t$, $f'(t) = 10 \cos t$. Now $10 \cos t = 0$ when $\cos t = 0$; that is, when $t = \frac{\pi}{2}$ or $t = \frac{3\pi}{2}$. $f(\frac{\pi}{2}) = 10 \sin \frac{\pi}{2} = 10$ and $f(\frac{3\pi}{2}) = 10 \sin \frac{3\pi}{2} = -10$. Hence, the velocity $f'(t)$ is 0 when the coordinate of the position of the particle is 10 or −10.

b Since $f'(t) = 10 \cos t$, the maximum velocity is 10. When $f(t) = 10 \sin t = 0$, $\sin t = 0$, so that $f(t) = 0$ when $t = 0$ or $t = \pi$. $f'(0) = 10 \cos 0 = 10$ and $f'(\pi) = 10 \cos \pi = -10$. $|10| = |-10| = 10$, which is the maximum velocity.

c $f''(t) = -10 \sin t$; hence, the greatest absolute value of the acceleration will be 10. Now $|-10 \sin t| = 10$ when $t = \frac{\pi}{2}$ and $t = \frac{3\pi}{2}$. From exercise 3a, the displacement of the particle from the center point is greatest when $t = \frac{\pi}{2}$ and when $t = \frac{3\pi}{2}$.

4 $f'(t) = cA \cdot e^{ct} = c \cdot f(t)$. Hence, $f'(t)/f(t) = c$.

5 a $v(t) = v_0 + at$. **b** $s(t) = v_0t + \frac{1}{2}at^2$.

6 a From exercise 5b, since $v_0 = 0$, we have $175 = 0 + \frac{1}{2}10t^2$. Hence, $t = \sqrt{35}$ and
$v(t) = 0 + 10\sqrt{35} = 10\sqrt{35}$.

b $v(t) = 0$ when $10\sqrt{35} - 5t = 0$; that is, when $t = 2\sqrt{35}$. $s(t) = (10\sqrt{35})(2\sqrt{35}) - \frac{5}{2}(2\sqrt{35})^2 = 350$ ft.

7 a $f'(t_0) = -cA \cdot e^{-ct_0} + B$. As t increases, $-cA \cdot e^{-ct}$ becomes smaller, so that $f'(t)$, which is the instantaneous velocity, increases and gets closer and closer to B.

b $f''(t_0) = c^2A \cdot e^{-ct_0}$. As t increases, $f''(t)$, which is the acceleration, decreases and approaches 0.

c Since the acceleration at $t = 0$ is g, we have $f''(0) = c^2A \cdot e^0 = c^2A = g$. Hence, $A = \frac{g}{c^2}$. Since the velocity at $t = 0$ is 0, we have
$$f'(0) = -cA \cdot e^0 + B = -cA + B = 0 \text{ or } B = cA.$$
Since $A = \frac{g}{c^2}$, $B = \frac{g}{c}$.

Page 584

1 $2^T = \left(\dfrac{W_0}{W(T)}\right)^h$. $2^T = (\frac{8}{1})^h$. $2^{T/h} = 8$; therefore, $\dfrac{T}{h} = 3$, or $T = 3h$. Since $h = 5730 \pm 40$, $T = 17,190 \pm 120$.

2 25%. 50% of the carbon 14 would be lost in approximately 5700 years, and another 50% of the remaining 50% would be lost in the next 5700 years.

3 A contemporary of Julius Caesar. $2^T = (\frac{5}{4})^{5730 \pm 40}$. Since $2^0 = 1$, $2^1 = 2$, and $1.25 \approx 2^{\frac{1}{3}}$, we have $2^T \approx (2^{\frac{1}{3}})^{5730 \pm 40}$, or $2^T \approx 2^{1910 \pm 13}$. Hence, $T \approx 1900$ years.

4 $\dfrac{W(T)}{W_0} = 2^{-T/h} \approx 2^{-25,000/5700} \approx 2^{-5}$. Hence, $\dfrac{W(T)}{W_0} \approx \frac{1}{32}$, which means that about 3% of the carbon 14 would be left after 25,000 years.

Chapter review
Pages 584-586

1 b	4 d	7 a	10 b	13 c	16 c
2 b	5 b	8 b	11 d	14 d	17 c
3 b	6 d	9 a	12 c	15 c	18 c

Cumulative review
Pages 586-587
1 a

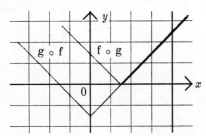

b $(f \circ g)(x) = |x - 3|$ and $(g \circ f)(x) = |x| - 3$. When $x \geq 3$, $(f \circ g)(x) = x - 3$ and $(g \circ f)(x) = x - 3$. Hence, for $x \geq 3$, $(f \circ g)(x) = (g \circ f)(x)$. When $0 < x < 3$, $(f \circ g)(x) = 3 - x$ and $(g \circ f)(x) = x - 3$. Therefore, for these values of x, $(f \circ g)(x) > 0$ and $(g \circ f)(x) < 0$. Hence, for $0 < x < 3$, $(f \circ g)(x) > (g \circ f)(x)$. When $x \leq 0$, $(f \circ g)(x) = 3 - x$ and $(g \circ f)(x) = -3 - x$, so that $(f \circ g)(x) - (g \circ f)(x) = (3 - x) - (-3 - x) = 6$. Hence, for $x \leq 0$, $(f \circ g)(x) > (g \circ f)(x)$. Thus, for all values of x, $(f \circ g)(x) \geq (g \circ f)(x)$.

2 54 square units

3 a $f(x) > 0$ for $\{x \mid x < 0$ or $0 < x < 4$ or $x > 4\}$; $f(x) = 0$ for $\{0, 4\}$; $f(x)$ is never less than 0.

b $f'(x) = 4x^3 - 24x^2 + 32x = 4x(x - 4)(x - 2)$. Hence, $f'(x) > 0$ for $\{x \mid 0 < x < 2$ or $x > 4\}$; $f''(x) = 0$ for $\{0, 2, 4\}$; $f'(x) < 0$ for $\{x \mid x < 0$ or $2 < x < 4\}$.

c $f''(x) = 4(3x^2 - 12x + 8)$. Hence, $f''(x) > 0$ for $\{x \mid x < 2 - \frac{2\sqrt{3}}{4}$ or $x > 2 + \frac{2\sqrt{3}}{3}\}$; $f''(x) = 0$ for $\{2 - \frac{2\sqrt{3}}{3}, 2 + \frac{2\sqrt{3}}{3}\}$; $f''(x) < 0$ for $\{x \mid 2 - \frac{2\sqrt{3}}{3} < x < 2 + \frac{2\sqrt{3}}{3}\}$.

d

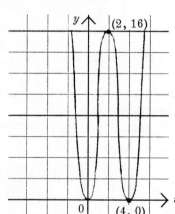

4 $(-2, -8)$, $(-1, -1)$, and $(3, 27)$

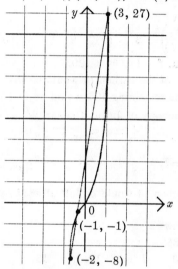

5 a $k = -14$.

b $(x + \frac{1}{2} - \sqrt{\frac{29}{2}})$ and $(x + \frac{1}{2} + \sqrt{\frac{29}{2}})$

6 a, b

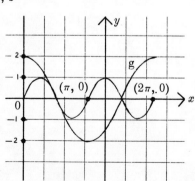

c $x = \frac{\pi}{2}$ and $x = \frac{3\pi}{2}$.

7 a $\dfrac{\csc x - 2 \sin x}{\cos^4 x - \sin^4 x} = \dfrac{\dfrac{1}{\sin x} - 2 \sin x}{(\cos^2 x - \sin^2 x)(\cos^2 x + \sin^2 x)} = \dfrac{\dfrac{1 - 2 \sin^2 x}{\sin x}}{\cos^2 x - \sin^2 x} =$

$\dfrac{\dfrac{1 - 2 \sin^2 x}{\sin x}}{(1 - \sin^2 x) - \sin^2 x} = \dfrac{\dfrac{1 - 2 \sin^2 x}{\sin x}}{1 - 2 \sin^2 x} = \dfrac{1}{\sin x} = \csc x.$

b $\cos 3x = \cos (2x + x) = \cos 2x \cos x - \sin 2x \sin x = (\cos^2 x - \sin^2 x)(\cos x) -$
$(2 \sin x \cos x) \sin x = \cos^3 x - \sin^2 x \cos x - 2 \sin^2 x \cos x = \cos^3 x -$
$3 \sin^2 x \cos x = \cos^3 x - 3(1 - \cos^2 x)\cos x = \cos^3 x - 3 \cos x + 3 \cos^2 x =$
$4 \cos^3 x - 3 \cos x.$

8 a Domain: $\{t \mid 0 \leqq t \leqq 30\}$; range: $\{G(t) \mid 0 \leqq G(t) \leqq 180{,}000\}$

b $G'(t) = -12{,}000 + 400t$; hence, the water is running out of the pool at the rate of 8000 gallons per minute after 10 minutes.

c $G(10) = 180{,}000 - 12{,}000(10) + 200(10)^2 = 80{,}000$; $G(0) = 180{,}000$. Hence, the average rate of change is 10,000 gallons per minute.

9 a $W(t) = W_0(\tfrac{1}{2})^{2t/3}.$

b $W(3n + 4) = W_0(\tfrac{1}{2})^{2n + 8/3}$; $W(3n - 2) = W_0(\tfrac{1}{2})^{2n - 4/3}.$

Hence, $\dfrac{W(3n + 4)}{W(3n - 2)} = \dfrac{\tfrac{1}{2}^{8/3}}{\tfrac{1}{2}^{-4/3}} = \dfrac{\tfrac{1}{2}^{8/3} \cdot \tfrac{1}{2}^{4/3}}{1} = (\tfrac{1}{2})^4 = \tfrac{1}{16}.$

c $250 = W_0(\tfrac{1}{2})^{2 \cdot 9/3} = W_0(\tfrac{1}{2})^6 = W_0 \tfrac{1}{64}$. Hence, $W_0 = 16{,}000$. $1000 = 16{,}000(\tfrac{1}{2})^{2t/3}$.
Hence, $t = 6.$

10 a $2 (\cos \tfrac{\pi}{3} + i \sin \tfrac{\pi}{3}) = 1 + \sqrt{3}i$; $2(\cos \tfrac{4\pi}{3} + i \sin \tfrac{4\pi}{3}) = -1 - \sqrt{3}i$;
$2 (\cos \tfrac{2\pi}{3} + i \sin \tfrac{2\pi}{3}) = -1 + \sqrt{3}i$; $2(\cos \tfrac{5\pi}{3} + i \sin \tfrac{5\pi}{3}) = 1 - \sqrt{3}i$;
$2 (\cos \pi + i \sin \pi) = -2 + 0i$; $2(\cos 2\pi + i \sin 2\pi) = 2 + 0i.$

b

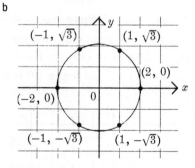

11 a $\tfrac{9}{4}$ **b** 3 **c** 0.25 **d** $\tfrac{27}{8}$

12 a $|(f \cdot g)(x)| = |f(x) \cdot g(x)| = |f(x)| \cdot |g(x)| = |f(x)| \cdot |\sin x|$. Now $0 \leqq |\sin x| \leqq 1$.
Therefore, $|(f \cdot g)(x)| = |f(x)|$ when $|\sin x| = 1$ and $|(f \cdot g)(x)| < |f(x)|$ when
$0 \leqq |\sin x| < 1$. Thus, $|(f \cdot g)(x)| \leqq |f(x)|.$

b $(f \cdot g)(x) = f(x)$ when $g(x) = 1$; that is, when $\sin x = 1$. Hence, $(f \cdot g)(x) = f(x)$ when $x = \frac{\pi}{2} + 2n\pi$, where n is a positive integer. $(f \cdot g)(x) = -f(x)$ when $g(x) = -1$; that is, when $x = \frac{3\pi}{2} + 2n\pi$, where n is a positive integer.

c $(f \cdot g)(x) = 0$ when $g(x) = 0$; that is, when $x = n\pi$, where n is a nonnegative integer.

d As x increases without bound, $(f \cdot g)(x)$ approaches 0, alternately from above the x-axis and from below the x-axis.

e

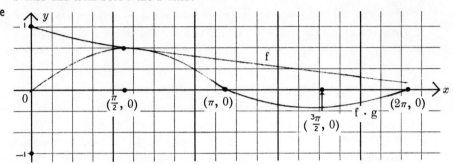

Chapter 11
Logarithmic functions

1 a $\log_2 64 = 6$.   **c** $\log_2 \sqrt{2} = \frac{1}{2}$.   **e** $\log_2 2\sqrt{2} = \frac{3}{2}$.

   b $\log_2 1 = 0$.   **d** $\log_2 0.25 = -2$.   **f** $\log_2 \frac{1}{8} = -3$.

2 a 5   **b** -1 **c** -7 **d** -4 **e** $\frac{1}{3}$ **f** $\frac{2}{3}$

3 a 8   **b** $\frac{1}{2}$ **c** $\frac{1}{16}$ **d** $4\sqrt{2}$ **e** $\frac{\sqrt{2}}{2}$ **f** 128

4 a 10   **b** $\frac{1}{2}$ **c** 0.3   **d** 5   **e** -3.2 **f** 12

5 a 10   **b** 6   **c** 8   **d** 13

6 $\log_2 x > 0$ for all $x > 1$. $\log_2 x < 0$ for all x such that $0 < x < 1$. Since $\log_2$ is the inverse of $\exp_2$, it follows that the domain of $\log_2$ is the range of $\exp_2$ and the range of $\log_2$ is the domain of $\exp_2$. We know that $x > 0$ leads to $\exp_2 x > 1$ and $x < 0$ leads to $0 < \exp_2 x < 1$. Hence, $\log_2 x > 0$ leads to $x > 1$ and $\log_2 x < 0$ leads to $0 < x < 1$.

7 a The graph of $\log_2$ is the reflection in the line $\ell(x) = x$ of the graph of $\exp_2$. This follows because the functions are inverses of each other.

b

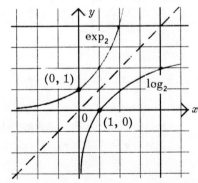

c The graph is increasing for its entire domain; that is, for all $x > 0$. The graph is never decreasing.

d The graph is never concave upward; the graph is concave downward for all $x > 0$.

8 If $\log_2\left(\frac{1}{b}\right) = x$, where $b > 0$, then $2^x = \frac{1}{b}$ by definition of $\log_2$. Hence, $2^{-x} = b$. Again by definition $\log_2 b = -x$, or $-\log_2 b = x$. Since $\log_2\left(\frac{1}{b}\right) = x$ and $-\log_2 b = x$, we have $\log_2\left(\frac{1}{b}\right) = -\log_2 b$.

Page 593

1 **a** 1   **b** 3   **c** $\frac{1}{2}$ **d** -1 **e** 5   **f** 0

2 **a** 125   **b** 0.001   **c** 8   **d** $\frac{1}{6}$ **e** 8   **f** $\frac{1}{2}$

3 **a** 10   **b** 2   **c** 9   **d** 9   **e** 16   **f** 2

4 **a** 5   **b** 4   **c** 1.2   **d** $\emptyset$ ($\exp_4 > 0$ for all x.)

5 **a** True. $\log_{10} 10{,}000 = 4$, $\log_{10} 1000 = 3$, and $\log_{10} 10 = 1$.

    b True. $\log_3 9 = 2$ and $\log_9 3 = \frac{1}{2}$.

    c False. $\log_7 7^3 = 3$ and $\log_3 3^7 = 7$.

    d True. $\log_{10} 10^{-1.5} = -1.5$ and $10^{\log_{10}(-1.5)} = -1.5$.

6 The function $\exp_1$ is not one-to-one since every domain element maps onto 1. Hence, $\exp_1$ cannot have an inverse, so the function $\log_1$ does not exist.

7 $\log_a x > 0$ for $x > 1$. This is so because $\exp_a x > 1$ whenever $x > 0$. $\log_a x < 0$ for $0 < x < 1$. This is so because $0 < \exp_a < 1$ whenever $x < 0$.

8 Suppose that $x_1 < x_2$ and that $\log_a x_1 = y_1$ and $\log_a x_2 = y_2$. Then $a^{y_1} = x_1$ and $a^{y_1} < a^{y_2}$. Since $\exp_a$ is a strictly increasing function, this means that $y_1 < y_2$, or $\log_a x_1 < \log_a x_2$.

Now suppose that $\log_a x_1 < \log_a x_2$ and let $\log_a x_1 = y_1$ and $\log_a x_2 = y_2$. Then $y_1 < y_2$ and, because $\exp_a$ is a strictly increasing function, $a^{y_1} < a^{y_2}$. But $a^{y_1} = a^{\log_a x_1} = x_1$ and $a^{y_2} = a^{\log_a x_2} = x_2$. Therefore, $x_1 < x_2$. Hence, $\log_a x_1 < \log_a x_2$ if and only if $x_1 < x_2$.

9 **a**

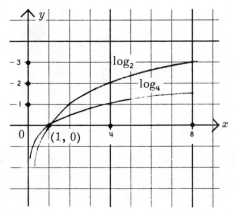

b Assume that $x_0 > 0$. Let $\log_2 x_0 = y_0$ and $\log_4 x_0 = y_1$. Then $2^{y_0} = x_0$ and $4^{y_1} = x_0$; so $2^{y_0} = 4^{y_1}$. But $4^{y_1} = (2^2)^{y_1} = 2^{2y_1}$. Hence, $y_0 = 2y_1$ and $\log_2 x_0 = 2 \log_4 x_0$. Since x_0 is an arbitrary positive real number, it follows that $\log_2 x = 2 \log_4 x$ for all $x > 0$. Thus, $f = 2g$.

10 a Assume that $x_0 > 0$ and let $\log_2 x_0 = y_0$ and $\log_a x_0 = y_1$. Then $2^{y_0} = x_0 = a^{y_1} = (2^a)^{y_1} = 2^{ay_1}$. Hence, $y_0 = ay_1$, or $\log_2 x_0 = a\log_a x_0$. Since x_0 is an arbitrary positive real number, it follows that $\log_2 x = a\log_a x$ for all $x > 0$. Therefore, $f = ag$.

b By the theorem in part a, since $8 = 2^3$, $\log_2 x = 3 \log_8 x$.

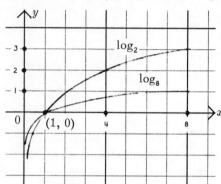

Pages 595-596

1 a $5, 10, 15, 20, 25$ **c** $13, 20, 27, 34, 41$ **e** $0, 1, 3, 6, 10$

b $1, 5, 25, 125, 625$ **d** $-\frac{1}{2}, \frac{1}{4}, -\frac{1}{8}, \frac{1}{16}, -\frac{1}{32}$ **f** $-\frac{1}{2}, \frac{1}{3}, -\frac{1}{8}, \frac{1}{30}, -\frac{1}{144}$

2 a $4 \cdot 3^{n-1}$ **b** $3 \cdot (-1)^{n-1}$ **c** $4 \cdot (\frac{3}{2})^{n-1}$ **d** $.3(-\frac{1}{10})^{n-1}$ or $-3(-\frac{1}{10})^n$

3 a 3 **b** 486 **c** 8th

4 a $\frac{1}{4}$ **b** 64 **c** 4th

5 2 **6** $\dfrac{1 + \sqrt{5}}{2}$

7 a $b, b + ba, b + ba + ba^2, b + ba + ba^2 + ba^3, b + ba + ba^2 + ba^3 + ba^4$

b $S_n = b + ba + ba^2 + \ldots + ba^{n-1}$; $aS_n = ba + ba^2 + ba^3 + \ldots + ba^n$. Hence,

$S_n - aS_n = b - ba^n$. Therefore, $S_n(1 - a) = b(1 - a^n)$, or $S_n = \dfrac{b(1 - a^n)}{1 - a}$.

c Suppose that $\left| S_n - \dfrac{b}{1 - a} \right| = \left| \dfrac{b(1 - a^n)}{1 - a} - \dfrac{b}{1 - a} \right| = \left| \dfrac{-ba^n}{1 - a} \right| = \dfrac{ba^n}{1 - a} < d$, where

d is a small positive number, and that $n > k$. Then $a^n < \dfrac{d(1 - a)}{b}$. Since $|a| < 1$,

let $a = \dfrac{1}{x}$ so that $|x| > 1$. Hence, $\left(\dfrac{1}{x}\right)^n < \dfrac{d(1 - a)}{b}$, or $x^n > \dfrac{b}{d(1 - a)}$. Hence,

$n > \log_x \dfrac{b}{d(1 - a)}$. Therefore, if $k = \left[\log_x \dfrac{b}{d(1 - a)}\right]$, where $x = \dfrac{1}{a}$, then

$\left| S_n - \dfrac{b}{1 - a} \right| < d$ when $n > k$.

1 a 1024   b 8192   c 4096   d 2048

2 a 7   c 2   e 7

   b $\sqrt[5]{\frac{5}{3}}$ d 5   f $\frac{4}{3}$

3 $\log_{10} 1 = 0.0000$. $\log_{10} 4 = 0.6020$. $\log_{10} 7 = 0.8451$.

   $\log_{10} 2 = 0.3010$. $\log_{10} 5 = 0.6990$. $\log_{10} 8 = 0.9030$.

   $\log_{10} 3 = 0.4771$. $\log_{10} 6 = 0.7781$. $\log_{10} 9 = 0.9542$.

4 a 2×10^1; $\log_{10} 20 = 1.3010$.

   b 8×10^4; $\log_{10} 80{,}000 = 4.9030$.

   c 4×10^2; $\log_{10} 400 = 2.6020$.

   d 9×10^3; $\log_{10} 9000 = 3.9542$.

   e 7×10^6; $\log_{10} 7{,}000{,}000 = 6.8451$.

   f 5×10^{-3}; $\log_{10} 0.005 = -2.3010$.

   g 3×10^{-1}; $\log_{10} 0.3 = -0.5229$.

   h 6×10^{-2}; $\log_{10} 0.06 = -1.2219$.

5 Since $x = a \times 10^n$, $\log_{10} x = \log_{10}(a \times 10^n) = \log_{10} a + \log_{10} 10^n$. Now $\log_{10} 10^n = n$; hence, $\log_{10}(x) = n + \log_{10} a$.

6 a 0.5877; 1.5877; $0.5877 - 2$ or -1.4123; 3.5877

   b 0.8645; 2.8645; $0.8645 - 1$ or -0.1355; $0.8645 - 3$ or -2.1355

   c 0.9258; 4.9258; $0.9258 - 1$ or -0.0742; 1.9258

   d 0.7372; $0.7372 - 4$ or -3.2628; 3.7372; $0.7372 - 2$ or 1.2628

1 a 3.8465   c 1.8145   e $0.7530 - 1$ or -0.2470

   b 2.5383   d 0.5330   f $0.6407 - 2$ or -1.3593

2 a 7175   c 195.0   e 72.13   g 899.5

   b 0.4777   d 0.03370   f 0.4500   h 45.91

3 a 1.9306   b 2.2320   c 0.8150   d $0.0913 - 1$ or -0.9087

4 a 90.4   c 1330   e 2,051,000

   b 298   d 776.8   f 2079

5 a No. Since $10^p = (2 \cdot 5)^p = 2^p \cdot 5^p$, 10^p is divisible by 5. However, 2^q is not divisible by 5 because 2 and 5 are relatively prime.

   b Assume that $\log_{10} 2 = \frac{p}{q}$, where p and q are positive integers. By definition of the log function, this means that $10^{p/q} = 2$. Hence, $(10^{p/q})^q = 2^q$, or $10^p = 2^q$. But by the answer for part a, this is impossible. Therefore, the log to the base 10 of 2 cannot be equal to the rational number $\frac{p}{q}$. Hence, $\log_{10} 2$ must be irrational.

6 $\log_a (x_1 \cdot x_2 \cdot x_3) = \log_a \Big((x_1 \cdot x_2) \cdot x_3 \Big)$

$\qquad\qquad\qquad = \log_a (x_1 \cdot x_2) + \log_a x_3$

$\qquad\qquad\qquad = \log_a x_1 + \log_a x_2 + \log_a x_3.$

1 a $r + s$ c $r + 2s$ e $\dfrac{r + s}{2}$

   b $r - s$ d $2r + 2s$ f $\dfrac{r - s}{3}$

2 a 2.51 c 13.2 e 3.90
   b 2.19 d 8.24 f 3.34

3 a 0.0546 b 0.354 c 0.776 d 0.208

4 Answers are given to the nearest hundredth.
   a 1.18 c 1.17 e 0.31
   b −2.10 d −0.55 f 0.91

5 e^{π} is greater.

Page 609

1 a 2.48 b 50.4 c 13.3 d 0.539

2 7.74 sec. 3 207 sq. units

4 a $2208 b 17.5 years

5 25.7 years 6 130

Page 612

1 a 5.248 c −0.811 e 4.847 g −1.198
   b 3.880 d −2.223 f 2.171 h −2.441

2 a 2.41 b 27.3 c 3.16 d 0.772

3 a By Theorem 54/11, $\dfrac{\log_a a}{\log_a b} = \dfrac{\log_b a}{\log_b b}$. Since $\log_a a = 1$ and $\log_b b = 1$, we have

   $\dfrac{1}{\log_a b} = \log_b a$.

4 Let x_0 be a positive real number. Now $g(x_0) = \log_a x_0 = \log_a e \cdot \log_e x_0 =$
   $\log_a e \cdot \ln x_0 = \log_a e \cdot f(x_0)$. Since x_0 was selected arbitrarily, it follows that
   $g(x) = \log_a e \cdot f(x)$ for all $x > 0$. Hence, $g = (\log_a e) \cdot f$.

5 $\{1, e^2\}$

6 $\log_a d = \log_a b \cdot \log_b d = \log_a b \cdot (\log_b c \cdot \log_c d) = \log_a b \cdot \log_b c \cdot \log_c d$.

Pages 614-615

1 $y = x - 1$; $y = ex - 2$; $x = \dfrac{1}{e - 1}$.

2 a $(\frac{1}{2}, -\ln 2)$ c $(10, \ln 10)$
   b $(1, \ln 1)$ d $(\frac{1}{100}, -\ln 100)$

3 a Let x_0 be a positive real number. Then $g(x_0) = \log_e cx = \log_e c + \log_e x_0$. Since
      $c \in \Re^+, \log_e c \in \Re$ and since x_0 was selected arbitrarily, it follows that $g(x) =$
      $\log_e x + k$, where $k = \log_e c$. Hence, the graph of g is the graph of $\log_e$ translated $k = \log_e c$ units vertically.

b 1) In part a it was established that the graph of g is a vertical translate of the graph of $\log_e$. Hence, the tangent line to the graph of g at the point $(x_0, \log_e cx_0)$ is also a vertical translate of the tangent line to the graph of $\log_e$ at the point $(x_0, \log_e x_0)$. From this, it follows that the two tangent lines have the same slope. Therefore, $g'(x_0) = \log_e'(x_0) = \dfrac{1}{x_0}$. Since x_0 is an arbitrary point in the domain of g, it follows that $g'(x) = \dfrac{1}{x}$.

2) $g(x) = \log_e c + \log_e x$. Hence, $g'(x) = \log_e' c + \log_e' x$. Since the slope function of a constant function is 0, we have $g'(x) = 0 + \dfrac{1}{x} = \dfrac{1}{x}$.

4 a The domain of g is $\{x \mid x < 0, x \in \Re\}$. The range of g is $\Re$.

b Because the graph of g is the reflection in the y-axis of the graph of $\log_e$, the tangent line to the graph of g at $(-x_0, \ln x_0)$ is the reflection in the y-axis of the tangent line to the graph of $\log_e$ at $(x_0, \ln x_0)$. Hence, the slope of this tangent to the graph of g is the negative of the slope of the tangent to the graph of $\log_e$. Therefore, $g'(-x_0) = -\dfrac{1}{-x_0} = \dfrac{1}{x_0}$. Since $-x_0$ is arbitrary, it follows that $g'(x) = \dfrac{1}{x}$.

c Function g is never increasing. Function g is decreasing for all x in its domain.

d $g''(x) = -\dfrac{1}{x^2}$. Hence, g is never concave upward, but is concave downward for all x in its domain.

e

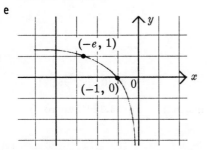

5 Because the graph of f is the graph of $\log_e$ translated horizontally $-a$ units, the tangent line to the graph of f at the point $\left(x_0 - a, \log_e (x_0 - a)\right)$ has the same slope as the tangent line to the graph of $\log_e$ at the point $(x_0, \log_e x_0)$. Since $\log_e'(x_0) = \dfrac{1}{x_0}$, it follows that $f'(x_0 - a) = \dfrac{1}{x_0}$. If $x = x_0 - a$, then $x_0 = x + a$. Hence, $f'(x) = \dfrac{1}{x + a}$. Since x_0 was selected arbitrarily, it follows that $f'(x) = \dfrac{1}{x + a}$ for all x for which f is defined.

6 In exercise 4b, it was established that if $g(x) = \log_e (-x)$, then $g'(x) = \dfrac{1}{x}$. Therefore, if $f(x) = \log_e cx$, where $c \in \Re^-$, then $f(x) = \log_e \left(k(-x)\right)$, where $k \in \Re^+$. From this, we have $f(x) = \log_e k + \log_e (-x)$ or $f'(x) = 0 + \dfrac{1}{x} = \dfrac{1}{x}$.

Chapter review
Pages 615-617

1 a	4 a	7 b	10 c	13 a	16 b	19 d
2 b	5 a	8 b	11 c	14 d	17 b	
3 c	6 d	9 a	12 a	15 c	18 d	

Cumulative review
Pages 616-617

1 a $x = \frac{5}{8}; y = \frac{1}{48}.$ b $x = 16\sqrt{3}; y = 16.$

2 a $f(1) = \frac{(1)^2 - 1}{1} = 0$ and $f(-1) = \frac{(-1)^2 - 1}{-1} = 0.$ Hence, if $k = 0$, then $f(-1) = k$ and $f(1) = k,$ so that f is not a one-to-one function.

  b If $x > 0$, then $\widehat{f}(x) = \frac{x^2 - 1}{x} = x - \frac{1}{x},$ which is a strictly decreasing function. Since every strictly decreasing function is one-to-one, $\widehat{f}$ is a one-to-one function.

3 $f(8) = 17.2.$

4 The graph of a function fulfilling these requirements is shown below.

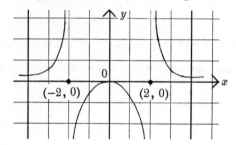

5 $k = -2.5.$ **6** a -5; b $= 3.$

7 a $\{\frac{\pi}{3}, \frac{2\pi}{3}, \frac{4\pi}{3}, \frac{5\pi}{3}\}$ b $\{0, \pi, 2\pi\}$ c $\{\frac{\pi}{6}, \frac{\pi}{2}, \frac{5\pi}{6}\}$ d $\{0, \frac{\pi}{2}, \frac{3\pi}{2}, 2\pi\}$

8 a $\{-\frac{1}{3}\}$ b $\{-\frac{1}{2}, \frac{1}{2}\}$ c $\{0.3010\}$ (approx.)   d $\{3.322\}$ (approx.)

9 a $2, 3, 5, 9, 17$ b $a_1 = 16.$

10 a $\ln v = \ln 4 + \frac{2}{3} \ln u.$

  b The graph is a straight line with slope $\frac{2}{3}$ and y-intercept $(0, \ln 4)$

11 Since $f'(x) = e^x$, $f'(\ln 2) = e^{\ln 2} = 2$, and since $g'(x) = \frac{1}{x}$, $g'(\frac{1}{2}) = \frac{1}{\frac{1}{2}} = 2.$ Because the two tangent lines have the same slope, they are parallel.

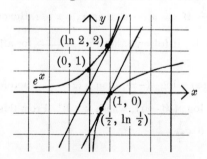

Pages 621-623

1 a $f(x) = 0$ when $x = 1$ and when $x = -1$. Hence, the x-intercepts are $(-1, 0)$ and
$(1, 0)$. $f(x) > 0$ for $\{x \mid -1 < x < 1 \text{ or } x > 1\}$ and $f(x) < 0$ for $\{x \mid x < -1\}$. $f'(x) = 0$
when $x = -\frac{1}{3}$ and when $x = 1$. Hence, f has a relative maximum point at $(-\frac{1}{3}, \frac{32}{27})$
and a relative minimum point at $(1, 0)$. $f'(x) > 0$ for $\{x \mid x < -\frac{1}{3} \text{ or } x > 1\}$ and
$f'(x) < 0$ for $\{x \mid -\frac{1}{3} < x < 1\}$. $f''(x) = 0$ when $x = \frac{1}{3}$; hence, the graph of f has an
inflection point at $(\frac{1}{3}, \frac{16}{27})$. $f''(x) > 0$ for $\{x \mid x > \frac{1}{3}\}$ and $f''(x) < 0$ for $\{x \mid x < \frac{1}{3}\}$.
See graph at left below.

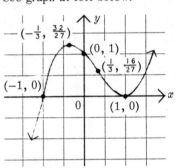

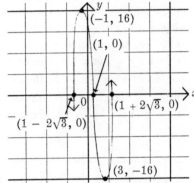

b $f(x) = 0$ when $x = 1$, when $x = 1 + 2\sqrt{3}$, and when $x = 1 - 2\sqrt{3}$. Hence, the
x-intercepts are $(1, 0)$, $(1 + 2\sqrt{3}, 0)$, and $(1 - 2\sqrt{3}, 0)$. $f(x) > 0$ for
$\{x \mid 1 - 2\sqrt{3} < x < 1 \text{ or } x > 1 + 2\sqrt{3}\}$. $f'(x) = 0$ when $x = 3$ and when $x = -1$.
Hence, f has a relative minimum point at $(3, -16)$ and a relative maximum point
at $(-1, 16)$. $f'(x) > 0$ for $\{x \mid x < -1 \text{ or } x > 3\}$ and $f'(x) < 0$ for $\{x \mid -1 < x < 3\}$.
$f''(x) = 0$ when $x = 1$; hence, the graph of f has an inflection point at $(1, 0)$.
$f''(x) > 0$ for $\{x \mid x > 1\}$ and $f''(x) < 0$ for $\{x \mid x < 1\}$. See graph at right above.

c $f(x) = 0$ when $x = 2$ and when $x = 0$. Hence, the x-intercepts are $(2, 0)$ and $(0, 0)$.
$f(x) > 0$ for $\{x \mid x < 0 \text{ or } x > 2\}$ and $f(x) < 0$ for $\{x \mid 0 < x < 2\}$. $f'(x) = 0$ when
$x = 0$ and when $x = \frac{3}{2}$. The graph has a relative minimum point at $(\frac{3}{2}, -\frac{27}{16})$.
$f'(x) > 0$ for $\{x \mid x > \frac{3}{2}\}$ and $f'(x) < 0$ for $\{x \mid x < \frac{3}{2}\}$. $f''(x) = 0$ when $x = 0$ and when
$x = 1$. Hence, the graph of f has inflection points at $(0, 0)$ and at $(1, -1)$. $f''(x) > 0$
for $\{x \mid x < 0 \text{ or } x > 1\}$ and $f''(x) < 0$ for $\{x \mid 0 < x < 1\}$. See graph at left below.

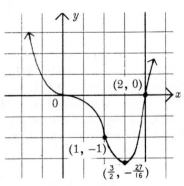

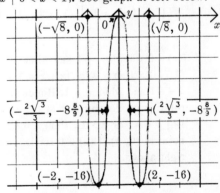

d $f(x) = 0$ when $x = 0$, when $x = \sqrt{8}$, and when $x = -\sqrt{8}$. Hence, the x-intercepts are $(0, 0)$, $(\sqrt{8}, 0)$ and $(-\sqrt{8}, 0)$. $f(x) > 0$ for $\{x \mid x < -\sqrt{8}$ or $x > \sqrt{8}\}$ and $f(x) < 0$ for $\{x \mid -\sqrt{8} < x < 0$ or $0 < x < \sqrt{8}\}$. $f'(x) = 0$ when $x = 0$, when $x = 2$, and when $x = -2$. The graph of f has a relative maximum point at $(0, 0)$ and relative minimum points at $(2, -16)$ and $(-2, -16)$. $f'(x) > 0$ for $\{x \mid -2 < x < 0$ or $x > 2\}$ and $f'(x) < 0$ for $\{x \mid x < -2$ or $0 < x < 2\}$. $f''(x) = 0$ when $x = \frac{2\sqrt{3}}{3}$ and when $x = -\frac{2\sqrt{3}}{3}$. Hence, the graph of f has inflection points at $(\frac{2\sqrt{3}}{3}, -8\frac{8}{9})$ and $(-\frac{2\sqrt{3}}{3}, -8\frac{8}{9})$. $f''(x) > 0$ for $\{x \mid x < -\frac{2\sqrt{3}}{3}$ or $x > \frac{2\sqrt{3}}{3}\}$ and $f''(x) < 0$ for $\{x \mid -\frac{2\sqrt{3}}{3} < x < \frac{2\sqrt{3}}{3}\}$. See graph at bottom right on preceding page.

e $f(x) = 0$ when $x = 2$ and when $x = -2$. Hence, the x-intercepts are $(2, 0)$ and $(-2, 0)$. $f(x) > 0$ for $\{x \mid x < -2$ or $x > 2\}$ and $f(x) < 0$ for $\{x \mid -2 < x < 2\}$. $f'(x) = 0$ when $x = 0$, when $x = 1$, and when $x = -1$. Hence, f has a relative maximum point at $(0, -8)$ and relative minimum points at $(1, -9)$ and $(-1, -9)$. $f'(x) > 0$ for $\{x \mid -1 < x < 0$ or $x > 1\}$ and $f'(x) < 0$ for $\{x \mid x < -1$ or $0 < x < 1\}$. $f''(x) = 0$ when $x = \frac{\sqrt{3}}{3}$ and when $x = -\frac{\sqrt{3}}{3}$. Hence, the graph of f has inflection points at $(\frac{\sqrt{3}}{3}, -8\frac{5}{9})$ and $(-\frac{\sqrt{3}}{3}, -8\frac{5}{9})$. $f''(x) > 0$ for $\{x \mid x < -\frac{\sqrt{3}}{3}$ or $x > \frac{\sqrt{3}}{3}\}$ and $f''(x) < 0$ for $\{x \mid -\frac{\sqrt{3}}{3} < x < \frac{\sqrt{3}}{3}\}$. See graph at left below.

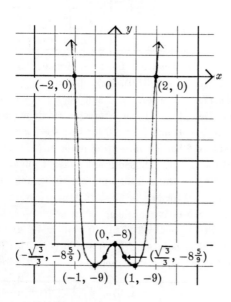

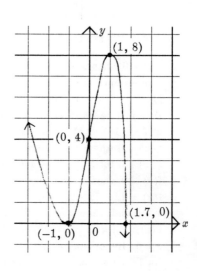

f $f(x) = 0$ when $x = -1$ and when $x \approx 1.7$. Hence, the x-intercepts are $(-1, 0)$ and $(1.7, 0)$. $f(x) > 0$ for $\{x \mid x < 1.7, x \neq 0\}$; $f(x) < 0$ for $\{x \mid x > 1.7\}$. $f'(x) = 0$ when $x = -1$ and when $x = 1$. Hence, f has a relative minimum point at $(-1, 0)$ and a relative maximum point at $(1, 8)$. $f'(x) > 0$ for $\{x \mid -1 < x < 1\}$ and $f'(x) < 0$ for $\{x \mid x < -1$ or $x > 1\}$. $f''(x) = 0$ for $x = 0$. Hence, the graph of f has an inflection point at $(0, 4)$. $f''(x) > 0$ for $\{x \mid x < 0\}$ and $f''(x) < 0$ for $\{x \mid x > 0\}$. See graph at right above.

2 a The function f is an even function with domain $\Re$ and range $\{y \mid 0 < y \leq 2\}$. f is increasing for $\{x \mid x \leq 0\}$ and decreasing for $\{x \mid x \geq 0\}$. The maximum value of $f(x)$ is 2, when $x = 0$, and $f'(x) = 0$ when $x = 0$. The function has inflection points at $(-2, 1)$ and $(2, 1)$. The function is concave upward for $\{x \mid x < -2 \text{ or } x > 2\}$ and concave downward for $\{x \mid -2 < x < 2\}$. As $|x|$ increases, the value of $f(x)$ approaches 0.

b The function f is an odd function with domain $\{x \mid |x| \neq 2, x \in \Re\}$ and range $\Re$. f is decreasing over its entire domain. $f'(x) = 0$ when $x = 0$. f has the lines $x = 2$ and $x = -2$ as vertical asymptotes and the x-axis as a horizontal asymptote when $|x|$ is large. $f(x) > 0$ for $\{x \mid -2 < x < 0 \text{ or } x > 2\}$ and $f(x) < 0$ for $\{x \mid x < -2 \text{ or } 0 < x < 2\}$. The function has an inflection point at $(0, 0)$. The function is concave upward for $\{x \mid -2 < x < 0 \text{ or } x > 2\}$ and concave downward for $\{x \mid x < -2 \text{ or } 0 < x < 2\}$.

c The function f is an even function with domain $\Re$ and range $\{y \mid y \leq 1\}$. f has x-intercepts $(-1, 0)$ and $(1, 0)$. The y-intercept, $(0, 1)$, is a maximum point on the graph of f. f has inflection points at $(-3, -1)$ and $(3, -1)$. The function is increasing for $\{x \mid x \leq 0\}$ and decreasing for $\{x \mid x \geq 0\}$. The function is concave upward for $\{x \mid -3 < x < 0 \text{ or } 0 < x < 3\}$ and concave downward for $\{x \mid x < -3 \text{ or } x > 3\}$.

d The function f is an even function with domain $\{x \mid |x| \neq 1, x \in \Re\}$ and range $\{y \mid y < 0 \text{ or } y \geq 1\}$. $f'(x) = 0$ for $x = 0$, and $(0, 1)$ is a relative minimum point on the graph of f. f has the vertical lines $x = -1$ and $x = 1$ as asymptotes and the x-axis as a horizontal asymptote when $|x|$ is large. f is increasing for $\{x \mid 0 < x < 1 \text{ or } x > 1\}$ and decreasing for $\{x \mid x < -1 \text{ or } -1 < x < 0\}$. The function is concave upward for $\{x \mid -1 < x < 1\}$ and concave downward for $\{x \mid x < -1 \text{ or } x > 1\}$.

3

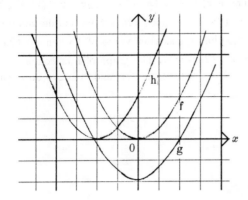

a g is an even function with domain $\Re$ and range $\{y \mid y \geq -2\}$. The x-intercepts are $(-2, 0)$ and $(2, 0)$. The function is increasing for $\{x \mid x > 0\}$ and decreasing for $\{x \mid x < 0\}$. $g(x) > 0$ for $\{x \mid x < -2 \text{ or } x > 2\}$ and $g(x) < 0$ for $\{x \mid -2 < x < 2\}$. g is concave upward for its entire domain. $g'(x) = 0$ when $x = 0$. The function has a minimum value at the point $(0, -2)$.

b The domain of h is $\Re$ and the range is $\{y \mid y \geq 0\}$. The x-intercept is $(-2, 0)$. The function is increasing for $\{x \mid x > -2\}$ and decreasing for $\{x \mid x < -2\}$. h is concave upward for its entire domain. $h'(x) = 0$ when $x = -2$. The function has a minimum value at the point $(-2, 0)$.

4

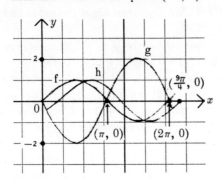

a g is an odd function with domain $\Re$ and range $\{y \mid -2 \leq y \leq 2\}$. g is periodic with fundamental period 2π and has x-intercepts at $(n\pi, 0)$, where n is an integer. $g(x) > 0$ for $\{x \mid (2n - 1)\pi < x < 2n\pi\}$ and $g(x) < 0$ for $\{x \mid 2n\pi < x < (2n + 1)\pi\}$. The function is increasing for $\{x \mid (4n + 1)\frac{\pi}{2} \leq x \leq (4n + 3)\frac{\pi}{2}\}$ and decreasing for $\{x \mid (4n - 1)\frac{\pi}{2} \leq x \leq (4n + 1)\frac{\pi}{2}\}$. $g(x)$ has a maximum value of 2 when $x = (4n - 1)\frac{\pi}{2}$ and a minimum value of -2 when $x = (4n + 1)\frac{\pi}{2}$. The graph of g is concave upward for the intervals $\{x \mid 2n\pi \leq x \leq (2n + 1)\pi\}$ and concave downward for the intervals $\{x \mid (2n - 1)\pi \leq x \leq 2n\pi\}$.

b Function h has domain $\Re$ and range $\{y \mid -1 \leq y \leq 1\}$. h is periodic with fundamental period 2π and has x-intercepts $(\frac{\pi}{4} + n\pi, 0)$, where n is an integer. $h(x) > 0$ for $\{x \mid (2n + \frac{1}{4})\pi < x < (2n + \frac{5}{4})\pi\}$ and $h(x) < 0$ for $\{x \mid (2n - \frac{3}{4})\pi < x < (2n + \frac{1}{4})\pi\}$. The function is increasing for $\{x \mid (2n - \frac{1}{4})\pi \leq x \leq (2n + \frac{3}{4})\pi\}$ and decreasing for $\{x \mid (2n + \frac{3}{4})\pi \leq x \leq (2n + \frac{7}{4})\pi\}$. $h(x)$ has a maximum value of 1 when $x = (2n + \frac{3}{4})\pi$ and a minimum value of -1 when $x = (2n + \frac{7}{4})\pi$. The graph of h is concave upward for the intervals $\{x \mid (2n + \frac{5}{4})\pi \leq x \leq (2n + \frac{9}{4})\pi\}$ and concave downward for the intervals $\{x \mid (2n + \frac{1}{4})\pi \leq x \leq (2n + \frac{5}{4})\pi\}$.

5

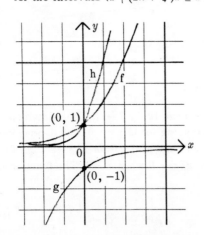

a The domain of g is $\Re$ and its range is $\{y \mid y < 0\}$. g is increasing for all x in $\Re$ and g is concave downward over its entire domain. g has the x-axis as a horizontal asymptote as x becomes large.

b The domain of h is $\Re$ and its range is $\{y \mid y > 0\}$. h is increasing for all x in $\Re$ and h is concave upward over its entire domain. h has the x-axis as a horizontal asymptote when $|x|$ is large, but $x < 0$.

6

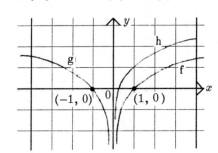

a The domain of g is $\{x \mid x < 0\}$ and its range is $\Re$. The x-intercept of g is $(-1, 0)$; $g(x) > 0$ for $\{x \mid x < -1\}$; and $g(x) < 0$ for $\{x \mid -1 < x < 0\}$. g is decreasing for all x in $\Re$ and g is concave downward over its entire domain. g has the y-axis as a vertical asymptote.

b The domain of h is $\{x \mid x > 0\}$ and its range is $\Re$. The x-intercept of h is $(\frac{1}{e}, 0)$; $h(x) > 0$ for $\{x \mid x > \frac{1}{e}\}$; and $h(x) < 0$ for $\{x \mid 0 < x < \frac{1}{e}\}$. h is increasing for all x in $\Re$ and h is concave downward over its entire domain. h has the y-axis as a vertical asymptote.

7 a See graph at left below. The domain of f^{-1} is $\{x \mid x \geq 0\}$ and its range is $\{y \mid y \geq -2\}$. The x-intercept of f^{-1} is $(1, 0)$; $f^{-1}(x) < 0$ for $\{x \mid 0 \leq x < 1\}$; and $f^{-1}(x) > 0$ for $\{x \mid x > 1\}$. f^{-1} is increasing for all x in its domain and f^{-1} is concave upward over its entire domain.

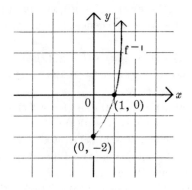
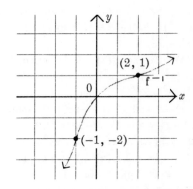

b See graph at right above. The domain of f^{-1} is $\Re$ and its range is $\Re$. The x-intercept of f^{-1} is $(0, 0)$; $f^{-1}(x) < 0$ for $\{x \mid x < 0\}$; and $f^{-1}(x) > 0$ for $\{x \mid x > 0\}$. f^{-1} is increasing for all x in $\Re$. f^{-1} has $(-1, -2)$ and $(2, 1)$ as inflection points. f^{-1} is concave upward for $\{x \mid x < -1$ or $x > 2\}$ and concave downward for $\{x \mid -1 < x < 2\}$.

8 a Since $f(x) = x^3$, $(f \circ f^{-1})(x) = \left(f^{-1}(x)\right)^3 = x$. Hence, $f^{-1}(x) = x^{\frac{1}{3}}$.

b

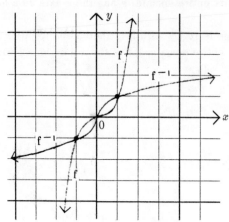

c f is an odd function with domain $\Re$ and range $\Re$. The x-intercept of f is $(0, 0)$; $f(x) < 0$ for $\{x \mid x < 0\}$; and $f(x) > 0$ for $\{x \mid x > 0\}$. $f'(x) = 0$ when $x = 0$ and f is increasing for all x in $\Re$. f is concave upward for $\{x \mid x > 0\}$ and f is concave downward for $\{x \mid x < 0\}$.

f^{-1} is an odd function with domain $\Re$ and range $\Re$. The x-intercept of f^{-1} is $(0, 0)$; $f^{-1}(x) < 0$ for $\{x \mid x < 0\}$; and $f^{-1}(x) > 0$ for $\{x \mid x > 0\}$. $(f^{-1})'(x)$ is never 0 and f^{-1} is increasing for all x in $\Re$. f^{-1} is concave upward for $\{x \mid x < 0\}$ and concave downward for $\{x \mid x > 0\}$.

Pages 626-627

1 a $f'(x) = 1$ and $g'(x) = 3$; hence, $(f \cdot g)'(x) = (f' \cdot g)(x) + (f \cdot g')(x) = (1)(3x + 2) +$ $3(x - 1) = 6x - 1$. $(f \cdot g)(x) = (x - 1)(3x + 2) = 3x^2 - x - 2$; hence, $(f \cdot g)'(x) = 6x - 1$.

b $f'(x) = 2x$ and $g'(x) = 2$; hence, $(f \cdot g)'(x) = (f' \cdot g)(x) + (f \cdot g')(x) = (2x)(2x - 1) +$ $(2)(x^2) = 6x^2 - 2x$. $(f \cdot g)(x) = (x^2)(2x - 1) = 2x^3 - x^2$; hence, $(f \cdot g)'(x) =$ $6x^2 - 2x$.

c $f'(x) = 2x$ and $g'(x) = 3x^2$; hence, $(f \cdot g)'(x) = (f' \cdot g)(x) + (f \cdot g')(x) =$ $(2x)(x^3 + 2) + (3x^2)(x^2 - 1) = 5x^4 - 3x^2 + 4x$. $(f \cdot g)(x) = (x^2 - 1)(x^3 + 2) =$ $x^5 - x^3 + 2x^2 - 2$; hence, $(f \cdot g)'(x) = 5x^4 - 3x^2 + 4x$.

d $f'(x) = 2$ and $g'(x) = -2x + 1$; hence, $(f \cdot g)'(x) = (f' \cdot g)(x) + (f \cdot g')(x) =$ $(2)(-x^2 + x - 1) + (-2x + 1)(2x + 3) = -6x^2 - 2x + 1$. $(f \cdot g)(x) =$ $(2x + 3)(-x^2 + x - 1) = -2x^3 - x^2 + x - 3$; hence, $(f \cdot g)'(x) = -6x^2 - 2x + 1$.

2 a $f'(x) = 2x$ and $g'(x) = 1$; hence, $(f \circ g)'(x) = (f' \circ g)(x) \cdot g'(x) = \left(2(x + 1)\right)(1) =$ $2x + 2$. $(f \circ g)(x) = (x + 1)^2 = x^2 + 2x + 1$; hence $(f \circ g)'(x) = 2x + 2$.

b $f'(x) = 3x^2$ and $g'(x) = 5$; hence, $(f \circ g)'(x) = (f' \circ g)(x) \cdot g'(x) = \left(3(5x)^2\right)(5) =$ $375x^2$. $(f \circ g)(x) = (5x)^3 = 125x^3$; hence, $(f \circ g)'(x) = 375x^2$.

c $f'(x) = 6x$ and $g'(x) = -1$; hence, $(f \circ g)'(x) = (f' \circ g)(x) \cdot g'(x) = \left(6(3 - x)\right)(-1) =$ $6x - 18$. $(f \circ g)(x) = 3(3 - x)^2 = 27 - 18x + 3x^2$; hence, $(f \circ g)'(x) = 6x - 18$.

d $f'(x) = 6x^2$ and $g'(x) = 2$; hence, $(f \circ g)'(x) = (f' \circ g)(x) \cdot g'(x) = \left(6(2x + 1)^2\right)(2) =$
$48x^2 + 48x + 12$. $(f \circ g)(x) = 2(2x + 1)^3 = 16x^3 + 24x^2 + 12x + 2$; hence,
$(f \circ g)'(x) = 48x^2 + 48x + 12$.

3 a $f'(x) = \cos x$ and $g'(x) = 2$; hence, $(f \circ g)'(x) = (f' \circ g)(x) \cdot g'(x) = (\cos 2x)(2) =$
$2 \cos 2x$.

b $(f \circ g)'(\frac{\pi}{2}) = 2 \cos 2 \cdot \frac{\pi}{2} = 2 \cos \pi = -2$. $(f \circ g)'(\frac{5\pi}{4}) = 2 \cos 2 \cdot \frac{5\pi}{4} = 2 \cos \frac{5\pi}{2} = 0$.

c $(f \circ g)(x) = \sin 2x$. The graph of $f \circ g$ is shown below, along with the tangents at
$x = \frac{\pi}{2}$ and $x = \frac{5\pi}{4}$, which have slopes -2 and 0, respectively.

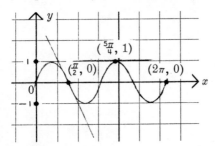

4 a $\left(\dfrac{f}{g}\right)'(x) = \dfrac{g \cdot f' - f \cdot g'}{g^2}$; hence, $f' = \dfrac{x \cdot 0 - 1 \cdot 1}{x^2} = -\dfrac{1}{x^2}$.

b $g'(x) = \dfrac{x^2 \cdot 0 - 1 \cdot 2x}{x^4} = -\dfrac{2}{x^3}$.

c Let h: $h(x) = a$ and g: $g(x) = x^{-n}$, where n is a negative integer. Thus,

$$f(x) = ax^n = \dfrac{a}{x^{-n}} = \dfrac{h(x)}{g(x)} = \dfrac{h}{g}(x).$$

Now $\left(\dfrac{h}{g}\right)'(x) = \dfrac{g(x) \cdot h'(x) - h(x) \cdot g'(x)}{(g(x))^2}$. Hence,

$$f'(x) = \left(\dfrac{h}{g}\right)'(x) = \dfrac{x^{-n}(0) - a(-nx^{-n-1})}{(x^{-n})^2} = \dfrac{anx^{-n-1}}{x^{-2n}} = anx^{n-1}.$$

Since the domain of f is $\{x \mid x \neq 0\}$, this last expression is defined for all x in
domain of f.

5 a $f'(x) = -\dfrac{1}{x^2}$; $f''(x) = \dfrac{2}{x^3}$. f is an odd function with domain $\{x \mid x \neq 0, x \in \Re\}$.

f(x) > 0 for $\{x \mid x > 0\}$ and f(x) < 0 for
$\{x \mid x < 0\}$. Since f'(x) < 0 for all x in
the domain, f is decreasing over its
entire domain. Since f''(x) > 0 for $x > 0$,
the graph is concave upward for $\{x \mid x > 0\}$,
and since f''(x) < 0 for $x < 0$, the graph
is concave downward for $\{x \mid x < 0\}$.
See graph at the right.

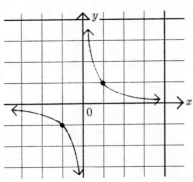

b $f'(x) = 1 - \dfrac{1}{x^2}$; $f''(x) = \dfrac{2}{x^3}$. f is an odd function with domain $\{x \mid x \neq 0,\ x \in \Re\}$ and

range $\{y \mid |y| \geqq 2\}$. $f(x) > 0$ for $\{x \mid x > 0\}$ and $f(x) < 0$ for $\{x \mid x < 0\}$. $f'(x) = 0$

when $x = \pm 1$; the function has a relative maximum of -2 when $x = -1$ and a

relative minimum of 2 when $x = 1$. Since $f'(x) > 0$ when $|x| > 1$, the function is

increasing for $\{x \mid |x| > 1\}$, and since $f'(x) < 0$ when $|x| < 1$, the function is

decreasing for $\{x \mid |x| < 1\}$. Since $f''(x) > 0$ for $x > 0$, the graph is concave upward

for $\{x \mid x > 0\}$, and since $f''(x) < 0$ for $x < 0$, the graph is concave downward for

$\{x \mid x < 0\}$.

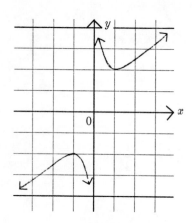

c $f'(x) = \dfrac{-2}{x^3}$; $f''(x) = \dfrac{6}{x^4}$. f is an even function with domain $\{x \mid x \neq 0,\ x \in \Re\}$ and

range $\{y \mid y > 0,\ y \in \Re\}$. Since $f'(x) > 0$ when $x < 0$, f is increasing for

$\{x \mid x < 0\}$, and since $f'(x) < 0$ when $x > 0$, f is decreasing for $\{x \mid x > 0\}$. Since

$f''(x) > 0$ for all x in the domain, the graph is concave upward over the entire

domain.

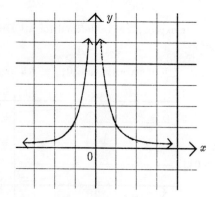

d $f'(x) = 1 + \dfrac{2}{x^3}$; $f''(x) = -\dfrac{6}{x^4}$. f has domain $\{x \mid x \neq 0, x \in \Re\}$ and range $\Re$. $f(x) = 0$

when $x = 1$; so the graph has x-intercept $(1, 0)$. $f(x) > 0$ for $\{x \mid x > 1\}$, and $f(x) < 0$ for $\{x \mid x < 0$ or $0 < x < 1\}$. Since $f'(x) = 0$ when $x = -\sqrt[3]{2}, f(x)$ has a relative maximum at approx. -1.89. Since $f'(x) > 0$ for $\{x \mid x \leq -\sqrt[3]{2}$ or $x > 0\}$, the function is increasing for this interval. Since $f'(x) < 0$ for $\{x \mid -\sqrt[3]{2} < x < 0\}$, the function is decreasing for this interval. Since $f''(x) < 0$ for all x in the domain, the function is concave downward over the entire domain.

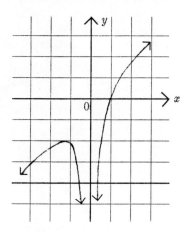

6 a 400; \$4000 **b** 800; \$3200 **c** $P(x) = 1000x + 4000 + \dfrac{4000}{x - 5}$.

d 300 first-line tires and 500 second-line tires; \$5000